Approximate Molecular Orbital Theory

JOHN A. POPLE
Carnegie Professor of Chemical Physics
Carnegie-Mellon University

DAVID L. BEVERIDGE
Associate Professor of Chemistry
Hunter College
City University of New York

McGRAW-HILL BOOK COMPANY
NEW YORK   ST. LOUIS   SAN FRANCISCO   DÜSSELDORF
LONDON   MEXICO   PANAMA   SYDNEY   TORONTO

APPROXIMATE MOLECULAR ORBITAL THEORY

Library of Congress Catalog Card Number 70-95820

50512

1 2 3 4 5 6 7 8 9 0   MAMM   7 9 8 7 6 5 4 3 2 1 0

This book was set in Modern by The Maple Press
Company and printed on permanent paper and bound
by The Maple Press Company.   The designer was
Edward Zytko; the drawings were done by John
Cordes, J & R Technical Services, Inc.   The editors
were James L. Smith and Andrea Stryker-Rodda.
Paul B. Poss supervised the production.

Preface

Since its inception in the early days of quantum mechanics, molecular orbital theory has become a powerful method for studying the electronic structure of molecules, illuminating many areas of chemistry. In quantitative form, it has developed both as an *ab initio* method for computing molecular wavefunctions directly from the fundamental equations of quantum mechanics and also as a semiempirical technique for interrelating various physical properties of atoms and molecules using a simplified formalism as a framework for parameterization. Until recently, *ab initio* calculations dealt mainly with very small systems while the semiempirical methods were oriented toward the π electrons of larger planar molecules. In the last few years, however, both approaches have become more concerned with general polyatomic molecules and they now overlap somewhat in their areas of application.

This book has the limited objective of presenting the background of self-consistent molecular orbital theory and following this with a description of certain elementary semiempirical schemes which use the general theory as a basic framework. These are methods based on zero-differential overlap (complete neglect of differential overlap, or CNDO, and intermediate neglect of differential overlap, or INDO) which are simple enough to be applied to a wide range of chemical problems without major computational effort. The necessary general theory is covered in Chaps. 1 and 2 leading up to simple examples of molecular orbital calculations for diatomics. In Chap. 3, the approximations involved in the semiempirical schemes and the corresponding parameterizations are discussed in detail. In Chap. 4 we survey applications of the methods which have been made to date, including studies of electronic charge distributions in molecules, dipole moments, equilibrium geometries, nuclear hyperfine structure in the electron spin resonance spectroscopy of organic free radicals and the spin coupling constants measured by nuclear magnetic resonance.

Many of the conclusions based on the simple methods described in this book will undoubtedly be modified by larger and more sophisticated calculations which are rapidly becoming possible. Nevertheless, we believe that theoretical studies at this simple level do provide a first approximation which is realistic, informative, and direct enough to allow widespread application. It is to facilitate such applications that we have collected the material in this volume.

Much of the work described herein has been the result of a collaborative effort with a number of colleagues at Carnegie-Mellon University. These include David P. Santry, Gerald Segal, Mark S. Gordon, Paul A. Dobosh, Neil S. Ostlund, and James W. McIver, Jr. Helpful discussions with Herbert

v

Fischer and Keith Miller are also acknowledged. The efforts of Kathryn Severn in preparing the typescript are greatly appreciated. Permission to reproduce material has been granted by the Journal of Chemical Physics and the Journal of the American Chemical Society.

The support of the U.S. Public Health Service, Grant 1-F2-CA-21,281-01 is gratefully acknowledged by David L. Beveridge.

JOHN A. POPLE
DAVID L. BEVERIDGE

Contents

1
Quantum-mechanical Background

1.1 INTRODUCTION

The main objective of any theory of molecular structure is to provide some insight into the various physical laws governing the chemical constitution of molecules in terms of the more fundamental universal physical laws governing the motions and interactions of the constituent atomic nuclei and electrons. In principle such theories can aim at a precise quantitative description of the structure of molecules and their chemical properties, since the underlying physical laws are now well understood in terms of quantum theory based on the Schroedinger equation. However, in practice mathematical and computational complexities make this goal difficult to attain, and one must usually resort to approximate methods.

The principal approximate methods considered in molecular quantum mechanics are valence bond theory and molecular orbital theory [1]. Valence bond theory originated in the work of Heitler

1

and London and was developed extensively by Pauling. Molecular orbital theory has its origins in the early research work in band spectroscopy of diatomic molecules and has been widely used to describe many aspects of molecular structure and diverse molecular properties such as electronic dipole moments, optical absorption spectra, and electron and nuclear magnetic resonance. Among those involved in the original works were Hund, Mulliken, Lennard-Jones, and Slater. We are concerned herein exclusively with molecular orbital theory, and particularly with the theories and problems encountered in carrying out the calculation of molecular orbitals for large molecules.

Molecular orbital theory provides a precise description of molecular electronic structure only for one-electron molecules, but for many-electron molecules it provides a sufficiently good approximate description to be generally useful. The full analytical calculation of the molecular orbitals for most systems of interest may be reduced to a purely mathematical problem [2], the central feature of which is the calculation and diagonalization of an effective interaction energy matrix for the system. The digital computer programs that have been prepared to carry out these calculations have been mostly the result of extensive work by highly coordinated research groups. A number of these groups have generously made their programs available to the scientific community at large [3], but even with the programs in hand the computer time involved in carrying out sufficiently accurate calculations is often prohibitively large, even for diatomic molecules. On the other hand, many applications of molecular orbital theory do not necessarily require accurate molecular orbitals for the system. In many chemical and physical problems, a qualitative or semi-quantitative knowledge of the form of the molecular orbitals is sufficient to extract the necessary information. Thus there is considerable interest in the development of good approximate molecular orbital theories to serve this purpose, and this constitutes the subject of the present book.

Approximate molecular orbital theories are based on schemes developed within the mathematical framework of molecular orbital theory, but with a number of simplifications introduced in the computational procedure. Often experimental data on atoms and prototype molecular systems are used to estimate values for quantities entering into the calculations as parameters, and for this reason the procedures are widely known as *semiempirical methods*.

Approximate molecular orbital theory may be approached from two basically different points of view. One approach involves choosing appropriate values for the elements of the aforementioned interaction energy matrix from essentially empirical considerations, and is characteristic of the so-called Hückel [4] and extended Hückel [5] methods. The other approach is based explicitly on the mathematical formalism, and involves introducing approximations for the atomic and molecular integrals entering the expression for the elements of the energy interaction matrix. The latter approach is referred to as approximate self-consistent field theory [6]. Both Hückel theory and approximate self-consistent field theory were originally developed within the framework of the π electron approximation, treating the π electrons of planar unsaturated organic molecules explicitly with the remaining σ electrons and atomic nuclei considered as part of a nonpolarizable core. Hückel π electron theory has been given a most definitive treatment by Streitweiser [4], and likewise π electron self-consistent field theory is developed in considerable detail in the recent books by Salem [7] and Murrell [8]. We thus restrict our consideration to more recent approximate molecular orbital theories applicable to all valence electrons of a general three-dimensional molecule.

In the following presentation, we have attempted to give the essentials of quantum mechanics and molecular orbital theory pertinent to the understanding and application of approximate molecular orbital calculations to chemical problems. The remainder of this chapter is a cursory and informal discussion of certain quantum-mechanical principles and an introduction to the orbital description of electronic structure. In Chap. 2, the methods of molecular orbital theory are introduced and illustrated in some detail. Chapters 3 and 4 are concerned with approximate molecular orbital theory, presenting first the formalism of acceptable approximation schemes followed by a discussion of applications reported to date. Appendix A contains a description and listing of a digital computer program for carrying out calculations by some of the more extensively tested approximate molecular orbital methods.

1.2 THE SCHROEDINGER EQUATION [9]

According to classical mechanics, the energy E of a system of interacting particles is the sum of a kinetic-energy contribution T and a potential-energy function V,

$$T + V = E \tag{1.1}$$

Schroedinger suggested that the proper way to describe the wave character of particles was to replace the classical kinetic- and potential-energy functions T, V with *linear operators*† $\mathbf{T}$, $\mathbf{V}$ and set up a wave equation of the form

$$\{\mathbf{T} + \mathbf{V}\}\Psi = E\Psi \tag{1.2}$$

The solution to Eq. (1.2), the so-called *wavefunction* Ψ, would describe the spatial motion of all the particles of the system moving in the field of force specified by the potential-energy operator $\mathbf{V}$.

In simple one-electron systems, such as the hydrogen atom, the problem is essentially to describe the motion of the electron in the coulombic force field of the nucleus. In this case the classical potential-energy function and the quantum-mechanical potential-energy operator are identical, and for an electron moving in the field of a nucleus of charge Ze,

$$\mathbf{V} = -Ze^2 r^{-1} \tag{1.3}$$

where r is the distance of the electron from the nucleus and e is the unit of electronic charge. With the coordinate system centered on the atomic nucleus, one need consider only the kinetic energy of the electron. Schroedinger's prescription required that the classical kinetic-energy expression for a single particle,

$$T = \frac{p^2}{2m} \tag{1.4}$$

where p and m are the momentum and mass of the particle, respectively, be replaced by the linear differential operator

$$\mathbf{T} = -\frac{h^2}{8\pi^2 m}\nabla^2 \tag{1.5}$$

where h is Planck's constant, m the electronic mass, and

$$\nabla^2 = \frac{\partial^2}{\partial x^2} + \frac{\partial^2}{\partial y^2} + \frac{\partial^2}{\partial z^2} \tag{1.6}$$

in cartesian coordinates. Thus the Schroedinger equation for the hydrogen atom takes the form

$$\left\{-\frac{h^2}{8\pi^2 m}\nabla^2 - \frac{Ze^2}{r}\right\}\Psi(1) = E\Psi(1) \tag{1.7}$$

In this one-electron system, the wavefunction $\Psi(1)$ contains only the coordinates of the single electron, and the 1 in parentheses signifies

---

† A linear operator $\mathbf{M}$, considered with functions ζ and η, obeys the equations

   (1) $\mathbf{M}(\zeta + \eta) = \mathbf{M}\zeta + \mathbf{M}\eta$
   (2) $\mathbf{M}(C\zeta) = C\mathbf{M}\zeta$ where C is a constant

a functional dependence on all the coordinates of an electron arbitrarily labeled electron 1. It is a useful convention for later considerations to denote wavefunctions depending on the coordinates of only one electron by lowercase psi, $\psi(1)$. Such functions are called *orbitals* and are the quantum-mechanical counterpart of planetary orbits in classical mechanics. Similarly, one-electron energies will be denoted by ε. The linear operator in braces in Eq. (1.7) is known as the *hamiltonian operator* for the system under consideration, and is denoted by $\mathcal{H}$. Thus the Schroedinger equation for the hydrogen atom may be written in the form

$$\mathcal{H}(1)\psi(1) = \varepsilon\psi(1) \tag{1.8}$$

The Schroedinger equation for a larger system consisting of a set of interacting electrons and nuclei is formulated in a similar manner. This first requires specification of the full hamiltonian for the system. The hamiltonian is again the sum of kinetic-energy operators for the nuclei and for the electrons together with the potential-energy terms representing the various coulombic interactions. These are repulsive for electron-electron and nucleus-nucleus pairs, but attractive between electrons and nuclei. If there are N nuclei and n electrons, the many-particle hamiltonian operator $\mathcal{H}^{\text{total}}$ is

$$\mathcal{H}^{\text{total}}(1,2, \ldots ,N;1,2, \ldots ,n) = -\frac{h^2}{8\pi^2} \sum_{A}^{N} M_A^{-1}\nabla_A^2$$

$$+ \sum_{A<B} e^2 Z_A Z_B r_{AB}^{-1} - \frac{h^2}{8\pi m^2} \sum_{p}^{n} \nabla_p^2 - \sum_{A} \sum_{p} e^2 Z_A r_{Ap}^{-1}$$

$$+ \sum_{p<q} e^2 r_{pq}^{-1} \tag{1.9}$$

Here M_A is the mass of nucleus A; m and e are the electronic mass and charge, respectively; $Z_A e$ is the charge on nucleus A; and r_{ij} is the distance between particles i and j. Summations involving indices A and B are over atomic nuclei and those involving p and q are over electrons.

The Schroedinger equation for the entire system is thus

$$\mathcal{H}^{\text{total}}(1,2, \ldots ,N;1,2, \ldots ,n)\Psi(1,2, \ldots ,N;1,2, \ldots ,n)$$
$$= E\Psi(1,2, \ldots ,N;1,2, \ldots ,n) \tag{1.10}$$

where Ψ is now a complete wavefunction for all particles in the molecule and E is the total energy of the system. Since each particle is described by three cartesian coordinates, this is a partial differential equation in $3N + 3n$ variables.

The full Schroedinger equation for any molecular system will have an infinite number of solutions, only certain of which are acceptable. If we are concerned with stationary or bound states of the system, the wavefunction Ψ, to be physically reasonable, must be continuous, single-valued, and vanish at infinity. Just as the wave equation for the vibrating string with fixed ends yields a discrete set of acceptable standing wave solutions, acceptable solutions of the Schroedinger equation occur only for certain values of the energy. The discrete energies may be labeled E_1, E_2, . . . and the corresponding wavefunctions Ψ_1, Ψ_2, . . . so that

$$\mathfrak{JC}^{total}\Psi_i = E_i\Psi_i \tag{1.11}$$

In accordance with usual nomenclature for differential equations of this type, the energies E_i are called the *eigenvalues* of the operator $\mathfrak{JC}^{total}$ and the corresponding wavefunctions Ψ_i are known as the *eigenfunctions*. It may happen that two or more wavefunctions arise with identical energies, and such solutions are said to be *degenerate*.

In practice, rather than attempt to find a wavefunction describing both electronic and nuclear motion together, it is usually sufficient to break the problem down into two parts and consider first the motion of electrons in the field of stationary nuclei. There is then a separate, purely electronic problem for each set of nuclear positions. This is a reasonable procedure because the masses of the nuclei are several thousand times larger than the masses of the electrons, so that the nuclei move much more slowly, and we may reasonably suppose the electrons to adjust themselves to new nuclear positions so rapidly that at any one instant their motion is just as it would be if the nuclei were at rest at the positions they occupy at that same instant. This simplification is referred to as the Born-Oppenheimer approximation [10]. In more quantitative terms, the Born-Oppenheimer approximation amounts to separating off the nuclear kinetic energy and nuclear-nuclear repulsion terms from $\mathfrak{JC}^{total}$, and considering only the part of the hamiltonian which depends on the positions but not the momenta of the nuclei. This is the *electronic hamiltonian operator* $\mathfrak{JC}^{el}$.

$$\mathfrak{JC}^{el} = \frac{-h^2}{8\pi m^2}\sum_p \nabla_p{}^2 - \sum_A\sum_p e^2 Z_A r_{Ap}{}^{-1} + \sum_{p<q} e^2 r_{pq}{}^{-1} \tag{1.12}$$

The electronic hamiltonian may be used in a modified Schroedinger equation,

$$\mathfrak{JC}^{el}(1,2, \ . \ . \ . \ ,n)\Psi^{el}(1,2, \ . \ . \ . \ ,n) = \mathcal{E}\Psi^{el}(1,2, \ . \ . \ . \ ,n) \tag{1.13}$$

the solutions of which are purely electronic wavefunctions Ψ^{el}, describing the motion of the electrons in the field of the fixed nuclei. The total energy E of the system of a given internuclear distance is then given as

$$E = \mathcal{E} + \sum_{A<B} e^2 Z_A Z_B r_{AB}^{-1} \tag{1.14}$$

where $\mathcal{E}$ is the electronic energy and the second term is the electrostatic internuclear repulsion energy. Molecular orbital theory is concerned with electronic wavefunctions only, and we henceforth drop the superscript el on the hamiltonian operator and the wavefunctions without ambiguity.

In dealing with the equations of quantum mechanics, it is convenient to introduce new units which are appropriate to atomic dimensions and which eliminate some of the constants from the wavefunction. These are referred to as *atomic units*. The atomic unit of length is defined as the quantity

$$a_0 = \frac{h^2}{4\pi^2 m e^2} = 0.529167 \times 10^{-8} \text{ cm} \tag{1.15}$$

and is the radius of the first orbit in the original Bohr theory of the hydrogen atom. It is frequently referred to as the Bohr radius. The atomic unit of electric charge is the protonic charge,

$$e = 4.80298 \times 10^{-10} \text{ esu} \tag{1.16}$$

The atomic unit of energy is the energy of interaction of two units of charge separated by one Bohr radius

$$\varepsilon_0 = \frac{e^2}{a_0} = 4.35942 \times 10^{-11} \text{ erg} \tag{1.17}$$

and is called a *Hartree*. The atomic unit of mass is the electron mass,

$$m = 9.0191 \times 10^{-28} \text{ g} \tag{1.18}$$

In this system, nuclear masses are measured as the number of electron masses. We shall use these units throughout the remainder of the book, unless otherwise specified. The electronic hamiltonian operator of Eq. (1.12) reduces in atomic units to

$$\mathcal{H} = -\sum_p \tfrac{1}{2}\nabla_p^2 - \sum_A \sum_p Z_A r_{Ap}^{-1} + \sum_{p<q} r_{pq}^{-1} \tag{1.19}$$

1.3 GENERAL PROPERTIES OF OPERATORS AND WAVEFUNCTIONS

In this section, we shall enumerate a number of general properties of the Schroedinger equation and related operators which will be of some value in developing orbital theories in later chapters. We begin by noting that the Schroedinger equation itself leaves the solution undetermined to the extent of a multiplicative constant [if Ψ satisfies Eq. (1.10), so does $c\Psi$, where c is any number]. To fix the magnitude of this constant, it is convenient to impose a *normalization condition*. For a one-electron wavefunction satisfying (1.8), we require

$$\int \psi_i^2(1) \, d\tau_1 = 1 \tag{1.20}$$

where $d\tau$ is the volume element for the electron. $\psi_i^2 \, d\tau$ is interpreted in quantum mechanics as the probability of finding the electron in a small volume element $d\tau$. The normalization condition then ensures the total probability of the electron being anywhere is unity. For a many-particle wavefunction Ψ_i, the corresponding normalization condition is

$$\int \cdots \int \Psi_i^2(1,2, \ldots) \, d\tau_1 \, d\tau_2 \cdots = 1 \tag{1.21}$$

where $d\tau_1$, $d\tau_2$, . . . are the volume elements for the individual particles. Again $\Psi_i^2(1,2, \ldots) \, d\tau_1$, $d\tau_2 \cdots$ (sometimes shortened to $\Psi_i^2 \, d\tau$) is the probability of particle 1 being in the volume element $d\tau_1$, particle 2 in $d\tau_2$, and so forth.

It is also a property of the wave equation that two different solutions, Ψ_i and Ψ_j, are mutually orthogonal, i.e.,

$$\int \Psi_i \Psi_j \, d\tau = 0 \tag{1.22}$$

This condition may be combined with normalization in the single statement

$$\int \Psi_i \Psi_j \, d\tau = \delta_{ij} \tag{1.23}$$

for all i, j. Here δ_{ij} is the Kronecker delta symbol: unity if $i = j$ and zero otherwise.

In general a wavefunction Ψ may be complex, in which case the probability density is more properly written $|\Psi^2|$ or $\Psi^*\Psi$, where the asterisk denotes complex conjugation. However, the actual use of complex wavefunctions can normally be avoided in the absence of external electromagnetic perturbations, but the asterisk notation is often retained for generality.

We have already seen that in Schroedinger treatment, the classical kinetic- and potential-energy functions are replaced by linear operators. In fact, every physical observable M (and many quantities closely related to observables) may be characterized by a linear operator $\mathbf{M}$. The operators encountered herein are listed in Table 1.1.

Table 1.1 Quantum-mechanical operators in terms of cartesian coordinates

Observable	Operator
Position	$\mathbf{r} = x\mathbf{i} + y\mathbf{j} + z\mathbf{k}$
Linear momentum	$\mathbf{p} = p_x\mathbf{i} + p_y\mathbf{j} + p_z\mathbf{k}$
	where $p_x = \dfrac{h}{2\pi i}\dfrac{\partial}{\partial x}$
	$p_y = \dfrac{h}{2\pi i}\dfrac{\partial}{\partial y}$
	$p_z = \dfrac{h}{2\pi i}\dfrac{\partial}{\partial z}$
Orbital angular momentum	$\mathbf{1} = l_x\mathbf{i} + l_y\mathbf{j} + l_z\mathbf{k}$
	where $l_x = \dfrac{h}{2\pi i}\left(y\dfrac{\partial}{\partial z} - z\dfrac{\partial}{\partial y} \right)$
	$l_y = \dfrac{h}{2\pi i}\left(z\dfrac{\partial}{\partial x} - x\dfrac{\partial}{\partial z} \right)$
	$l_z = \dfrac{h}{2\pi i}\left(x\dfrac{\partial}{\partial y} - y\dfrac{\partial}{\partial x} \right)$
Spin angular momentum	$\mathbf{s} = s_x\mathbf{i} + s_y\mathbf{j} + s_z\mathbf{k}$
Kinetic energy	$\mathbf{T} = \dfrac{p^2}{2m}$
Potential energy	$\mathbf{V} = r^{-1}$
Dipole moment	$\mathbf{\mu} = e\mathbf{r}$
Charge density	$\varrho(\mathbf{R}) = \delta(\mathbf{R} - \mathbf{r})$
Spin density	$\varrho^{\mathrm{spin}}(\mathbf{R}) = 2\mathbf{s}_z\,\delta(\mathbf{R} - \mathbf{r})$

The quantum-mechanical expectation value of the observable M is given by

$$\int \Psi_i^* \mathbf{M} \Psi_i \, d\tau \tag{1.24}$$

where the integration extends over all variables. Thus the energy of the system is the expectation value of the hamiltonian operator,

$$\mathcal{E}_i = \int \Psi_i^* \mathcal{H} \Psi_i \, dr \tag{1.25}$$

and the dipole moment of the system is the expectation value of the dipole-moment operator, etc.

At this point it is convenient to introduce the alternative matrix notation used for integrals of the type of Eq. (1.24), sometimes referred to as Dirac notation [11]. Given any set of functions involving the coordinates of all the particles, and any operator M, we may define a set of matrix elements $\langle \Psi_i | \mathbf{M} | \Psi_j \rangle$

$$\langle \Psi_i | \mathbf{M} | \Psi_j \rangle = \int \Psi_i^* \mathbf{M} \Psi_j \, d\tau \tag{1.26}$$

The symbols M_{ij} and $(i|\mathbf{M}|j)$ are also frequently encountered in the literature for the same quantities. Note that complex conjugation is implied for the left-hand element enclosed in brackets. The vertical bars are inserted only for clarity and have no mathematical significance.

Since experimental measurements invariably result in real and not complex numbers, an additional restriction must be imposed on the linear operators to assure that expectation values as in Eq. (1.24) are real. This will be so if the operator M is hermitian, i.e., if the operator $\mathbf{M}$ has the property

$$\langle \Psi_j | \mathbf{M} | \Psi_i \rangle = \langle \Psi_i | \mathbf{M} | \Psi_j \rangle \tag{1.27}$$

Thus linear operators associated with observables must be hermitian.

Other important features of wavefunctions follow from the commutation properties of various operators with the hamiltonian. Two operators $\mathbf{L}$ and $\mathbf{M}$ are said to *commute* if

$$\mathbf{LM} = \mathbf{ML} \tag{1.28}$$

that is, if the order of operations on any function is immaterial. It should be noted that commutation often fails with differential operators. Thus $\partial/\partial x (x\psi) \neq x(\partial/\partial x)\psi$.

It can be shown quite generally that if the operators $\mathbf{L}$ and $\mathbf{M}$ commute, then there exists a complete set of functions which are simultaneously eigenfunctions of both operators. (A complete set of functions has the property that any function can be expressed as a linear combination of members of the set.) If this set of functions is Λ_i, then

$$\mathbf{L}\Lambda_i = l_i \Lambda_i \qquad \text{and} \qquad \mathbf{M}\Lambda_i = m_i \Lambda_i \tag{1.29}$$

where l_i and m_i are eigenvalues.

We shall be particularly concerned with operators which commute with the hamiltonian $\mathfrak{IC}$. The eigenfunctions of $\mathfrak{IC}$ are the stationary wavefunctions Ψ_i. Hence, if $\mathbf{M}$ commutes with $\mathfrak{IC}$, then we may expect that

$$\mathbf{M}\Psi_i = m\Psi_i \tag{1.30}$$

so that the observable M has a definite value m_i in each state; Eq. (1.30) must be true for nondegenerate wavefunctions, and for degenerate wavefunctions we may adopt appropriate linear combinations so that Eq. (1.30) is always satisfied.   Another important consequence is that the off-diagonal matrix elements of **M** are zero,

$$\langle \Psi_i | \mathbf{M} | \Psi_j \rangle = 0 \tag{1.31}$$

again provided that the operator **M** commutes with the hamiltonian. This follows from Eq. (1.30) and the orthogonality of Ψ_i and Ψ_j. Important examples of operators which commute with the hamiltonian are angular-momentum operators and certain symmetry operators. According to the above analysis, we may classify states according to the values m_i of these other operators.   Further, we shall often find it possible and useful to construct eigenfunctions of these operators for use as trial wavefunctions, knowing in advance that the final solution must be of this form.

1.4 THE VARIATIONAL METHOD

The complete treatment of a quantum-mechanical problem involving electronic structure is equivalent to the complete solution of the appropriate Schroedinger equation.   A direct approach in terms of a mathematical treatment of the partial differential equation is practicable only for one-electron systems, and for many-electron systems solutions are usually obtained by the variational method.   This method in its *full* form is completely equivalent to the differential equations, but it has many advantages in the ways it can be adapted to approximate wavefunctions.

Solutions of the Schroedinger equation give *stationary values* of the energy.   That is, if Ψ is a solution to Eq. (1.13), for any small change $\delta\Psi$,

$$\delta \mathcal{E} = \delta \langle \Psi | \mathcal{3C} | \Psi \rangle = 0 \tag{1.32}$$

If this criterion is applied to a completely flexible function Ψ (in the appropriate number of dimensions), all wavefunctions Ψ_i for the hamiltonian $\mathcal{3C}$ will be obtained.   The great advantage of the variational method in approximate quantum mechanics is that the same criteria can be applied to *incompletely* flexible functions to obtain *approximations* to correct wavefunctions.   Thus, if the only flexibility allowed in a particular type of calculation is the variation of a finite number of numerical parameters $c_1, c_2, \ldots$ so that $\Psi = \Psi(c_1, c_2, \ldots)$, then the estimate of the energy according to Eq. (1.25) will be a function of these parameters, $\mathcal{E}(c_1, c_2, \ldots)$, and the stationary values of E will satisfy

$$\delta \mathcal{E}(c_1, c_2, \ldots) = \frac{\partial \mathcal{E}}{\partial c_1} \delta c_1 + \frac{\partial \mathcal{E}}{\partial c_2} \delta c_2 + \cdots = 0 \tag{1.33}$$

Solution of these algebraic equations will then lead to approximations to the energies $\mathcal{E}_i$ and the wavefunctions Ψ_i for the stationary states. As the flexibility of the variation function Ψ increases (e.g., by increasing the number of adjustable parameters), the calculated energies and wavefunctions will become closer approximations to the correct values. From the variation theorem, the lowest energy calculated from any incompletely flexible variation function represents an upper bound for the true energy for the lowest state of the system.

A very common use of the variational method is with a linear combination of fixed functions Φ_1, Φ_2, . . .

$$\Psi(c_1, c_2, \ldots) = c_1 \Phi_1 + c_2 \Phi_2 + \cdots \tag{1.34}$$

The given functions Φ_i are often referred to as a *basis* or as *basis functions*. If the basis functions are linearly independent (that is, if no one can be written as a linear combination of the others), the variational method then leads directly to a set of approximate energies and wavefunctions. As will be seen in the following chapter, this approach is the basis of the systematic calculation of approximate electronic wavefunctions via molecular orbital theory.

1.5 THE ORBITAL APPROXIMATION [12, 13]

The orbital approach to approximate solutions of the many-electron Schroedinger equation is an attempt to construct a satisfactory approximate many-electron wavefunction from a combination of functions, each dependent upon the coordinates of one electron only. For an n electron system, the simplest way to do this is to associate the n electrons with n one-electron functions ψ_1, ψ_2, . . . , ψ_n and write the total wavefunction $\Psi(1, 2, \ldots, n)$ as a product of the one-electron functions,

$$\Psi(1, 2, \ldots, n) = \psi_1(1) \psi_2(2) \cdots \psi_n(n) \tag{1.35}$$

Such one-electron functions ψ_i are called *orbitals* and the product function as such is known as a *Hartree product* [13]. The probability density function Ψ^2 computed from Eq. (1.35) is, of course, just the product of one-electron probability densities ψ_i^2. From elementary probability theory, this situation arises only when the events associated with each of the probabilities ψ_i^2 occur independently of one another.

Thus the physical model involved in the approximation of many-electron wavefunctions by products of orbitals is an *independent electron* model.

If the many-electron hamiltonian operator $\mathfrak{IC}(1,2,3, \ldots ,n)$ *could* be written as a sum of one-electron operators $\mathbf{H}(i)$, it would be possible to obtain solutions for the Schroedinger equation by a straightforward separation of variables, and the solutions would indeed be in the form of a product of one-electron functions such as Eq. (1.35). In fact, the many-electron hamiltonian operator can *not* be written simply as a sum of one-electron operators, since it contains interelectron repulsion operators of the form r_{ij}^{-1}, which depend on the instantaneous relative coordinates of the two electrons i and j. Nevertheless, orbital theories attempt to develop approximate many-electron wavefunctions from product functions. It is useful in this regard to consider for the moment the many-electron hamiltonian operator as being approximated by a modified many-electron hamiltonian-type operator $\mathfrak{F}(1,2, \ldots ,n)$ which *can* be written as a sum of "effective" one-electron hamiltonian operators $\mathbf{F}(i)$,

$$\mathfrak{F}(1,2, \ldots ,n) = \sum_p \mathbf{F}(p) = \sum_p [-\tfrac{1}{2}\nabla_p{}^2 + \mathbf{V}(p)] \qquad (1.36)$$

Here $\mathbf{V}(p)$ is an unspecified one-electron potential-energy function based on the potential field of the atomic nuclei and the average of the instantaneous fields presented by the other $n - 1$ electrons. The operator $\mathfrak{F}(1,2, \ldots ,n)$ may be employed in a Schroedinger-type equation for the system under consideration,

$$\mathfrak{F}(1,2, \ldots ,n)\Psi(1,2, \ldots ,n) = \mathcal{E}\Psi(1,2, \ldots ,n) \qquad (1.37)$$

for which the solutions now factor into a product of orbitals such as Eq. (1.35) with each of the individual orbitals ψ_i satisfying a one-electron Schroedinger equation of the form

$$\mathbf{F}(1)\psi_i(1) = \varepsilon_i\psi_i(1) \qquad (1.38)$$

where ε_i is the orbital energy.

The effective potential $\mathbf{V}(p)$ in a one-electron hamiltonian should include the average field due to the other electrons. This potential must therefore depend on the location or spatial distribution of these electrons, which in fact is determined by the molecular orbitals. In other words, it is really necessary to know the molecular orbitals ψ_i before it is possible to construct an effective one-electron potential to use in a one-electron orbital equation. If the molecular orbitals that are obtained by solving the one-electron equation turn out to be identical to those used in constructing the potential $V(p)$, these orbitals are described as *self-consistent*, that is, consistent with their own potential field. This is a central concept which will be developed later in quantitative detail. It is sufficient for present purposes to state that determination of self-consistent orbitals depends on the variational principle, these same orbitals being those which will minimize the calculated energy $\langle \Psi | \mathfrak{K} | \Psi \rangle$, $\mathfrak{K}$ being the *correct* many-electron hamiltonian. Use of the variational principle, in fact, permits us to develop a precise orbital theory leading to one-electron eigenvalue equations of the form of Eq. (1.38) *without* making the approximation of Eq. (1.36).

1.6 ELECTRON SPIN [14]

Although an orbital as such gives a complete specification of the spatial distribution of an electron, it is still incomplete in that it does not specify the state of electron spin. In addition to spatial motion, reflected in orbital angular momentum, an electron may possess an additional intrinsic angular momentum identified with electron spin. The spin angular momentum is represented by the vector operator s and has components s_x, s_y, and s_z which satisfy the basic commutation relations characteristic of general angular-momentum operators. The spin operators all commute with the general hamiltonian operator, which contains no spin coordinates, so that one may hope to gain simplification by constructing approximate wavefunctions which are already eigenfunctions of appropriate spin-angular-momentum operators. The components s_x, s_y, and s_z all commute with the spin-squared operator s^2 but not with each other. Thus the most one can hope for is a function which is simultaneously an eigenstate of s^2 and one of the components of s, usually taken arbitrarily as s_z.

The spin angular momentum is quantized such that the z component may assume only two possible values, $\pm h/4\pi$. These two spin states may be represented by two mutually orthogonal spin wave-functions $\alpha(\xi)$ and $\beta(\xi)$, where ξ is the spin coordinate. The quantization condition is thus

$$s^2 \eta(\xi) = s(s+1)\eta(\xi) \tag{1.39}$$
$$s_z \eta(\xi) = m_s \eta(\xi) \tag{1.40}$$

where $\eta(\xi)$ may be $\alpha(\xi)$ or $\beta(\xi)$ and m_s may take the value $\pm \frac{1}{2}$ in units of $h/2\pi$, with $+\frac{1}{2}$ resulting from operation of s_z on $\alpha(\xi)$ and $-\frac{1}{2}$ resulting from operation on $\beta(\xi)$. In accord with the general quantum-mechanical theory of angular momentum, m_s takes the values $s, s-1, \ldots, -s$, and in the case of one electron $s = \frac{1}{2}$, again in units of $h/2\pi$.

The complete wavefunction for a single electron is a product of a spatial function and a spin function $\psi_i(\mathbf{r})\eta(\xi)$, called a *spin orbital*. A given spatial orbital $\psi_i(\mathbf{r})$ may be associated with either α or β spin functions, giving rise to the two spin orbitals $\psi_i(\mathbf{r})\alpha(\xi)$ and $\psi_i(\mathbf{r})\beta(\xi)$.

A product wavefunction including electron spin is obtained directly as a Hartree product of spin orbitals,

$$\Psi(1,2, \ldots ,n) = \psi_1(1)\alpha(1)\psi_2(2)\beta(2) \cdots \psi_n(n)\beta(n) \qquad (1.41)$$

where the 1 signifies the appropriate spatial or spin coordinates of electron 1, etc. Wavefunctions of the form of Eq. (1.40) are often written in the contracted notation

$$\Psi(1,2, \ldots ,n) = \psi_1(1)\bar{\psi}_2(2) \cdots \psi_{n-1}(n-1)\bar{\psi}_n(n) \qquad (1.42)$$

where the barred orbitals $\bar{\psi}_i$ have β spin functions and an α spin function is implied for the unbarred orbitals.

Just as the spin orbitals are taken to be eigenfunctions of the one-electron spin-angular-momentum operators $\mathbf{s}^2$ and $\mathbf{s}_z$, it is for the same reason desirable for the many-electron wavefunction Ψ to be an eigenfunction of the many-electron spin operators $\mathbf{S}^2$ and $\mathbf{S}_z$,

$$\mathbf{S}^2 = \mathbf{S}_x{}^2 + \mathbf{S}_y{}^2 + \mathbf{S}_z{}^2 \qquad (1.43)$$

and

$$\mathbf{S}_z = \sum_p \mathbf{s}_{pz} \qquad (1.44)$$

where the summation runs over all electrons in the system. The eigenrelations for the many-electron wavefunctions are

$$\mathbf{S}^2\Psi = S(S+1)\Psi \qquad (1.45)$$

where S takes positive integral or half-integral values $0, \frac{1}{2}, 1, \frac{3}{2}, \ldots$ and

$$\mathbf{S}_z\Psi = M_s\Psi \qquad (1.46)$$

where M_s takes the $2S+1$ values $S, (S-1), \ldots, -(S-1), -S$. Thus a state of the system is characterized in part by the pair of spin quantum numbers (S,M_S), with S being a measure of the resultant spin magnitude and M_S being a measure of the orientation. By application of the operator S_z to a product wavefunction of the form of Eq. (1.41), it is seen that the M_S for the many-electron system is a sum of the m_S for the individual spin orbitals,

$$M_s = \sum_p (m_s)_p \tag{1.47}$$

Of the various types of states commonly encountered in the study of molecules, the simplest states are those with zero resultant spin, so that $S = 0$ and $M_S = 0$. The *multiplicity* of a state is defined as the number of different M_S components possible, and in this case the multiplicity is 1 and the state is known as a *singlet*. For $S = \frac{1}{2}$, there will be two components $M_S = +\frac{1}{2}$ and $M_S = -\frac{1}{2}$, and such states are known as *doublets*. For $S = 1$, there are three components, $M_S = 1$, $M_S = 0$, and $M_S = -1$, and the state is a *triplet*. States of higher multiplicity are, of course, also possible.

1.7 THE ANTISYMMETRY PRINCIPLE AND DETERMINANTAL WAVEFUNCTIONS

One very important feature of many-electron wavefunctions which has not been discussed so far concerns their symmetry under interchange of electron coordinates. Since electrons are essentially indistinguishable particles, no physical property of the system can be affected if we simply rename or renumber the electrons. If we consider the many-electron density function $\rho(1,2, \ldots ,n)$,

$$\rho(1,2, \ldots ,n) = \Psi^2(1,2, \ldots ,n) \tag{1.48}$$

this must be *unaffected* if we interchange the coordinates of any two electrons. For this to be so, Ψ itself must be changed only by a factor of $+1$ or -1 under such an interchange,

$$\Psi(1,2, \ldots ,i,j, \ldots ,n) = \pm \Psi(1,2, \ldots ,j,i, \ldots ,n) \tag{1.49}$$

In the former case Ψ is said to be symmetric with respect to the interchange, and in the latter case Ψ is antisymmetric, and these are the only two possibilities compatible with the invariance of Ψ^2. In fact, the antisymmetric property is appropriate for electrons, since it leads naturally to the Pauli exclusion principle [15] in orbital theory which states that no two electrons may be assigned to identical spin orbitals. This will become clear shortly.

The antisymmetry principle may be formulated as

$$\mathbf{P}_{ij}\Psi(1,2, \ldots ,n) = -\Psi(1,2, \ldots ,n) \tag{1.50}$$

where $\mathbf{P}_{ij}$ is a *permutation operator* which interchanges all the coordinates (including spin coordinates) of electrons i and j.

A single-product wavefunction

$$\Psi(1,2, \ldots ,n) = \psi_1(1)\alpha(1)\psi_2(2)\beta(2) \cdots \psi_n(n)\beta(n) \qquad (1.51)$$

does *not* satisfy the antisymmetry principle and is therefore not a suitable approximate form to use. For example, the two-electron function $\Psi(1,2)$,

$$\Psi(1,2) = \psi_1(1)\alpha(1)\psi_1(2)\beta(2) \qquad (1.52)$$

is transformed by application of a two-electron permutation operator according to the equation

$$\mathbf{P}_{12}\Psi(1,2) = \psi_1(2)\alpha(2)\psi_1(1)\beta(1) \qquad (1.53)$$

from which it is clear that $\mathbf{P}_{12}\Psi(1,2)$ is not the negative of $\Psi(1,2)$. However, a combination of Hartree products may be constructed which is antisymmetric. Consider

$$\Psi(1,2) = \psi_1(1)\alpha(1)\psi_1(2)\beta(2) - \psi_1(2)\alpha(2)\psi_1(1)\beta(1) \qquad (1.54)$$

Now

$$\mathbf{P}_{12}\Psi(1,2) = \psi_1(2)\alpha(2)\psi_1(1)\beta(1) - \psi_1(1)\alpha(1)\psi_1(2)\beta(2) \qquad (1.55)$$

which by comparison with Eq. (1.50) is seen to be just $-\Psi(1,2)$ as desired. Thus for the two-electron system under consideration, the correct form for an orbital approximation to the wavefunction would be given by Eq. (1.54).

With the general form of the orbital approximation to the two-electron wavefunction thus established, it remains only to multiply the right-hand side of Eq. (1.54) by a constant factor $\mathfrak{N}$ such that the combination of Hartree products is normalized to unity. This will be considered for the general case in the following chapter.

It should be noted at this point that the properly antisymmetrized form of the orbital approximation to the two-electron wavefunction may be generated from the original Hartree product by operating on the Hartree product with a linear combination of permutation operators $\mathbf{P}_k$ each resulting in one of the 2! distinct permutations of i and j possible, in the example under consideration,

$$\Psi(1,2) = \mathfrak{N} \sum_{k}^{2!} (-1)^P \mathbf{P}_k \psi_1(1)\alpha(1)\psi_1(2)\beta(2) \qquad (1.56)$$

where $(-1)^P$ is $+1$ for an even permutation and -1 for an odd permutation. This is just the same process as one encounters in the definition of a determinant of elements of a square matrix, and indeed it is found that the combination of Hartree products necessary for a properly antisymmetrized function may be found by writing the spin orbitals as elements of a square matrix, with the electron label as the column index and the orbital label as the row index, and forming the determinant of this matrix. For the two-electron examples under consideration,

$$\Psi(1,2) = \mathfrak{N} \begin{vmatrix} \psi_1(1)\alpha(1) & \psi_1(1)\beta(1) \\ \psi_1(2)\alpha(2) & \psi_1(2)\beta(2) \end{vmatrix} \quad (1.57)$$

This is the simplest example of a general method of constructing approximate wavefunctions from products of one-electron spin orbitals. The many-electron wavefunction for a $2n$ electron system, with two electrons per spatial orbital as a determinant of the $2n$ spin orbitals involved, is

$$\Psi(1,2,\ldots,n) = \mathfrak{N} \begin{vmatrix} \psi_1(1)\alpha(1) & \psi_1(1)\beta(1) & \psi_2(1)\alpha(1) \cdots \psi_n(1)\beta(1) \\ \psi_1(2)\alpha(2) & \psi_1(2)\beta(2) & \cdots \\ \cdots & \cdots & \cdots \\ \psi_1(2n)\alpha(2n) & \cdots & \psi_n(2n)\beta(2n) \end{vmatrix}$$
$$(1.58)$$

with the normalization constant appropriately adjusted. Equation (1.58) is often abbreviated as the product of the diagonal elements of the matrix enclosed in bars

$$\Psi(1,2,\ldots,n) = |\psi_1(1)\alpha(1)\psi_1(2)\beta(2) \cdots \psi_n(2n)\beta(2n)| \quad (1.59)$$

where the appropriate normalization is implied. Such determinants of spin orbitals are known as Slater determinants [16]. A single Slater determinant is the simplest orbital wavefunction which satisfies the antisymmetry principle. Slater determinants in the literature to molecular orbital theory are often written in the contracted notation introduced in Eq. (1.42), in which Eq. (1.59) would be written

$$\Psi(1,2,\ldots,n) = |\psi_1(1)\bar{\psi}_1(2) \cdots \psi_n(2n-1)\bar{\psi}_n(2n)| \quad (1.60)$$

or, even more simply,

$$\Psi(1,2,\ldots,n) = |\psi_1\bar{\psi}_1 \cdots \psi_n\bar{\psi}_n| \quad (1.61)$$

A number of well-known theorems concerning determinants have important consequences for orbital wavefunctions. For example, the antisymmetry property itself follows directly from the theorem that the interchange of two rows changes the sign of the determinant. The Pauli exclusion principle corresponds to the theorem that a determinant with two identical columns vanishes, so that a nonzero function cannot be constructed if two electrons are assigned to the same spin orbital.

A theorem of determinants which will prove useful in the interpretation of orbital wavefunctions allows that the n spin orbitals of the determinant may be subjected to any orthogonal transformation without essentially changing the determinantal product function. This latter property sometimes allows transformation of molecular orbitals delocalized over an entire molecule into orbitals localized in regions associated with classical chemical bonds [17].

1.8 ELECTRONIC CONFIGURATIONS AND ELECTRONIC STATES

Having dealt with some of the general features of the orbital approach to approximate solutions of the Schroedinger equation, we consider now the manner in which the orbitals obtained describe the electronic structure of the system. For a molecule with $2n$ electrons, a solution of the Schroedinger equation in the orbital approximation results in $2n$ molecular spin orbitals, each associated with a discrete orbital energy. In a spin-restricted orbital wavefunction, a given spatial orbital may be associated with both an electron of α spin and an electron of β spin, with the orbital energies of the two resulting spin orbitals being, of course, degenerate. For the ground state of the $2n$ electron system, the n spatial orbitals will be occupied. Such a system is said to have an *electronic configuration* $\psi_1^2 \psi_2^2 \cdots \psi_n^2$.

Electronic configurations may be represented schematically by orbital energy-level diagrams as shown in Fig. 1.1. In Fig. 1.1a the orbital energy-level diagram for a four-electron system is given. A configuration such as this with all occupied orbitals containing their maximum of two electrons is known as a *closed-shell* configuration. Since there are an identical number of α and β electrons, it follows that $S = 0$ and the closed-shell configuration gives rise to a singlet state.

In constructing orbital wavefunctions for a given state of the system, it is advantageous to choose a form which is an eigenfunction of $\mathbf{S}^2$ and $\mathbf{S}_z$ for the state. In general, this may be done by choosing an appropriate linear combination of Slater determinants. In the case of closed-shell singlet states, it turns out that a single determinant as such is an eigenfunction of $\mathbf{S}^2$ and $\mathbf{S}_z$. Thus the spin-correct form for an orbital wavefunction for a closed-shell singlet with $2n$ electrons is, in contracted notation,

$$^1\Psi(1, 2, \ldots, 2n - 1, 2n) = |\psi_1(1)\bar{\psi}_1(2) \cdots \psi_n(2n - 1)\bar{\psi}_n(2n)| \tag{1.62}$$

If the number of electrons is odd, $2n + 1$, the ground-state electronic configuration will be $\psi_1^2 \psi_2^2 \cdots \psi_n^2 \psi_{n+1}$ and may be repre-

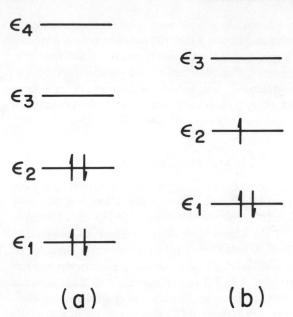

Fig. 1.1 Orbital energy-level diagram for ground electronic configuration of (a) closed-shell and (b) open-shell system.

sented by the orbital energy-level diagram such as that given in Fig. 1.1b. A configuration of this sort is a type of *open-shell* configuration and is characteristic of free radicals. With an odd number of electrons, $M_s = +\frac{1}{2}$ or $M_s = -\frac{1}{2}$ and this open-shell configuration gives rise to a doublet state. The spin-correct form of orbital wavefunctions for the two components of the doublet state are

$$^2\Psi = |\psi_1(1)\bar{\psi}_1(2) \cdots \psi_n(2n-1)\bar{\psi}_n(2n)\psi_{n+1}(2n+1)| \\ (M_s = \tfrac{1}{2})$$

$$^2\Psi = |\psi_1(1)\bar{\psi}_1(2) \cdots \psi_n(2n-1)\bar{\psi}_n(2n)\bar{\psi}_{n+1}(2n+1)| \\ (M_s = -\tfrac{1}{2})$$

(1.63)

In determining the orbitals for such a state, it is sufficient to consider explicitly only one or the other of the M_s components, since they are energetically degenerate.

Electronic configurations with more than one unpaired electron arise when systems with ground-state configurations such as those shown in Fig. 1.1 are exposed to electromagnetic radiation, usually in the form of visible or ultraviolet light. Electronic transitions are induced, resulting in the promotion of an electron from occupied orbital ψ_i to a previously unoccupied orbital ψ_k. This electronic excitation gives rise to excited configurations as shown in Fig. 1.2. From Fig. 1.2a four possible values of M_s may result. The contribution to M_s from any doubly occupied orbitals is of course zero, and it is sufficient to consider only the unpaired electrons. With both unpaired electrons of parallel spin, we have the $\alpha\alpha$ combination giving $M_s = +1$ and the $\beta\beta$ combination giving $M_s = -1$. The antiparallel combinations are $\alpha\beta$ and $\beta\alpha$, both giving $M_s = 0$ components. The $M_s = 1$, $M_s = -1$, and one of the $M_s = 0$ belong to a triplet state, and the remaining $M_s = 0$ component is a singlet state. Thus the configuration with two open shells gives rise to *two* states, a triplet and a singlet. These two states have different energies, even though the electronic configuration is the same. This is because the relative distribution of electrons with parallel spin differs from those with antiparallel spin, and so the electron-electron repulsion differs. In general, states of higher multiplicity are found at lower energies since electrons of parallel spins are kept apart by the antisymmetry condition. The spin-correct orbital wavefunctions for the singlet and triplet arising

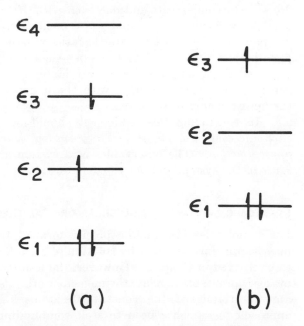

Fig. 1.2 Orbital energy-level diagrams for excited electronic configurations.

from two open shells are

$$^1\Psi(1, 2, \ldots, j, l, \ldots, 2n - 1, 2n)$$
$$= (2)^{-\frac{1}{2}}\{|\psi_1(1)\bar\psi_1(2) \cdots \psi_i(j)\bar\psi_k(l) \cdots \psi_n(2n - 1)\bar\psi_n(2n)|$$
$$- |\psi_1(1)\bar\psi_1(2) \cdots \bar\psi_i(j)\psi_k(l) \cdots \psi_n(2n - 1)\bar\psi_n(2n)|\} \quad (1.64)$$

$$^3\Psi(1, 2, \ldots, j, l, \ldots, 2n - 1, 2n)$$
$$= |\psi_1(1)\bar\psi_1(2) \cdots \psi_i(j)\psi_k(l) \cdots \psi_n(2n - 1)\bar\psi_n(2n)|$$
$$(M_s = 1)$$

$$^3\Psi(1, 2, \ldots, j, l, \ldots, 2n - 1, 2n)$$
$$. = (2)^{-\frac{1}{2}}\{|\psi_1(1)\bar\psi_1(2) \cdots \psi_i(j)\bar\psi_k(l) \cdots \psi_n(2n - 1)\bar\psi_n(2n)|$$
$$+ |\psi_1(1)\bar\psi_1(2) \cdots \bar\psi_i(j)\psi_k(l) \cdots \psi_n(2n - 1)\bar\psi_n(2n)|\} \quad (1.65)$$
$$(M_s = 0)$$

$$^3\Psi(1, 2, \ldots, j, l, \ldots, 2n - 1, 2n)$$
$$= |\psi_1(1)\psi_1(2) \cdots \bar\psi_i(j)\bar\psi_k(l) \cdots \psi_n(2n - 1)\bar\psi_n(2n)|$$
$$(M_s = -1)$$

The excited open-shell configuration shown in Fig. 1.2b has three unpaired electrons. We know from the previous paragraph that two unpaired spins may be combined to give two $M_s = 0$ components, an $M_s = 1$ and an $M_s = -1$ component. Combining a third unpaired spin with these two results in three $M_s = \frac{1}{2}$ components, three $M_s = -\frac{1}{2}$ components and one each with $M_s = \frac{3}{2}$ and $M_s = -\frac{3}{2}$. The $M_s = \frac{3}{2}$, $\frac{1}{2}$, $-\frac{1}{2}$, and $-\frac{3}{2}$ components comprise the four components of a quartet state, and the remaining components form two doublet states. Thus the open-shell configuration with three unpaired electrons gives rise to two doublets and a quartet state, all generally of different energy, with the quartet state usually having the lowest energy of the three.

In concluding this section, it should be carefully noted that *electronic configurations as such are constructs arising from the orbital approximation.* The observables of a system are always referred to *states* of the system and not to configurations.

1.9 ATOMIC ORBITALS IN MOLECULAR ORBITAL THEORY

For a molecular system, the precise form of the molecular orbitals may in principle be found by solution of certain differential equations to be derived in Chap. 2. However, the nature of chemical problems makes it profitable to relate the molecular orbitals to the corresponding atomic orbitals of the constituent atoms. The most rewarding approach to date has been to seek combinations of atomic orbitals which will be good approximations to the molecular orbitals of the system, the simplest such approximation being a simple sum with appropriate linear weighting coefficients. Considering a set of atomic functions ϕ_μ, $\mu = 1, 2, \ldots$, associated with the various atoms of the molecule, one can try to represent any particular molecular orbital ψ_i as

$$\psi_i = c_{1i}\phi_1 + c_{2i}\phi_2 + c_{3i}\phi_3 + \cdots \tag{1.66}$$

where the $c_{\mu i}$ are numerical coefficients which may be of either sign and may be real or complex numbers. This type of expansion is known as a *linear combination of atomic orbitals* [2], abbreviated henceforth as LCAO. Expansions of the LCAO type thus provide a mathematical framework for detailed calculations, with the actual computation of the molecular wavefunction for the system reduced to the determination of the linear expansion coefficients $c_{\mu i}$ for each of the orbitals.

In carrying out numerical calculations of molecular orbitals, it is necessary to have a convenient analytical form for the atomic orbitals of each type of atom in the molecule. The solutions of the Schroedinger equation for one-electron atomic systems can be written in the form [18]

$$\phi(r,\theta,\phi) = R_{nl}(r)Y_{lm}(\theta,\phi) \tag{1.67}$$

where r, θ, and ϕ are the spherical polar coordinates centered on the atom. The angular parts $Y_{lm}(\theta,\phi)$ are the well-known spherical harmonics, defined as

$$Y_{lm}(\theta,\phi) = \Theta_{lm}(\theta)\Phi_m(\phi) \tag{1.68}$$

where, in real space

$$\Theta_{lm}(\theta) = \left[\frac{(2l+1)(l-m)!}{2(l+m)!}\right]^{1/2} P_l^m(\cos\phi) \tag{1.69}$$

$$\Phi_m(\phi) = \begin{cases} (2\pi)^{-1/2} \\ (\pi)^{-1/2} \end{cases} \cos m\phi \qquad \begin{matrix} m = 0 \\ m \neq 0 \end{matrix} \tag{1.70}$$

$$\Phi_{\bar{m}}(\phi) = (\pi)^{-1/2} \sin m\phi$$

with the $P_l^m(\cos\phi)$ being associated Legendre polynomials.

The spherical harmonics depend on the angular-momentum quantum numbers l and m, which arise in the course of the solution of the differential equations involving angular coordinates θ and ϕ to insure that the total wavefunction will be unchanged if θ is replaced by $\theta + 2\pi$ or if ϕ is replaced by $\phi + 2\pi$. The angular properties of

Table 1.2   Real angular parts of s, p, and d atomic orbitals, referred to spherical polar coordinates (r,θ,ϕ)

s functions, $l = 0$	p functions, $l = 1$	d functions, $l = 2$
$s: \left(\dfrac{1}{4\pi}\right)^{\frac{1}{2}}$	$p_x: \left(\dfrac{3}{4\pi}\right)^{\frac{1}{2}} \cos\theta$	$d_{3z^2-r^2}: \left(\dfrac{5}{16\pi}\right)^{\frac{1}{2}} \left(3\cos^2\theta - 1\right)$
	$p_y: \left(\dfrac{3}{4\pi}\right)^{\frac{1}{2}} \sin\theta\cos\phi$	$d_{xz}: \left(\dfrac{15}{4\pi}\right)^{\frac{1}{2}} \sin\theta\cos\theta\cos\phi$
	$p_z: \left(\dfrac{3}{4\pi}\right)^{\frac{1}{2}} \sin\theta\sin\phi$	$d_{yz}: \left(\dfrac{15}{4\pi}\right)^{\frac{1}{2}} \sin\theta\cos\theta\sin\phi$
		$d_{x^2-y^2}: \left(\dfrac{15}{16\pi}\right)^{\frac{1}{2}} \sin^2\theta\cos 2\phi$
		$d_{xy}: \left(\dfrac{15}{16\pi}\right)^{\frac{1}{2}} \sin^2\theta\sin 2\phi$

the atomic orbitals may be classified according to their characteristic values of l and m, and this classification is of great importance both in regard to electron distribution in atoms and the nature of directed valency of atoms in molecules. The quantum number l, known as the *azimuthal* quantum number, takes the integral values $0, 1, 2, \ldots$ and is a measure of the total orbital angular momentum of the electron about the nucleus, the absolute magnitude of which is $l(l + 1)$ in units of $h/2\pi$. The second quantum number m takes the $2l + 1$ different integral values $l, l - 1, \ldots, -(l - 1), -l$ and is the magnitude, again in units of $h/2\pi$, of the component of angular momentum along the polar axis. The quantum number m is known as the *magnetic* quantum number, and specifies the orientation of the orbital angular-momentum vector.

Atomic orbitals are labeled by letters according to the value of the quantum number l; s, p, d, and f are used for $l = 0, 1, 2, 3$, etc. The analytical forms for the angular parts of the atomic orbitals commonly encountered in molecular problems are listed in Table 1.2. It is frequently convenient to refer the different kinds of angular functions to cartesian-coordinate axes. If these axes are chosen so that z is the polar axis $\theta = 0$ and x corresponds to $\theta = 90°$, $\phi = 0$ (Fig. 1.3), then

$$x = r \sin\theta \cos\phi$$
$$y = r \sin\theta \sin\phi \qquad\qquad (1.71)$$
$$z = r \cos\theta$$

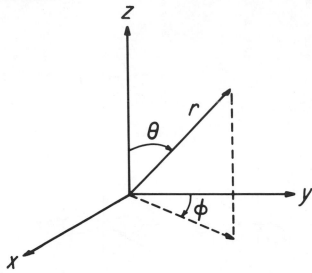

Fig. 1.3 Relation of spherical polar coordinates (r,θ,ϕ) to cartesian coordinates (x,y,z).

The s function in Table 1.2 is independent of angle and needs no further suffix. The three p functions have the same angular dependence as the coordinates x, y, and z and are usually referred to as p_x, p_y, and p_z. The d functions have the same angular dependence as quadratic expressions in x, y, and z and are labeled $d_{3z^2-r^2}$, d_{zx}, d_{zy}, $d_{x^2-y^2}$, and d_{xy}.

All of these angular functions have characteristic *nodes* (surfaces where the function changes sign and therefore vanishes). The s functions are independent of angle and have no *angular nodes*, although they may have *radial nodes* on spherical surfaces where the wavefunction vanishes for a particular value of r. The three p functions p_x, p_y, p_z have nodes in the planes $x = 0$, $y = 0$, and $z = 0$, respectively. Each will have opposite signs on opposite sides of the nodal plane so that they may be represented diagrammatically by positive and negative lobes as shown in Fig. 1.4. The four d functions d_{zx}, d_{zy}, $d_{x^2-y^2}$, d_{xy}, also shown in Fig. 1.4, have two nodal planes each and can be represented by four lobes. The remaining linearly independent d function is zero on the cone defined by $\cos \theta = (\frac{1}{3})^{\frac{1}{2}}$. The signs associated with the lobes of atomic functions do not affect the observable properties of an electron, since these depend not on ψ but on ψ^2. The signs *are* significant in the case of overlapping atomic functions in molecules, for the relative signs of the lobes involved determine whether the interaction will be constructive or destructive.

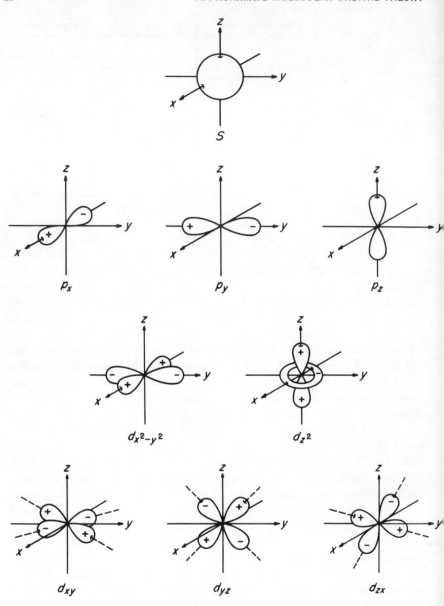

Fig. 1.4 Schematic representation of s, p, and d atomic orbitals.

Table 1.3   Radial parts of hydrogenic atomic orbitals

n	l	$R_{nl}(r)$
1	0	$2\zeta^{3/2} \exp(-\zeta r)$
2	0	$2\zeta^{3/2}(1 - \zeta r) \exp(-\zeta r)$
	1	$(\tfrac{4}{3})^{1/2}\zeta^{5/2}\, r \exp(-\zeta r)$
3	0	$(\tfrac{2}{3})\zeta^{3/2}(3 - 6\zeta r + 2\zeta^2 r^2) \exp(-\zeta r)$
	1	$(\tfrac{8}{9})^{1/2}\zeta^{5/2}(2 - \zeta r)\, r \exp(-\zeta r)$
	2	$(\tfrac{8}{45})^{1/2}\zeta^{7/2}\, r^2 \exp(-\zeta r)$

The radial part of the atomic functions $R_{nl}(r)$ are polynomials in the radial distance r multiplied by a decaying exponential $e^{-\zeta r}$, where ζ is the *orbital exponent*.   The normalized radial parts of the wavefunctions for the hydrogen atom are given in Table 1.3, where $\zeta = Z/n$, Z being the nuclear charge and n being the principal quantum number of the shell.   In choosing analytical forms for atomic functions of many-electron atoms, it is possible to use radial functions of the general form given in Table 1.3, with the orbital exponent adjusted to reflect the electrostatic screening of the nucleus by inner-shell electrons.   With these so-called hydrogenic functions, many of the integrals required in the calculation of molecular orbitals are rather difficult to evaluate, partially due to the complicated polynomial in r. The complicated form of the polynomial arises in establishing the radial nodes in the function.   Slater [19] proposed a much simpler analytical form for $R_{nl}(r)$:

$$R_{nl}(r) = (2\zeta)^{n+1/2}[(2n)!]^{-1/2}r^{n-1} \exp(-\zeta r) \tag{1.72}$$

These are nodeless functions, now widely known as Slater-type orbitals (STO).   The orbital exponent ζ is given as

$$\zeta = \frac{Z - s}{n^*} \tag{1.73}$$

where s is a screening constant and n^* is an effective principal quantum number.   The parameters s and n^* could be determined so as to give good values for, e.g., energy levels of atoms, atomic and ionic radii, etc.   Slater gave the following empirical rules for choosing s and n^* to give good approximations to the best atomic orbitals of this type:

1. The parameter n^* is identical with the principal quantum number n up to the value 3.   For higher n, values of n^* are as in Table 1.4.

Table 1.4 Values of the effective principal quantum number n^* in Slater atomic orbitals

n	n^*
1	1.0
2	2.0
3	3.0
4	3.7
5	4.0
6	4.2

2. The numerator of Eq. (1.73) may be considered an effective nuclear charge, with s being a measure of the shielding effect of other electrons. It is determined by dividing electrons into the shells $(1s)$, $(2s, 2p)$, $(3s, 3p)$, $(3d)$, $(4s, 4p)$, $(4d, 4f)$, $(5s, 5p)$, $(5d)$, each having a different shielding constant s. The shells are considered to be arranged from inside out in the order named and the total value of s is built up from the following contributions:

(a) Nothing from any shell outside the one considered

(b) 0.35 from each other electron in the same shell (except for $1s$, where 0.30 is used instead)

(c) If the shell is an s, p shell, 0.85 from each electron with principal quantum number less by one, and an additional 1.00 for each electron further in

(d) If the shell is d or f, 1.00 from each electron inside it

The effective nuclear charges calculated according to these rules for neutral atoms up to krypton are given in Table 1.5.

As Slater orbitals are frequently used in molecular calculations, it is useful to give explicit forms for the radial functions for $n = 1, 2, 3$ to be used in association with the angular functions of Table 1.2. These are

$$R_{1s}(r) = 2\zeta^{3/2} \exp(-\zeta r)$$

$$R_{2s}(r) = R_{2p}(r) = \left(\frac{4\zeta^5}{3}\right)^{1/2} r \exp(-\zeta r)$$

$$R_{3s}(r) = R_{3p}(r) = R_{3d}(r) = \left(\frac{16\zeta^7}{15}\right)^{1/2} r^2 \exp(-\zeta r)$$

(1.74)

One limitation of the simple form of Slater atomic orbitals is that they are not at all orthogonal to each other (as no allowance is made for radial nodes). This may be corrected by using a set of *orthogonalized Slater orbitals.* These are constructed by leaving the $1s$ function ϕ_{1s} unaltered, but replacing the simple Slater $2s$ function ϕ_{2s} by a linear combination

$$\phi'_{2s} = (1 - S_{1s,2s}{}^2)^{-\frac{1}{2}}(\phi_{2s} - S_{1s,2s}\phi_{1s}) \tag{1.75}$$

where $S_{1s,2s}$ is the overlap integral $\int \phi_{1s}(1)\phi_{2s}(1)\, d\tau_1$. Then ϕ_{2s} is normalized and orthogonal to ϕ_{1s}. Similarly, ϕ_{3s} can be made orthogonal to both ϕ_{1s} and ϕ_{2s} by subtracting an appropriate linear combination of both. The p and d series of orbitals can be treated in the same way, ϕ_{2p} and ϕ_{3d} being unaltered and ϕ_{3p} and ϕ_{4d} being modified.

Although Slater orbitals are the most popular analytical forms for radial parts of atomic orbitals in molecular orbital calculations, they are by no means the only possibility. Alternatively, one may consider *gaussian functions* [20], wherein the radial functions are similar to Slater functions except that the exponent of the decaying exponential

Table 1.5   Values of the parameter Z^* in Slater atomic orbitals

Z	Atom	Effective nuclear charge Z^*			Z	Atom	Effective nuclear charge Z^*				
		$1s$	$2s, p$	$3s, p$			$1s$	$2s, p$	$3s, p$	$3d$	$4s, p$
1	H	1.00			19	K	18.70	14.85	7.75		2.20
2	He	1.70			20	Ca	19.70	15.85	8.75		2.85
3	Li	2.70	1.30		21	Sc	20.70	16.85	9.75	3.00	3.00
4	Be	3.70	1.95		22	Ti	21.70	17.85	10.75	3.65	3.15
5	B	4.70	2.60		23	V	22.70	18.85	11.75	4.30	3.30
6	C	5.70	3.25		24	Cr	23.70	19.85	12.75	5.60	2.95
7	N	6.70	3.90		25	Mn	24.70	20.85	13.75	5.60	3.60
8	O	7.70	4.55		26	Fe	25.70	21.85	14.75	6.25	3.75
9	F	8.70	5.20		27	Co	26.70	22.85	15.75	6.90	3.90
10	Ne	9.70	5.85		28	Ni	27.70	23.85	16.75	7.55	4.05
11	Na	10.70	6.85	2.20	29	Cu	28.70	24.85	17.75	8.85	3.70
12	Mg	11.70	7.85	2.85	30	Zn	29.70	25.85	18.75	8.85	4.35
13	Al	12.70	8.85	3.50	31	Ga	30.70	26.85	19.75	9.85	5.00
14	Si	13.70	9.85	4.15	32	Ge	31.70	27.85	20.75	10.85	5.65
15	P	14.70	10.85	4.80	33	As	32.70	28.85	21.75	11.85	6.30
16	S	15.70	11.85	5.45	34	Se	33.70	29.85	22.75	12.85	6.95
17	Cl	16.70	12.85	6.10	35	Br	34.70	30.85	23.75	13.85	7.60
18	A	17.70	13.85	6.75	36	Kr	35.70	31.85	24.75	14.85	8.25

depends on r^2 rather than r. The gaussian radial functions fall off more sharply with distance than Slater orbitals and also round off rather than peak in the region of the cusp. Despite these deficiencies in the shapes, it is much easier to carry out the integrations involved in molecular calculations using gaussian functions, and for this reason they are quite often used for calculations of molecular orbitals for polyatomic molecules. Another possibility is the so-called *lobe function* [21], wherein spherical or elliptical functions, usually of gaussian form, are distributed so as to reproduce the conventional shapes of atomic orbitals. For example, an atomic p_x function could be constructed by two spherical gaussians located on either side of the atomic nucleus.

REFERENCES

1. For a historical account, the reader is referred to Slater, J. C.: "Quantum Theory of Molecules and Crystals," vol. 1, McGraw-Hill Book Company, New York, 1963, and the Nobel Prize address by R. S. Mulliken, reprinted in *Science*, **157**:13 (1967).
2. Roothaan, C. C. J.: *Rev. Mod. Phys.*, **23**:69 (1951).
3. Quantum Chemistry Program Exchange, Department of Chemistry, University of Indiana, Bloomington, Ind.
4. Hückel, E.: *Z. Physik*, **70**:204 (1931); A. Streitwieser: "Molecular Orbital Theory for Organic Chemists," John Wiley & Sons, Inc., New York, 1959.
5. Hoffman, R.: *J. Chem. Phys.*, **39**:1397 (1963); Pople, J. A., and D. P. Santry: *Mol. Phys.*, **7**:269 (1964), **9**:301 (1965).
6. Pople, J. A.: *Trans. Faraday Soc.*, **49**:1375 (1953).
7. Salem, L.: "The Molecular Orbital Theory of Conjugated Systems," W. A. Benjamin, Inc., New York, 1966.
8. Murrell, J. N.: "The Theory of the Electronic Spectra of Organic Molecules," John Wiley & Sons, Inc., New York, 1968.
9. Schroedinger, E.: *Ann. Physik*, **79**:361 (1926).
10. Born, M., and J. R. Oppenheimer: *Ann. Physik*, **84**:457 (1927).
11. Dirac, P. A. M.: "The Principles of Quantum Mechanics," Oxford University Press, London, 1958.
12. Hund, F.: *Z. Physik*, **40**:742 (1927), **42**:93 (1927); R. S. Mulliken: *Phys. Rev.*, **32**:186 (1928), **32**:761 (1928), **33**:730 (1929).
13. Hartree, D. R.: *Proc. Cambridge Phil. Soc.*, **24**:89, 111, 426 (1928).
14. Uhlenbeck, G., and S. Goudsmit: *Naturwissenschaften*, **13**:953 (1925).
15. Pauli, W.: *Z. Physik*, **31**:765 (1925).
16. Slater, J. C.: *Phys. Rev.*, **35**:509 (1930), **34**:1293 (1959).
17. Lennard-Jones, J. E.: *Proc. Roy. Soc. (London)*, **A198**:1, 14 (1949).
18. Pauling, L., and E. B. Wilson: "Introduction to Quantum Mechanics," McGraw-Hill Book Company, New York, 1935.
19. Slater, J. C.: *Phys. Rev.*, **36**:57 (1930).
20. Boys, S. F.: *Proc. Roy. Soc. (London)*, **A200**:542 (1950).
21. Whitten, J. L.: *J. Chem. Phys.*, **39**:349 (1963), **44**:359 (1966).

2
Self-consistent Field
Molecular Orbital Theory

2.1 INTRODUCTION

Having considered some general aspects of the orbital description of electronic structure, we turn now to a more detailed discussion of the actual calculation of orbitals for a many-electron system. The general approach is based on the variational method introduced in Sec. 1.4 and involves a systematic determination of the stationary values of the energy of the system. In the following presentation, an analytical expression for the energy expectation value of a closed-shell system suitable for use in a variational approach is derived in Sec. 2.2, and the Hartree-Fock equations for the orbitals are derived in the following section. The LCAO approximation to Hartree-Fock orbitals, leading to the Roothaan equations, is presented in Sec. 2.4, followed by an illustrative example. Analogous considerations on open-shell systems conclude the chapter. This material serves as the theoretical basis for the approximate molecular orbital theories presented and discussed in the remainder of the book.

2.2 THE ENERGY EXPRESSION FOR A CLOSED–SHELL CONFIGURATION

The variational approach to approximate solutions of the Schroedinger equation involves working with the energy expectation value $\langle \Psi | \mathcal{H} | \Psi \rangle$, and for algebraic manipulation it is necessary to have a convenient expression for this quantity in terms of the orbitals involved. Generalizing Eq. (1.55) to a closed-shell form with $2n$ electrons, the orbital wavefunction Ψ may be written in the form

$$\Psi = \mathfrak{N} \sum_{\mathbf{P}} (-1)^P \mathbf{P} \{ \psi_1(1)\alpha(1)\psi_1(2)\beta(2) \cdots \psi_n(2n)\beta(2n) \} \qquad (2.1)$$

where $\mathbf{P}$ is a permutation of $1, 2, \ldots, 2n$ and $(-1)^P$ is $+1$ or -1 for even or odd permutations, respectively. The orbitals ψ_i may be considered orthonormal without loss of generality, i.e.,

$$S_{ij} = \int \psi_i(1)\psi_j(1) \, d\tau_1 = \delta_{ij} \qquad (2.2)$$

The operator $\mathbf{P}$ permutes the coordinates of the electrons (not the suffixes of the molecular orbitals). For example, if $\mathbf{P}$ is the (odd) permutation 3421 of the numbers 1234, then

$$\mathbf{P}_{3421} \{ \psi_1(1)\alpha(1)\psi_1(2)\beta(2)\psi_2(3)\alpha(3)\psi_2(4)\beta(4) \}$$
$$= \psi_1(3)\alpha(3)\psi_1(4)\beta(4)\psi_2(2)\alpha(2)\psi_2(1)\beta(1) \qquad (2.3)$$

To find the normalization constant $\mathfrak{N}$, we must first evaluate the many-electron integral

$$\int \Psi^* \Psi \, d\tau_1 \cdots d\tau_{2n}$$
$$= \mathfrak{N}^2 \sum_{\mathbf{P}} \sum_{\mathbf{P}'} (-1)^P (-1)^{P'} \int \cdots \int \mathbf{P} \{ \psi_1(1)\alpha(1) \cdots \psi_{2n}(2n)\beta(2n) \}$$
$$\times \mathbf{P}' \{ \psi_1(1)\alpha(1) \cdots \psi_{2n}(2n)\beta(2n) \} \, d\tau_1 \cdots d\tau_{2n} \qquad (2.4)$$

The integration, of course, is over the spin and spatial coordinates of all the electrons. There is a double summation over all permutations $\mathbf{P}$ and $\mathbf{P}'$. Now the multiple integral in Eq. (2.4) associated with a particular pair of permutations $\mathbf{P}$ and $\mathbf{P}'$ will vanish unless $\mathbf{P}$ and $\mathbf{P}'$ are identical, since integration over the coordinates of at least one electron will involve two spin orbitals differing either in space or spin parts, giving zero by virtue of the orthogonality condition, Eq. (2.2). If $\mathbf{P}$ and $\mathbf{P}'$ are identical, the multiple integral is unity since all the orbitals are normalized. The right-hand side of Eq. (2.4) is therefore equal to $\mathfrak{N}^2$ multiplied by the number of permutations, which is $(2n)!$. For the total wave to be normalized, therefore, we must have

$$\mathfrak{N} = [(2n)!]^{-\frac{1}{2}} \qquad (2.5)$$

We can now proceed to the evaluation of the energy expectation value $\langle \Psi | \mathfrak{IC} | \Psi \rangle$, where Ψ is the determinantal wavefunction of Eq. (2.4). The hamiltonian operator may be separated into one- and two-electron parts,

$$\mathfrak{IC} = \mathfrak{IC}_1 + \mathfrak{IC}_2 \tag{2.6}$$

where

$$\mathfrak{IC}_1 = \sum_p \mathbf{H}^{\text{core}}(p) \tag{2.7}$$

with

$$\mathbf{H}^{\text{core}}(p) = -\tfrac{1}{2}\nabla_p{}^2 - \sum_A Z_A r_{pA}{}^{-1} \tag{2.8}$$

and

$$\mathfrak{IC}_2 = \sum_{p<q}\sum r_{pq}{}^{-1} \tag{2.9}$$

The quantity $\mathbf{H}^{\text{core}}$ is the one-electron hamiltonian corresponding to motion of an electron in the field of the bare nuclei, the charge of nucleus A being Z_A. Substituting Eq. (2.6) into the energy expectation value allows a corresponding separation of the electronic energy into one-electron and two-electron parts,

$$\langle \Psi | \mathfrak{IC} | \Psi \rangle = \langle \Psi | \mathfrak{IC}_1 | \Psi \rangle + \langle \Psi | \mathfrak{IC}_2 | \Psi \rangle \tag{2.10}$$

which are conveniently treated separately. For the one-electron part, using Eq. (2.7),

$$\langle \Psi | \mathfrak{IC}_1 | \Psi \rangle = \sum_p^{2n} \langle \Psi | \mathbf{H}^{\text{core}}(p) | \Psi \rangle \tag{2.11}$$

Now since the electrons are indistinguishable and are treated on an equal footing in Ψ, the expectation value of $\mathbf{H}^{\text{core}}(p)$ must be the same for all $2n$ values of p. Thus we need only consider $\mathbf{H}^{\text{core}}(1)$, noting that

$$\langle \Psi | \mathfrak{IC}_1 | \Psi \rangle = 2n \langle \Psi | \mathbf{H}^{\text{core}}(1) | \Psi \rangle \tag{2.12}$$

Substituting the full expansion for Ψ, we obtain

$$\langle \Psi | \mathfrak{IC}_1 | \Psi \rangle = [(2n-1)!]^{-1} \sum_{\mathbf{P}} \sum_{\mathbf{P}'} (-1)^P (-1)^{P'}$$
$$\times \int \cdots \int \mathbf{P}\{\psi_1(1)\alpha(1)\psi_1(2)\beta(2) \cdots\} \mathbf{H}^{\text{core}}(1)$$
$$\times \mathbf{P}'\{\psi_1(1)\alpha(1)\psi_1(2)\beta(2) \cdots\} \, d\tau_1 \, d\tau_2 \cdots d\tau_{2n} \tag{2.13}$$

Again it is possible to eliminate all terms with $\mathbf{P} \neq \mathbf{P}'$ in this double expansion by integration over the full coordinates of electrons 2, 3, . . . , $2n$. Because of the orthogonality of the orbitals, the spatial and spin functions associated with all of these electrons must match in the products $\mathbf{P}\{\ \}$ and $\mathbf{P}'\{\ \}$, otherwise integration would give a factor of zero. However, if any permutation of the numbers 1, 2, . . . , $2n$ leaves all symbols but one unchanged, the last symbol must be unchanged also. Hence, only terms with $\mathbf{P} = \mathbf{P}'$ survive in Eq. (2.13), which now becomes

$$\langle \Psi | \mathfrak{IC}_1 | \Psi \rangle = [(2n - 1)!]^{-1}$$
$$\times \sum_{\mathbf{P}} \int \cdots \int \mathbf{P}\{\psi_1(1)\alpha(1)\psi_1(2)\beta(2) \cdots\} \mathbf{H}^{\text{core}}(1)$$
$$\times \mathbf{P}\{\psi_1(1)\alpha(1)\psi_1(2)\beta(2) \cdots\} \, d\tau_1 \, d\tau_2 \cdots d\tau_{2n} \quad (2.14)$$

Integration over electrons 2, 3, 4, . . . , $2n$ in Eq. (2.14) gives unity in each term, so that the full expression becomes a sum of one-electron integrals over the space and spin coordinates of electron 1. Since $\mathbf{H}^{\text{core}}$ is independent of spin, integration over the spin coordinates of electron 1 gives another factor of unity and the final result is

$$\langle \Psi | \mathfrak{IC}_1 | \Psi \rangle = 2 \sum_{i=1}^{n} H_{ii} \qquad (2.15)$$

where H_{ii} is the expectation value of the one-electron core hamiltonian corresponding to the *molecular* orbital

$$H_{ii} = \int \psi_i(1)^* \mathbf{H}^{\text{core}} \psi_i(1) \, d\tau_1 \qquad (2.16)$$

The factor 2 in Eq. (2.15) corresponds to the fact that there are two electrons in each of the molecular orbitals ψ_i.

The expectation value of the two-electron hamiltonian $\mathfrak{IC}_2$ can be evaluated in a similar manner. There are $\frac{1}{2}(2n)(2n - 1)$ electron-electron repulsion terms, and again because of the indistinguishability of electrons, each will give the same contribution. Thus,

$$\langle \Psi | \mathfrak{IC}_2 | \Psi \rangle = \frac{1}{2}(2n)(2n - 1)\langle \Psi | r_{12}^{-1} | \Psi \rangle = \frac{1}{2}[(2n - 2)!]^{-1}$$
$$\times \sum_{\mathbf{P}} \sum_{\mathbf{P}'} (-1)^P (-1)^{P'} \int \cdots \int \mathbf{P}\{\psi_1(1)\alpha(1)\psi_1(2)\beta(2) \cdots\} r_{12}^{-1}$$
$$\times \mathbf{P}'\{\psi_1(1)\alpha(1)\psi_1(2)\beta(2) \cdots\} \, d\tau_1 \, d\tau_2 \cdots d\tau_{2n} \quad (2.17)$$

Again, orthogonality of the molecular orbitals leads to zero terms in Eq. (2.17) unless the permutations $\mathbf{P}$ and $\mathbf{P}'$ are identical in all but the spin orbitals to which electrons 1 and 2 are assigned. For each permutation, this leaves two possibilities for $\mathbf{P}$:

1. $\mathbf{P}'$ is identical to $\mathbf{P}$.
2. $\mathbf{P}'$ differs from $\mathbf{P}$ by interchanging the assignation of electrons 1 and 2.

These two parts can be considered separately. If $\mathbf{P}$ and $\mathbf{P}'$ are identical, there will be $(2n - 2)!$ permutations for each assignation of electrons 1 and 2 to spin orbitals. This cancels the factor $[(2n - 2)!]^{-1}$ in Eq. (2.17). If electrons 1 and 2 are assigned to *different* spatial molecular orbitals ψ_i and ψ_j, both may have α or β spin and there will be four contributions each equal to $\frac{1}{2}J_{ij}$, where

$$J_{ij} = \iint \psi_i^*(1)\psi_j^*(2) \frac{1}{r_{12}} \psi_i(1)\psi_j(2) \, d\tau_1 \, d\tau_2 \qquad (2.18)$$

this being a six-dimensional integral over space coordinates only. If electrons 1 and 2 are assigned to the same molecular orbital ψ, they must have opposite spins and there are only two terms $\frac{1}{2}J_{ii}$. The total contribution is thus

$$2 \sum_i \sum_{j(\neq i)} J_{ij} + \sum_i J_{ii} \qquad (2.19)$$

There remain the contributions in which the permutation $\mathbf{P}'$ differs from $\mathbf{P}$ by interchanging the assignation of 1 and 2. If 1 and 2 are assigned to different spatial orbitals ψ_i and ψ_j, there are the four following possibilities:

$\mathbf{P}$		$\mathbf{P}'$	
$\psi_i(1)\alpha(1)$	$\psi_j(2)\beta(2)$	$\psi_j(1)\alpha(1)$	$\psi_i(2)\alpha(2)$
$\psi_i(1)\alpha(1)$	$\psi_j(2)\beta(2)$	$\psi_j(1)\beta(1)$	$\psi_i(2)\alpha(2)$
$\psi_i(1)\beta(1)$	$\psi_j(2)\alpha(2)$	$\psi_j(1)\alpha(1)$	$\psi_i(2)\beta(2)$
$\psi_i(1)\beta(1)$	$\psi_j(2)\beta(2)$	$\psi_j(1)\beta(1)$	$\psi_i(2)\beta(2)$

Of these, the second and third give vanishing terms by integration over the spin coordinates. The first and fourth both give $-\frac{1}{2}K_{ij}$, where

$$K_{ij} = \iint \psi_i^*(1)\psi_j^*(2) \frac{1}{r_{12}} \psi_j(1)\psi_i(2) \, d\tau_1 \, d\tau_2 \qquad (2.20)$$

The negative sign arises because $\mathbf{P}$ and $\mathbf{P}'$ are of different parity, since $\mathbf{P}'$ can be obtained from $\mathbf{P}$ by a single interchange. Thus $(-1)^P(-1)^{P'} = -1$. If electrons 1 and 2 are assigned to the *same* spatial orbital, they must have different spin, and the corresponding integral vanishes by integration over spin coordinates.

Collecting terms, the final expression for the electronic energy is

$$\varepsilon = 2 \sum_i^n H_{ii} + \sum_i^n J_{ii} + \sum_i^n \sum_{j(\neq i)}^n (2J_{ij} - K_{ij}) \qquad (2.21)$$

Alternately, noting that $K_{ii} = J_{ii}$, this may be rearranged into the more compact form

$$\mathcal{E} = 2 \sum_i^n H_{ii} + \sum_i^n \sum_j^n (2J_{ij} - K_{ij}) \tag{2.22}$$

This important formula has reduced the many-electron integration to the set of three- and six-dimensional integrals H_{ii}, J_{ij}, and K_{ij}. J_{ij} and K_{ij} are known as *coulomb integrals* and *exchange integrals*, respectively.

The various terms in Eqs. (2.21) and (2.22) can readily be given a rough physical significance. The one-electron integral H_{ii} represents the energy of an electron in a molecular orbital ψ_i in the field of the bare nuclei, and this is multiplied by 2 since there are two electrons in each orbital. The two-electron integral J_{ij} represents the interaction of the smoothed-out charge distributions $\psi_i^* \psi_i$ and $\psi_j^* \psi_j$. It is associated with a factor 4 for each pair of different orbitals since there are two electrons in each. For the two electrons in the same orbital, there is clearly only one such term. These coulomb integrals in Eq. (2.21) give the value that the total electron-electron repulsion would have if all electrons moved independently in the orbitals to which they are assigned. The exchange integrals K_{ij} enter with a negative sign and reduce the energy of interaction between electrons with parallel spins in different orbitals ψ_i and ψ_j. This is a result of the antisymmetry principle and reflects the energy stabilization due to the partial correlation of electrons of parallel spin.

It is useful to define a set of one-electron *orbital energies* $\mathcal{E}_i$,

$$\mathcal{E}_i = H_{ii} + \sum_j^n \{2J_{ij} - K_{ij}\} \tag{2.23}$$

This is essentially the energy of an electron in ψ_i interacting with the core and the other $2n - 1$ electrons. With the assumption that there is no reorganization of the other $2n - 1$ electrons on ionization, $-\mathcal{E}_i$ may be associated with the *ionization potential* of an electron in ψ_i. This is sometimes referred to as a *Koopmans* [1], or *vertical*, ionization potential. Using orbital energies, the total electronic energy can then be written in the useful alternative forms

$$\mathcal{E} = 2 \sum_i^n \mathcal{E}_i - \sum_i^n \sum_j^n (2J_{ij} - K_{ij}) \tag{2.24}$$

or

$$\mathcal{E} = \sum_i (\mathcal{E}_i + H_{ii}) \tag{2.25}$$

It should be noted that the total electronic energy $\mathcal{E}$ is *not* equal to the sum of the one-electron energies. This is because the sum of one-electron energies includes each electron-electron interaction twice (the repulsion between electrons 1 and 2 contributes to the one-electron energies associated with both electrons). The second term in Eq. (2.24) corrects for this.

2.3 THE HARTREE–FOCK EQUATIONS FOR MOLECULAR ORBITALS

Having established the proper form for the many-electron wavefunction for closed shells as a single determinant of spin orbitals and developed a convenient expression for the electronic energy, we proceed now to the details of the actual determination of the spatial orbitals ψ_i for a closed-shell system. If no restriction (other than orthonormality) is imposed on these functions (that is, if they are completely flexible functions of the coordinates of one electron), then we can deduce differential equations for the *optimum* forms of the molecular orbitals by appealing to the variational method. These differential equations were first derived by Fock [2] based on earlier work by Hartree [3], and are now generally known as the Hartree-Fock equations.

According to the variational principle, if we adjust an approximate many-electron wavefunction such as Eq. (2.1) to lower the energy, then the accurate solution of the many-electron wave equation will be approached. The best molecular orbitals, therefore, are obtained by varying all the contributing one-electron functions $\psi_1, \psi_2, \ldots, \psi_n$ in the determinant until the energy achieves its minimum value. This will not, of course, give the *correct* many-electron Ψ for a closed-shell system, but rather the closest possible approach in the form of a single determinant of orbitals. Such orbitals are referred to as *self-consistent*, or *Hartree-Fock*, molecular orbitals. Thus the central mathematical problem is the determination of the orbitals giving a stationary value of $\langle \Psi | \mathfrak{H} | \Psi \rangle$, with Ψ being a many-electron orbital wavefunction. In addition, we impose the constraint that the orbitals remain orthonormal, that is, Eq. (2.2) is satisfied throughout. If this stationary point does in fact correspond to the energy minimum, the corresponding wavefunction Ψ is the self-consistent solution for the electronic ground state.

Constrained variational problems of this type are handled mathematically by the calculus of variations, using the method of undetermined multipliers. This involves minimizing the function

$$G = \varepsilon - 2 \sum_i \sum_j \varepsilon_{ij} S_{ij} = 2 \sum_i H_{ii}$$
$$+ \sum_i \sum_j (2J_{ij} - K_{ij}) - 2 \sum_i \sum_j \varepsilon_{ij} S_{ij} \quad (2.26)$$

where the energy expression is just that developed in the previous section and the ε_{ij} are as yet undetermined constants. (The factor 2 in the last term on the left-hand side is introduced for convenience.)

A stationary point of the function G is such that the variation in G, δG, is zero to first order,

$$\delta G = 0 \tag{2.27}$$

The variation in G consequent on changing all orbitals ψ_i by an infinitesimal amount to $\psi_i + \delta\psi_i$ is, in full,

$$\delta G = 2 \sum_i \delta H_{ii} + \sum_i \sum_j (2\delta J_{ij} - \delta K_{ij}) - 2 \sum_i \sum_j \varepsilon_{ij} \, \delta S_{ij} \tag{2.28}$$

where

$$\left(\int \delta \psi_i^* H \psi_i \right)^* = \int \delta \psi_i H \psi_i^*$$
$$= \int \psi_i^* H \delta \psi_i$$

$$\delta H_{ii} = \int \delta\psi_i^*(1)\mathbf{H}^{\text{core}}(1)\psi_i(1) \, d\tau_1 + \text{complex conjugate} \tag{2.29}$$

$$\delta J_{ij} = \int \delta\psi_i^*(1)\mathbf{J}_j(1)\psi_i(1) \, d\tau_1 + \int \delta\psi_j^*(1)\mathbf{J}_i(1)\psi_j(1) \, d\tau_1 + \text{complex conjugate} \tag{2.30}$$

$$\delta K_{ij} = \int \delta\psi_i^*(1)\mathbf{K}_j(1)\psi_i(1) \, d\tau + \int \delta\psi_j^*(1)\mathbf{K}_i(1)\psi_j(1) \, d\tau_1 + \text{complex conjugate} \tag{2.31}$$

$$\delta S_{ij} = \int \delta\psi_i^*(1)\psi_j(1) \, d\tau_1 + \text{complex conjugate} \tag{2.32}$$

Here the coulomb operator $\mathbf{J}_j$ is defined by

$$\mathbf{J}_j(1) = \int \psi_j^*(2) \frac{1}{r_{12}} \psi_j(2) \, d\tau_2 \tag{2.33}$$

The exchange operator $\mathbf{K}_j$ cannot be written as a simple function but has the property that

$$\mathbf{K}_j(1)\psi_i(1) = \left[\int \psi_j^*(2) \frac{1}{r_{12}} \psi_i(2) \, d\tau_2 \right] \psi_j(1) \tag{2.34}$$

Since the orbitals and their complex conjugates can be varied independently, exactly the same equations follow if we restrict our consideration to real functions and real variations. The condition for a stationary point is thus

$$\delta G = 2 \sum_i \int \delta\psi_i^* \left[\mathbf{H}^{\text{core}}\psi_i + \sum_j (2\mathbf{J}_j - \mathbf{K}_j)\psi_i - \sum_j \varepsilon_{ij}\psi_j \right] d\tau = 0 \tag{2.35}$$

and since the variation $\delta\psi$ is arbitrary, Eq. (2.35) is satisfied only if the quantity in square brackets is equal to zero for each and every i.

This leads directly to the differential equations

$$\left[\mathbf{H}^{\text{core}} + \sum_j (2\mathbf{J}_j - \mathbf{K}_j) \right]\psi_i = \sum_j \varepsilon_{ij}\psi_j \qquad i = 1, \ldots, n \qquad (2.36)$$

These are n one-electron wave equations for the orbitals $\psi_1, \psi_2, \ldots,$ ψ_n. The quantity in square brackets is known as the Fock hamiltonian operator $\mathbf{F}$, and the wave equations may be written in the form

$$\mathbf{F}\psi_i = \sum_j \varepsilon_{ij}\psi_j \qquad i = 1, \ldots, n \qquad (2.37)$$

Here $\mathbf{F}$ may be considered an effective one-electron hamiltonian for the electron in the molecular environment, and its various terms have a simple physical interpretation. $\mathbf{H}^{\text{core}}$ is the one-electron hamiltonian for an electron moving in the field of bare nuclei. $\mathbf{J}_i$ ($= \mathbf{K}_i$) is the potential due to the other electron occupying the same molecular orbital ψ_i. Similarly $2\mathbf{J}_j$, where j is not equal to i, is the averaged electrostatic potential of the two electrons in the orbital ψ_j. The exchange potential $\mathbf{K}_j$ is somewhat more complicated, but it arises from the effect of the antisymmetry of the total wavefunction on the correlation between electrons of parallel spin.

The differential equations of Eq. (2.37) differ from ordinary one-electron wave equations in that they each have a whole set of constants ε_{ij} on the right-hand sides instead of a single eigenvalue, and this arises because the solutions to the set of wave equations are not unique. To appreciate the reasons for this, it is necessary to return to the general properties of determinants. We have already noted in Sec. 2.4 that any multiple of one column may be added to another without altering the value of the determinant. This is actually a special case of a more general theorem which states that any unitary transformation (or just an orthogonal transformation if only real quantities are involved) of the elements leaves the value of the determinant unchanged. In the case considered herein, this means that the orbitals ψ_i may be replaced by a new set ψ_i', where

$$\psi_i' = \sum_j T_{ij}\psi_j \qquad (2.38)$$

as long as the elements T_{ij} form a unitary matrix,

$$\sum_k T_{ik}^* T_{kj} = \delta_{ij} \qquad (2.39)$$

where δ_{ij} is the Kronecker delta. A simple example of an orthogonal transformation of this type is the replacement of a pair of orbitals ψ_1 and ψ_2 by new orbitals ψ_1' and ψ_2' proportional to their sum and difference,

$$\psi_1' = \frac{\psi_1 + \psi_2}{\sqrt{2}} \tag{2.40}$$

$$\psi_2' = \frac{\psi_1 - \psi_2}{\sqrt{2}} \tag{2.41}$$

If we substitute a transformation of the form of Eq. (2.38) into the differential equations, Eq. (2.37), it is found that a similar set results (with appropriate redefinition of the coulomb and exchange operators), the only real difference being that the constants ε_{ij} are replaced by a new set ε_{kl}', given by

$$\varepsilon_{kl}' = \sum_{ij} T_{ki} \varepsilon_{ij} T_{jl} \tag{2.42}$$

It is clearly desirable to remove this indeterminacy from the problem and to fix the molecular orbitals uniquely. Since the ε_{ij} form a hermitian matrix, there exists a unitary transformation of the form of Eq. (2.38) which will bring the matrix of lagrangian multipliers to diagonal form, that is, all $\varepsilon_{ij} = 0$ unless $i = j$. Applying that transformation to the orbitals, the differential equations are brought into the form analogous to a standard eigenvalue problem,

$$F\psi_i = \varepsilon_i \psi_i \qquad i = 1, n \tag{2.43}$$

These are commonly known as the Hartree-Fock equations and state that the best molecular orbitals are all eigenfunctions of the Hartree-Fock hamiltonian operator $\mathbf{F}$, which is in turn is defined in terms of these orbitals through the coulomb and exchange operators $\mathbf{J}_j$ and $\mathbf{K}_j$. The general procedure for solving the Hartree-Fock equations is essentially a trial-and-error process, first assuming a set of trial solutions ψ_1', ψ_2', . . . which allows computation of the coulomb and exchange operators and thus the calculation of a first approximation to the Hartree-Fock hamiltonian operator. The eigenfunctions ψ_1'', ψ_2'', . . . of this operator constitute a second set of trial functions, and the entire procedure is continued until the orbital no longer changes (within a certain tolerance) on further iteration. These orbitals are then said to be self-consistent with the potential field they generate, and the whole procedure is called the self-consistent field method. In addition to the n occupied orbitals, there will be other eigenfunctions of $\mathbf{F}$ corresponding to higher eigenvalues ε_i. Such unoccupied orbitals are sometimes called *virtual orbitals*.

The general expression for the eigenvalues of the Hartree-Fock hamiltonian operator is

$$\epsilon_i = H_{ii}{}^{core} + \sum_j (2J_{ij} - K_{ij}) \tag{2.44}$$

which are just those quantities associated with the energy of an electron in orbital ψ_i (Sec. 2.2) and are thus known as *orbital energies*.

The molecular orbitals corresponding to a diagonal ϵ_{ij} matrix are in general spatially delocalized over all the atoms in the molecule. This description of the motion of electrons in molecules provides a good basis for electronic excitation and ionization but has the disadvantage that a chemical bond in the classical sense must be described by a superposition of occupied, delocalized molecular orbitals. The sets of orbitals for the system which do not correspond to completely diagonal ϵ_{ij} matrices, of course, still give rise to the same many-electron wavefunction, and certain of these sets provide a useful alternative way of interpreting ground-state electronic structure in detail. Orbitals associated with nonvanishing off-diagonal lagrangian multipliers are no longer completely delocalized but may be localized in some region or other of the molecule. Judicious choice of a transformation T_{ij} can lead to orbitals which are localized in the regions of classical chemical bonds. This can provide an illuminating physical interpretation of the orbital wavefunction.

The usual way of obtaining such orbitals, proposed by Lennard-Jones [5], is to first determine the molecular orbitals for the system and then to apply a unitary transformation to the new set of functions, known as *equivalent orbitals*. The problem of determining such orbitals directly in a Hartree-Fock procedure and choosing appropriate criteria for localization is an area of current active research, notably by Edmiston and Ruedenberg [6].

2.4 LCAO MOLECULAR ORBITALS FOR CLOSED-SHELL SYSTEMS

In the previous section, we have seen how optimum molecular orbitals may be defined as solutions of a set of coupled nonlinear differential equations. For molecular systems of any size, however, direct solution of these equations is impractical and more approximate methods are required. The most rewarding approach to date has been to approximate Hartree-Fock orbitals with linear combinations of atomic orbitals as introduced in Sec. 1.9. This method has the further advantage that it aids the interpretability of the results, since the nature of chemical problems frequently involves relating properties of molecules to those of the constituent atoms.

In this approach, each molecular orbital is considered in the form

$$\psi_i = \sum_{\mu} c_{\mu i} \phi_{\mu} \tag{2.45}$$

where the ϕ_{μ} are real atomic functions. This form is used within the determinantal wavefunction, Eq. (2.1). We shall adopt the convention of using Greek letters as suffixes for atomic orbitals in expansions such as Eq. (2.45), retaining Roman letters as suffixes for molecular orbitals. We shall again require that the orbitals ψ_i form an orthonormal set, and for this to be possible it is necessary that the number of atomic orbitals in the basis is greater than or equal to the number of occupied molecular orbitals. The requirement that the molecular orbitals be orthonormal in the LCAO approximation demands that

$$\sum_{\mu\nu} c_{\mu i}^{*} c_{\nu j} S_{\mu\nu} = \delta_{ij} \tag{2.46}$$

where δ_{ij} is the Kronecker delta and $S_{\mu\nu}$ is the overlap integral for atomic functions ϕ_{μ} and ϕ_{ν},

$$S_{\mu\nu} = \int \phi_{\mu}(1)\phi_{\nu}(1)\, d\tau_1 \tag{2.47}$$

Molecular orbitals may be obtained to essentially any accuracy desired by appropriate adjustment of the number of basis functions employed in the LCAO expansion. We distinguish here three types of basis sets commonly encountered: (1) *Minimal basis sets*, comprised of those atomic orbitals up to and including the orbitals of the valence shell o each atom of the system; (2) *extended basis sets*, amounting to a minimal basis set plus any number of atomic orbitals lying outside the valence shell for each atom; (3) *valence basis sets*, comprised of just those orbitals of the valence shell of each atom in the system. For example, the valence basis set for the LiH molecule would be the $2s$, $2p_x$, $2p_y$, and $2p_z$ lithium atomic functions plus the hydrogen $1s$ function. Adding the $1s$ lithium orbital brings the valence basis set to a minimal basis set. Adding $3s$, $3p$, $3d$, . . . functions on lithium and $2s$, $2p$, $3s$, . . . functions on hydrogen would give an extended basis set.

At this point it is useful to write down the expression for the electron charge density in the LCAO approximation. The charge density ρ at position $\mathbf{R}$ is obtained by working out the expectation value of the charge density operator $\varrho(\mathbf{R})$ defined in Table 1.1. The operator $\varrho(\mathbf{R})$ is a one-electron operator, and the algebraic reduction proceeds analogously to that developed previously for the one-electron contribution to the total energy in Sec. 2.2. Proceeding in this manner,

$$\rho(\mathbf{R}) = \langle \Psi | \varrho(\mathbf{R}) | \Psi \rangle = 2 \sum_i^{occ} \psi_i^*(\mathbf{R}) \psi_i(\mathbf{R}) \tag{2.48}$$

Using Eq. (2.45),

$$\rho(\mathbf{R}) = \sum_{\mu\nu} P_{\mu\nu} \phi_\mu(\mathbf{R}) \phi_\nu(\mathbf{R}) \tag{2.49}$$

where

$$P_{\mu\nu} = 2 \sum_i^{occ} c_{\mu i}^* c_{\nu i} \tag{2.50}$$

The integral of $\rho(\mathbf{R})$ over all $\mathbf{R}$ should be equivalent to the total number of electrons in the system, i.e.,

$$2n = \int \rho(\mathbf{R}) \, d\mathbf{R} = \sum_{\mu\nu} P_{\mu\nu} \int \phi_\mu(\mathbf{R}) \phi_\nu(\mathbf{R}) \, d\mathbf{R} = \sum_{\mu\nu} P_{\mu\nu} S_{\mu\nu} \tag{2.51}$$

By means of Eq. (2.51), the electronic charge distribution may be decomposed into contributions associated with the various basis functions of the LCAO expansion. This provides a convenient interpretation of the wavefunction in terms of constituent atoms and their orbitals. A quantity $P_{\mu\nu} S_{\mu\nu}$ may be considered the electronic population of the atomic overlap distribution $\phi_\mu \phi_\nu$, and diagonal terms such as $P_{\mu\mu} S_{\mu\mu}$ may be associated with the net electronic charges residing in orbital ϕ_μ. An indication of contributions to chemical binding is given by off-diagonal terms $P_{\mu\nu} S_{\mu\nu}$ with ϕ_μ and ϕ_ν centered on different atoms. The matrix of elements $P_{\mu\nu}$ is thus known as the density matrix. A detailed analysis of Eq. (2.51) constitutes a *population analysis*, developed by Mulliken [7].

The total electronic energy can also be written in terms of integrals over atomic orbitals if we substitute the linear expansion of Eq. (2.45) in the molecular orbital integrals. Thus

$$H_{ii} = \sum_{\mu\nu} c_{\mu i}^* c_{\nu i} H_{\mu\nu} \tag{2.52}$$

where $H_{\mu\nu}$ is the matrix of the core hamiltonian with respect to *atomic* orbitals

$$H_{\mu\nu} = \int \phi_\mu(1) \mathbf{H}^{core} \phi_\nu(1) \, d\tau_1 \tag{2.53}$$

Similarly we may write

$$J_{ij} = \sum_{\mu\lambda\nu\sigma} c_{\mu i}^* c_{\lambda j}^* c_{\nu i} c_{\sigma j} (\mu\nu|\lambda\sigma) \tag{2.54}$$

$$K_{ij} = \sum_{\mu\lambda\nu\sigma} c_{\mu i}^* c_{\lambda j}^* c_{\nu i} c_{\sigma j} (\mu\lambda|\nu\sigma) \tag{2.55}$$

where $(\mu\nu|\lambda\sigma)$ is the general two-electron interaction integral over atomic orbitals,

$$(\mu\nu|\lambda\sigma) = \int\int \phi_\mu(1)\phi_\nu(1) \frac{1}{r_{12}} \phi_\lambda(2)\phi_\sigma(2) \, d\tau_1 \, d\tau_2 \tag{2.56}$$

This six-dimensional integral gives the coulomb interaction between two local product densities $\phi_\mu\phi_\nu$ and $\phi_\lambda\phi_\sigma$.

If these expressions are substituted in Eq. (2.22) for the total electronic energy, we obtain

$$\mathcal{E} = \sum_{\mu\nu} P_{\mu\nu}H_{\mu\nu} + \tfrac{1}{2} \sum_{\mu\nu\lambda\sigma} P_{\mu\nu}P_{\lambda\sigma}[(\mu\nu|\lambda\sigma) - \tfrac{1}{2}(\mu\lambda|\nu\sigma)] \tag{2.57}$$

If all the integrals $H_{\mu\nu}$ and $(\mu\nu|\lambda\sigma)$ can be evaluated, Eq. (2.57) gives $\mathcal{E}$ as a quadratic function of the density matrix elements $P_{\mu\nu}$ or, using Eq. (2.50), as a quartic function of the coefficients $c_{\mu i}$.

The next important step is to find the optimum values of the coefficients $c_{\mu i}$, leading to a set of self-consistent LCAO or LCAO self-consistent field (SCF) *molecular orbitals*. Using the criterion of lowest calculated total energy, such orbitals will be the best for any particular set of basis functions ϕ_μ. This can be carried out by methods similar to the Hartree-Fock procedure described in the previous section. The small variation of the molecular orbital ψ_i is now given as

$$\delta\psi_i = \sum_\mu \delta c_{\mu i}\phi_\mu \tag{2.58}$$

and the condition for a stationary point in the function G, Eq. (2.26), becomes

$$\delta G = 2 \sum_i^{occ} \delta c_{\mu i}^* c_{\nu i}H_{\mu\nu}$$

$$+ \sum_{ij}^{occ} \sum_{\mu\nu\lambda\sigma} (\delta c_{\mu i}^* c_{\lambda j}^* c_{\nu i}c_{\sigma j} + c_{\mu i}^* \delta c_{\lambda j}^* c_{\nu i}c_{\sigma j})[2(\mu\nu|\lambda\sigma) - (\mu\lambda|\nu\sigma)]$$

$$- 2 \sum_{ij} \sum_{\mu\nu} \mathcal{E}_{ij}\delta c_{\mu i}^* c_{\nu j}S_{\mu\nu} + \text{complex conjugate} = 0 \tag{2.59}$$

The equations determining the optimum values of the $c_{\mu i}$ are obtained by recognizing that since the $\delta c_{\mu i}^*$ are arbitrary, the complete coefficient of each $\delta c_{\mu i}^*$ must equate to zero, leading to

$$\sum_\nu \left\{ c_{\nu i}H_{\mu\nu} + \sum_j^{occ} \sum_{\lambda\nu\sigma} c_{\lambda j}^* c_{\nu i}c_{\sigma j}[2(\mu\nu|\lambda\sigma) - (\mu\lambda|\nu\sigma)] \right\}$$

$$= \sum_j \mathcal{E}_{ij} \sum_\nu c_{\nu j}S_{\mu\nu} \tag{2.60}$$

Just as in the previous section, we are at liberty to choose the off-diagonal lagrangian multipliers ε_{ij} to be zero, to assure unique specification of the molecular orbitals. The equations then take the final form   *one equation for each μ.*

$$\sum_{\nu} (F_{\mu\nu} - \varepsilon_i S_{\mu\nu})c_{\nu i} = 0 \qquad (2.61)$$

where the elements of the matrix representation of the Hartree-Fock hamiltonian operator F are

$$F_{\mu\nu} = H_{\mu\nu} + \sum_{\lambda\sigma} P_{\lambda\sigma}[(\mu\nu|\lambda\sigma) - \tfrac{1}{2}(\mu\lambda|\nu\sigma)] \qquad (2.62)$$

It is seen that the equations for the LCAO self-consistent field molecular orbitals, Eq. (2.61), differ from the Hartree-Fock equations of the preceding section in that they are algebraic equations rather than differential equations. They were originally set forth independently by Hall [8] and by Roothaan [9], and are now generally known as the *Roothaan equations.*

The Roothaan equations for the LCAOSCF coefficients are cubic, since the Fock matrix $F_{\mu\nu}$ is itself a quadratic function of the $c_{\mu i}$. This is the mathematical consequence of the fact that the potential experienced by one electron will depend on the number and distribution of other electrons in the system. As a result, the equations have to be solved by an iterative procedure.

If we write the equations in the matrix form

$$\mathbf{FC} = \mathbf{SCE} \qquad (2.63)$$

where $\mathbf{E}$ is the diagonal matrix of the ε_i, they may be usefully transformed by defining new matrices

$$\mathbf{F}^\tau = \mathbf{S}^{-1/2}\mathbf{FS}^{-1/2} \qquad (2.64)$$
$$\mathbf{C}^\tau = \mathbf{S}^{1/2}\mathbf{C} \qquad (2.65)$$

where $\mathbf{S}^{1/2}$ is the square root of $\mathbf{S}$ (corresponding to all positive eigenvalues). Then Eq. (2.63) becomes

$$\mathbf{F}^\tau\mathbf{C}^\tau = \mathbf{C}^\tau\mathbf{E} \qquad (2.66)$$

and is in the form of a standard eigenvalue problem. The elements ε_i of $\mathbf{E}$ will be roots of the determinantal equation

$$|F_{\mu\nu}{}^\tau - \varepsilon\delta_{\mu\nu}| = 0 \qquad (2.67)$$

the lowest roots corresponding to the occupied molecular orbitals.

For each root ε_i, the coefficients $c_{\mu i}{}^\tau$ can be found from the linear equations

$$\sum_\nu (F_{\mu\nu}{}^\tau - \varepsilon_i \delta_{\mu\nu}) c_{\nu i}{}^\tau = 0 \tag{2.68}$$

and the coefficients then determined from

$$\mathbf{C} = \mathbf{S}^{-\frac{1}{2}} \mathbf{C}^\tau \tag{2.69}$$

The matrix elements of the Hartree-Fock hamiltonian operator are dependent on the orbitals through the elements $P_{\mu\nu}$, and the Roothaan equations are solved by first assuming an initial set of linear expansion coefficients $c_{\mu i}$, generating the corresponding density matrix $P_{\mu\nu}$ and computing a first guess at $F_{\mu\nu}$. The diagonalization procedure is effected by standard matrix eigenvalue techniques, and a new matrix of linear expansion coefficients $\mathbf{C}$ is obtained. The whole process is then repeated until the coefficients no longer change within a given tolerance on repeated iteration.

2.5 AN LCAOSCF EXAMPLE: HYDROGEN FLUORIDE

At this point, it may be helpful to give a numerical example of an LCAO self-consistent field wavefunction. We shall describe a simple calculation on hydrogen fluoride published by Ransil in 1960 [10].

Cartesian axes may be chosen with the fluorine nucleus at the origin and the proton at the point $(0,0,R)$, where R is the bondlength. The actual value of R used is 1.733 a.u. (0.9171 Å). The first step in the quantum-mechanical calculation is to specify the atomic orbital basis set ϕ_μ. This is a minimal set consisting of $1s$, $2s$, $2px$, $2py$, $2pz$ on the fluorine atom and $1s$ on hydrogen. The following Slater functions are used (see Sec. 1.8).

Fluorine:

$$\phi_1 = \phi(\text{F};1s) = \left(\frac{\zeta_1{}^3}{\pi}\right)^{\frac{1}{2}} \exp\left(-\zeta_1 r\right)$$

$$\phi_2 = \phi(\text{F};2s) = \left(\frac{\zeta_2{}^5}{3\pi}\right)^{\frac{1}{2}} r \exp\left(-\zeta_2 r\right)$$

$$\phi_3 = \phi(\text{F};2pz) = \left(\frac{\zeta_2{}^5}{\pi}\right)^{\frac{1}{2}} z \exp\left(-\zeta_2 r\right) \tag{2.70}$$

$$\phi_4 = \phi(\text{F};2px) = \left(\frac{\zeta_2{}^5}{\pi}\right)^{\frac{1}{2}} x \exp\left(-\zeta_2 r\right)$$

$$\phi_5 = \phi(\text{F};2py) = \left(\frac{\zeta_2{}^5}{\pi}\right)^{\frac{1}{2}} y \exp\left(-\zeta_2 r\right)$$

Hydrogen:

$$\phi_6 = \phi(\text{H};1s) = \left(\frac{\zeta_3{}^3}{\pi}\right)^{\frac{1}{2}} \exp\left(-\zeta_3 r\right) \tag{2.71}$$

The values of the exponents are chosen according to Slater's rules (Sec. 1.8) so that

$$\begin{aligned}
\zeta_1 &= 8.7 \\
\zeta_2 &= 2.6 \\
\zeta_3 &= 1.0
\end{aligned} \tag{2.72}$$

Using these functions, we may calculate the overlap integrals (see Appendix B) leading to the following 6×6 *overlap matrices:*

$$\mathbf{S} = \begin{bmatrix}
1.0000 & 0.2377 & 0 & 0 & 0 & 0.0548 \\
0.2377 & 1.0000 & 0 & 0 & 0 & 0.4717 \\
0 & 0 & 1.0000 & 0 & 0 & 0.2989 \\
0 & 0 & 0 & 1.0000 & 0 & 0 \\
0 & 0 & 0 & 0 & 1.0000 & 0 \\
0.0548 & 0.4717 & 0.2989 & 0 & 0 & 1.0000
\end{bmatrix} \tag{2.73}$$

The one-electron core hamiltonian has the form

$$\mathbf{H}^{\text{core}} = -\tfrac{1}{2}\nabla^2 - 9r_{\text{F}}^{-1} - r_{\text{H}}^{-1} \tag{2.74}$$

where r_{F} and r_{H} are the distances of the electron from the fluorine and hydrogen nuclei. All integrals of the type $H_{\mu\nu}$ can be evaluated by elementary methods and lead to the *core hamiltonian matrix.*

$$\mathbf{H}_{\mu\nu} = \begin{bmatrix}
-41.0320 & -9.4019 & -0.0162 & 0 & 0 & -2.1798 \\
-9.4019 & -11.1462 & -0.1775 & 0 & 0 & -4.3051 \\
-0.0162 & -0.1775 & -8.9692 & 0 & 0 & -2.2822 \\
0 & 0 & 0 & -8.8548 & 0 & 0 \\
0 & 0 & 0 & 0 & -8.8548 & 0 \\
-2.1798 & -4.3051 & -2.2822 & 0 & 0 & -5.2499
\end{bmatrix} \tag{2.75}$$

It should be noted that zeros appear in the matrices $S_{\mu\nu}$ and $H_{\mu\nu}$ in off-diagonal positions between atomic orbitals of different symmetry. The four functions ϕ_1, ϕ_2, ϕ_3, and ϕ_6 have σ symmetry (axially symmetric), while ϕ_4 and ϕ_5 are two components of π symmetry. As a consequence of these symmetry properties, the matrices separate into blocks.

The most difficult part of the calculation is the evaluation of the two-electron integrals $(\mu\nu|\lambda\sigma)$ defined in Eq. (2.56). Many of these vanish by symmetry and there are a number of other clear equalities

Table 2.1   Two-electron integrals $(\mu\nu|\lambda\sigma)$ for hydrogen fluoride

μ	ν	λ	σ	$(\mu\nu|\lambda\sigma)$
1	1	1	1	5.43750
2	1	1	1	0.79103
2	1	2	1	0.14633
2	2	1	1	1.29075
2	2	2	1	0.29564
2	2	2	2	0.94453
3	1	3	1	0.03104
3	2	3	1	0.04683
3	2	3	2	0.20877
3	3	1	1	1.29075
3	3	2	1	0.29564
3	3	2	2	0.94453
3	3	3	3	1.01766
4	3	4	3	0.05484
4	4	3	3	0.90797
6	1	1	1	0.19478
6	1	2	1	0.03452
6	1	2	2	0.06818
6	1	3	1	0.00120
6	1	3	2	0.00234
6	1	3	3	0.06835
6	1	4	4	0.06809
6	1	6	1	0.00825
6	2	1	1	0.44958
6	2	2	1	0.10438
6	2	2	2	0.36762
6	2	3	1	0.00611
6	2	3	2	0.04344
6	2	3	3	0.37464
6	2	4	4	0.36411
6	2	6	1	0.02442
6	2	6	2	0.16424
6	3	1	1	0.23671
6	3	2	1	0.05581
6	3	2	2	0.21070
6	3	3	1	0.01567
6	3	3	2	0.09473
6	3	3	3	0.22809
6	3	4	4	0.20200
6	3	6	1	0.01371
6	3	6	2	0.11704
6	3	6	3	0.11216
6	4	4	1	0.01255
6	4	4	2	0.06914

Table 2.1   Two-electron integrals $(\mu\nu|\lambda\sigma)$ for hydrogen fluoride (continued)

μ	ν	λ	σ	$(\mu\nu|\lambda\sigma)$
6	4	4	3	0.00955
6	4	6	4	0.02771
6	6	1	1	0.52693
6	6	2	1	0.12466
6	6	2	2	0.50168
6	6	3	1	0.01059
6	6	3	2	0.10245
6	6	3	3	0.52778
6	6	4	4	0.48863
6	6	6	1	0.02939
6	6	6	2	0.27072
6	6	6	3	0.23056
6	6	6	6	0.62500

[for example, $(42|51) = (32|51)$ and $(33|21) = (55|21)$]. A list of independent nonvanishing integrals is given in Table 2.1. We shall not give details of methods used to evaluate two-electron integrals. Those listed were obtained using a computer program written by Corbato and Switendick [11].

Having specified all the integrals needed, the next step is to make an initial guess at the LCAO coefficients to initiate the self-consistent cycling. The simplest way to do this is to use the eigenvectors of the core hamiltonian. This is equivalent to completely neglecting the field of the other electrons as a zero level of approximation. The eigenvalues and eigenvectors of $H_{\mu\nu}$ are listed in Table 2.2.

Table 2.2   Eigenvalues (ε) and eigenvectors of core hamiltonian for hydrogen fluoride

Molecular orbital ψ_i $\rightarrow$	1σ	2σ	3σ	1π	1π	4σ
Atomic orbital ε_i	-41.037	-9.740	-8.938	-8.855	-8.855	-4.272
1	1.003	-0.014	-0.001	0	0	0.004
2	-0.227	1.051	0.407	0	0	-0.208
3	0.079	-0.335	0.953	0	0	-0.072
4	0	0	0	0	0	0
5	0	0	0	1.000	1.000	0
6	0.036	-0.434	-0.238	0	0	1.188

These molecular orbitals are listed in order of increasing energy. To obtain the molecular orbital configuration, the ten electrons are assigned in pairs to the five orbitals with lowest energy, leading to the electronic configuration

$$(1\sigma)^2(2\sigma)^2(3\sigma)^2(1\pi)^4 \tag{2.76}$$

Since the ordering of energy levels using the core hamiltonian may differ from that using the full Fock matrix, there is some danger that electrons may be assigned to the wrong molecular orbitals by this process. In this case, the configuration given in (2.76) is the one leading to lowest calculated total energy and no difficulty arises. However, possible necessity of taking other configurations at this stage of the calculation should be borne in mind.

Given that the first five molecular orbitals in Table 2.2 are occupied, the next step is the calculation of the first approximation to the 6×6 density matrix $P_{\mu\nu}$ from

$$P_{\mu\nu} = \sum_{i=1}^{5} c_{\mu i} c_{\nu i} \tag{2.77}$$

From this matrix and the lists of integrals, it is now possible to calculate the first approximation to the electronic energy from Eq. (2.57) and the first approximation to the Fock hamiltonian matrix $F_{\mu\nu}$ from Eq. (2.62). The second approximation to LCAOSCF coefficients is then obtained from the eigenvectors of $F_{\mu\nu}$ and the cyclic procedure continues according to the scheme

$$H \to C \to P \to E \to F \to C \to P \to E \to, \text{ etc.} \tag{2.78}$$

The total electronic energies calculated in successive iterations are:

Iteration 1: -103.93973
2:     -104.66070
3:     -104.67176
4:     -104.67184
5:     -104.67184
6:     -104.67184

from which it is clear that convergence is rapid. However, in some other cases, convergence can be slow or oscillatory behavior can take place; special extrapolation procedures are then required.

The final set of molecular orbitals and the final density matrix are given in Tables 2.3 and 2.4.

Table 2.3   Eigenvalues (ε) and eigenvectors of SCF Fock matrix for hydrogen fluoride

Molecular orbital $\psi_i \rightarrow$	1σ	2σ	3σ	1π	1π	4σ
ε_i *Atomic orbital*	-26.139	-1.476	-0.566	-0.465	-0.465	0.477
1	0.9963	0.0163	0.0024	0	0	-0.0046
2	-0.2435	0.9322	0.0907	0	0	0.1606
3	0.0839	0.4715	0.6870	0	0	0.5761
4	0	0	0	1.000	0	0
5	0	0	0	0	1.000	0
6	0.0800	-0.5599	-0.8065	0	0	1.0502

Table 2.4   Density matrix for hydrogen fluoride

	1	2	3	4	5	6
1	2.1178	-0.5005	0.0760	0	0	0.0093
2	-0.5005	2.1830	0.4787	0	0	-0.2440
3	0.0760	-0.4787	0.9603	0	0	0.8206
4	0	0	0	2.0000	0	0
5	0	0	0	0	2.0000	0
6	0.0093	-0.2440	0.8206	0	0	1.0502

2.6   MOLECULAR ORBITALS FOR OPEN–SHELL SYSTEMS

The construction of orbital wavefunctions for open-shell systems was discussed in some detail in Sec. 1.8, and it was noted that in general linear combinations of Slater determinants were involved.   However, a spin-correct wavefunction for at least one component of the lowest energy state of an open-shell configuration can be written as a single Slater determinant, and for the calculation of self-consistent field molecular orbitals we focus on this component.   For a system with $q\ \beta$ electrons and $p\ (>q)\ \alpha$ electrons, this wavefunction is

$$^{p-q+1}\Psi = |\psi_1(1)\alpha(1)\psi_1(2)\beta(2)$$
$$\cdots\ \psi_q(2q)\beta(2q)\psi_{q+1}(2q+1)\alpha(2q+1)$$
$$\cdots\ \psi(p+q)\alpha(p+q)| \quad (2.79)$$

where the multiplicity is $p - q + 1$.   Wavefunctions of this type are termed *restricted single determinants* because the α electron associated with one of the doubly occupied orbitals $\psi_1, \psi_2, \ldots, \psi_q$ is described by the same spatial function as the β electron with which it is paired.   However, since the total number of α electrons differs from the total number of β electrons, the environment of these two electrons is not the same and their assignment to the *same* spatial orbital involves a restriction on the wavefunction and, consequently, a restriction on their spatial distribution.

A more general wavefunction is one in which the p α electrons and the q β electrons are assigned to two *completely independent* sets of molecular orbitals $\psi_1{}^\alpha$, $\psi_2{}^\alpha$, . . . , $\psi_p{}^\alpha$ and $\psi_1{}^\beta$, $\psi_2{}^\beta$, . . . , $\psi_q{}^\beta$. The corresponding determinantal wavefunction is

$$\begin{aligned}
{}^{p-q+1}\Psi = |&\psi_1{}^\alpha(1)\alpha(1)\psi_1{}^\beta(2)\beta(2)\psi_2{}^\alpha(3)\alpha(3) \\
\cdots \; &\psi_q{}^\beta(2q)\beta(2q)\psi_{q+1}^\alpha(2q+1)\alpha(2q+1)\psi_{q+2}^\alpha(2q+2)\alpha(2q+2) \\
&\cdots \; \psi_{p+q}^\alpha(p+q)\alpha(p+q)| \quad (2.80)
\end{aligned}$$

Such a wavefunction is described as an *unrestricted single determinant*. In diagrammatic terms, it may be said to represent a configuration of the type shown in Fig. 2.1b rather than Fig. 2.1a.

Since the restricted determinantal function is a particular case of the unrestricted function, it follows from the variational theorem that use of unrestricted functions must lead to lower (or possibly equal) calculated total energies. In this sense, the unrestricted

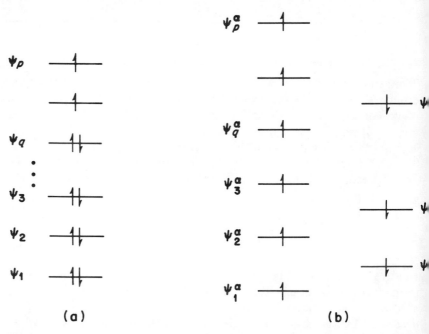

(a)   (b)

Fig. 2.1

wavefunction is superior. On the other hand, it can be shown that the unrestricted wavefunction is not generally an eigenfunction of the spin operator $\mathbf{S}^2$. Thus, if $p - q = 1$, the unrestricted single determinant does not describe a pure doublet state, but has "contaminating" components of other multiplicities [12]. However, it is still an eigenfunction of $\mathbf{S}_z$, the total spin component in the z direction, with eigenvalue $p - q$. It follows that the contaminating states are of higher multiplicity only. If $p - q = 2$, for example, where there are two extra α electrons, an unrestricted function would be an eigenfunction of $\mathbf{S}_z$ with eigenvalue unity. It can therefore have no singlet character and the contaminating components must be quintets, septets, and so forth. As a leading approximation, such contamination may be neglected, and we shall be principally concerned with unrestricted functions as approximations to pure spin states.

The self-consistent field approach to unrestricted molecular orbitals was set forth by Slater [13] and Pople and Nesbet [14]. The development of an expression for the total electronic energy using the unrestricted determinantal wavefunction of Eq. (2.80) follows similar lines to the closed-shell theory given in Sec. 2.2. Again, we may carry out linear transformations among the ψ^α orbitals to ensure that they are mutually orthogonal, and similarly with the ψ^β set. The functions $\psi_i^\alpha \alpha$ and $\psi_j^\beta \beta$ will automatically be orthogonal by virtue of the spin functions.

As in the restricted formalism, the total electronic energy can be conveniently calculated by separating the hamiltonian into a one-electron part $\mathcal{K}_1$ and a two-electron part $\mathcal{K}_2$ as in Eqs. (2.7) and (2.9), respectively. The expectation value of the one-electron part is given directly as

$$\langle \Psi | \mathcal{K}_1 | \Psi \rangle = \sum_{i=1}^{p+q} H_{ii} \tag{2.81}$$

which is an immediate generalization of Eq. (2.15). In this equation, the i summation is over α and β orbitals. The two-electron part can also be handled in a similar manner, it being necessary only to replace the spatial function ψ by ψ^α when it is multiplied by an α spin factor and by ψ^β when it is multiplied by a β spin factor. Thus (2.17) is replaced by

$$\langle \Psi | \mathcal{K}_2 | \Psi \rangle = \tfrac{1}{2}(p + q)(p + q - 1)\langle \Psi | r_{12}^{-1} | \Psi \rangle$$
$$= \tfrac{1}{2}[(p + q - 2)!]^{-1} \sum_P \sum_{P'} (-1)^P (-1)^{P'} \int \cdots \int$$

$$\mathbf{P}\{\psi_1{}^\alpha(1)\alpha(1)\psi_1{}^\beta(2)\beta(2) \cdots\} r_{12}^{-1}$$
$$\times \mathbf{P}'\{\psi_1{}^\alpha(1)\alpha(1)\psi_1{}^\beta(2)\beta(2) \cdots\} \, d\tau_1 \, d\tau_2 \cdots d\tau_{p+q} \tag{2.82}$$

As before, the only pairs of permutations that need be considered are
(1) those with $P = P'$ and (2) those in which electrons 1 and 2 are
assigned to different spatial orbitals but with the same spin.   Generalization of the previous argument leads to the following expression
for the electronic energy:

$$\mathcal{E} = \sum_{i}^{p+q} H_{ii} + \frac{1}{2}\Big(\sum_{i}^{p+q} \sum_{j}^{p+q} J_{ij} - \sum_{i}^{p} \sum_{j}^{p} K_{ij}{}^{\alpha} - \sum_{i}^{q} \sum_{j}^{q} K_{ij}{}^{\beta}\Big) \qquad (2.83)$$

Here the sums $\sum_{i}^{p}$ and $\sum_{i}^{q}$ are over α and β orbitals, respectively, and

the molecular orbital exchange integrals are given by

$$K_{ij}{}^{\alpha} = \int\int \psi_i{}^{\alpha}(1)\psi_j{}^{\alpha}(2)\frac{1}{r_{12}}\psi_j{}^{\alpha}(1)\psi_i{}^{\alpha}(2)\,d\tau_1\,d\tau_2 \qquad (2.84)$$

and similarly for $K_{ij}{}^{\beta}$.   It is easily confirmed that Eq. (2.83) reduces to
Eq. (2.22) if the set of functions ψ^{α} is identical with the set $\psi_i{}^{\beta}$.
   If we define a set of one-electron energies for α orbitals by

$$\varepsilon_i{}^{\alpha} = H_{ii}{}^{\alpha} + \sum_{j}^{p}(J_{ij} - K_{ij}{}^{\alpha}) + \sum_{j}^{q} J_{ij} \qquad (2.85)$$

and a similar set $\varepsilon_i{}^{\beta}$ for the β orbitals, then the total energy may be
written

$$\mathcal{E} = \frac{1}{2}\sum_{i}^{p}(\varepsilon_i{}^{\alpha} + H_{ii}{}^{\alpha}) + \frac{1}{2}\sum_{i}^{q}(\varepsilon_i{}^{\beta} + H_{ii}{}^{\beta}) \qquad (2.86)$$

   In the LCAO approximation, both sets of molecular orbitals are
written as linear combinations of atomic orbitals ϕ_{μ},

$$\psi_i{}^{\alpha} = \sum_{\mu} c_{\mu i}{}^{\alpha}\phi_{\mu}$$

$$\psi_i{}^{\beta} = \sum_{\mu} c_{\mu i}{}^{\beta}\phi_{\mu} \qquad (2.87)$$

A separate electron density function can be obtained for α and β electrons, and we may write

$$\rho^{\alpha}(\mathbf{R}) = \sum_{i}^{p} \psi_i{}^{\alpha}(\mathbf{R})^*\psi_i{}^{\alpha}(\mathbf{R}) = \sum_{\mu\nu} P_{\mu\nu}{}^{\alpha}\phi_{\mu}^{*}(\mathbf{R})\phi_{\nu}(\mathbf{R})$$

$$\rho^{\beta}(\mathbf{R}) = \sum_{i}^{q} \psi_i{}^{\beta}(\mathbf{R})^*\psi_i{}^{\beta}(\mathbf{R}) = \sum_{\mu\nu} P_{\mu\nu}{}^{\beta}\phi_{\mu}^{*}(\mathbf{R})\phi_{\nu}(\mathbf{R}) \qquad (2.88)$$

where $P_{\mu\nu}{}^\alpha$ and $P_{\mu\nu}{}^\beta$ are density matrices defined by

$$P_{\mu\nu}{}^\alpha = \sum_i^p c_{\mu i}{}^\alpha c_{\nu i}{}^\alpha \qquad \text{and} \qquad P_{\mu\nu}{}^\beta = \sum_i^q c_{\mu i}{}^\beta c_{\nu i}{}^\beta \qquad (2.89)$$

The full density matrix P is the sum of these two

$$P_{\mu\nu} = P_{\mu\nu}{}^\alpha + P_{\mu\nu}{}^\beta \qquad (2.90)$$

It is also possible to define a *spin density* function which is the *excess* of α electron density over β electron density at a given point. This is given by

$$\rho^{\text{spin}}(\mathbf{R}) = \rho^\alpha(\mathbf{R}) - \rho^\beta(\mathbf{R}) = \sum_{\mu\nu} \rho_{\mu\nu}{}^{\text{spin}} \phi_\mu^*(\mathbf{R}) \phi_\nu(\mathbf{R}) \qquad (2.91)$$

where the elements of *spin density matrix* are given by

$$\rho_{\mu\nu}{}^{\text{spin}} = P_{\mu\nu}{}^\alpha - P_{\mu\nu}{}^\beta \qquad (2.92)$$

For a closed-shell system, $P_{\mu\nu}{}^\alpha = P_{\mu\nu}{}^\beta$ and the spin density is zero everywhere. However, for radicals and triplet states, $\rho_{\mu\nu}{}^{\text{spin}}$ provides detailed information about the distribution of electron spin throughout the molecule.

If the LCAO molecular orbitals of Eq. (2.87) are used, the electronic energy expression of Eq. (2.83) can be rewritten in terms of integrals over atomic orbitals,

$$\mathcal{E} = \sum_{\mu\nu} P_{\mu\nu} H_{\mu\nu} + \tfrac{1}{2} \sum_{\mu\nu\lambda\sigma} (P_{\mu\nu} P_{\lambda\sigma} - P_{\mu\lambda}{}^\alpha P_{\nu\sigma}{}^\alpha - P_{\mu\lambda}{}^\beta P_{\nu\sigma}{}^\beta)(\mu\nu|\lambda\sigma)$$

$$(2.93)$$

This can now be used to find equations for the optimum values of the coefficients $c_{\mu i}{}^\alpha$ and $c_{\mu i}{}^\beta$ by carrying out *independent* variations of the α and β orbitals. This leads to two sets of coupled equations

$$\sum_\nu (F_{\mu\nu}{}^\alpha - \varepsilon_i{}^\alpha S_{\mu\nu}) c_{\nu i}{}^\alpha = 0$$

$$\sum_\nu (F_{\mu\nu}{}^\beta - \varepsilon_i{}^\beta S_{\mu\nu}) c_{\nu i}{}^\beta = 0 \qquad (2.94)$$

where there are two Fock hamiltonian matrices with elements given by

$$F_{\mu\nu}{}^\alpha = H_{\mu\nu} + \sum_{\lambda\sigma} [P_{\lambda\sigma}(\mu\nu|\lambda\sigma) - P_{\lambda\sigma}{}^\alpha(\mu\sigma|\lambda\nu)]$$

$$F_{\mu\nu}{}^\beta = H_{\mu\nu} + \sum_{\lambda\sigma} [P_{\lambda\sigma}(\mu\nu|\lambda\sigma) - P_{\lambda\sigma}{}^\beta(\mu\sigma|\lambda\nu)] \qquad (2.95)$$

These are generalizations of the Roothaan equations derived in Sec. 2.4, and have to be solved by a similar iterative procedure. Given an initial guess for the density matrices $P_{\mu\nu}{}^{\alpha}$ and $P_{\mu\nu}{}^{\beta}$, first approximations to the two Fock matrices $F_{\mu\nu}{}^{\alpha}$ and $F_{\mu\nu}{}^{\beta}$ may be computed. The two sets of Eqs. (2.95) may then be solved for two sets of coefficients by the method described in Sec. 2.3. This leads to a pair of new density matrices and the cycling procedure may be continued until self-consistency is achieved within a specified level of accuracy.

From the point of view adopted herein, the unrestricted approach to molecular orbital wavefunctions is more suitable than other approaches since a more realistic description of the unpaired spin density in the system is obtained. This is of considerable importance in the application of molecular orbital theory to the study of coupling constants obtained by electron spin resonance (cf. Sec. 4.3) and nuclear magnetic resonance (Sec. 4.4). Other methods for treating open-shell systems are available, and these have been concisely reviewed by Berthier [15].

REFERENCES

1. Koopmans, T.: *Physica*, **1**:104 (1933).
2. Fock, V.: *Z. Physik*, **61**:126 (1930).
3. Hartree, D. R.: *Proc. Cambridge Phil. Soc.*, **24**:89 (1928).
4. Margenau, H., and G. Murphy: "The Mathematics of Physics and Chemistry," D. Van Nostrand Company, Inc., Princeton, N.J., 1956.
5. Lennard-Jones, J. E.: *Proc. Roy. Soc. (London)*, **A198**:1, 14 (1949), and later papers.
6. Edmiston, C., and K. Ruedenberg: *Rev. Mod. Phys.*, **34**:457 (1963); *J. Chem. Phys.*, **43**:597 (1965).
7. Mulliken, R. S.: *J. Chem. Phys.*, **23**:1833, 1841 (1955); **36**:3428 (1962).
8. Hall, G. G.: *Proc. Roy. Soc. (London)*, **A205**:541 (1951).
9. Roothaan, C. C. J.: *Rev. Mod. Phys.*, **23**:69 (1951).
10. Ransil, B. J.: *Rev. Mod. Phys.*, **32**:239, 245 (1960).
11. Corbato, F. J., and A. C. Switendick: Quantum Chemistry Program Exchange, no. 29, Department of Chemistry, University of Indiana, Bloomington, Ind. Modified for the CDC 1604 by N. S. Ostlund.
12. Sasaki, F., and K. Ohno: *J. Math. Phys.*, **4**:1140 (1963).
13. Slater, J. C.: *Phys. Rev.*, **35**:210 (1930).
14. Pople, J. A., and R. K. Nesbet: *J. Chem. Phys.*, **22**:571 (1954).
15. Berthier, G.: in P. O. Lowdin and B. Pullman (eds.), "Molecular Orbitals in Chemistry, Physics and Biology," pp. 57 ff., Academic Press, Inc., New York, 1964.

3
Approximate Molecular Orbital Theories

3.1 INTRODUCTION

Up to this point we have considered molecular orbital theory from an *ab initio* viewpoint, with the calculation of a wavefunction involving the evaluation of a number of integrals followed by an algebraic self-consistent procedure. In this chapter we shall use this theory as a framework for the development of a more approximate approach which avoids the evaluation of many difficult integrals and which makes some use of experimental data in selecting values of others. Approximate molecular orbital theories are by nature *semiempirical*, in that one no longer attempts to derive molecular properties directly from the principles of quantum mechanics, but rather seeks to interpret correlations within experimental data.

Before describing the simplifying approximations in detail, it is pertinent to note some of the general conditions that should be satisfied by an approximate molecular orbital treatment if it is to provide a critical qualitative background for simple discussions of the electronic structure of large molecules. These may be listed as follows:

1. The methods must be simple enough to permit application to moderately large molecules without excessive computational effort. Although quite accurate molecular orbital wavefunctions now exist for many diatomic and polyatomic molecules, it is unlikely that comparable functions will be readily available in the near future for larger molecules. To be widely accessible, a quantum-mechanical theory necessarily has to be approximate.

2. Even though approximations have to be introduced, these should not be so severe that they eliminate any of the primary physical forces determining structure. For example, the relative stabilities of electrons in different atomic energy levels, the directional character of the bonding capacity of atomic orbitals, and electrostatic repulsion between electrons are all gross features with major chemical consequences and they should all be retained in a realistic treatment.

3. In order to be useful as an independent study, the approximate wavefunctions should be formulated in an unbiased manner, so that no preconceived ideas derived from conventional qualitative discussions are built in implicitly. For example, a critical theoretical study of the localization of a two-electron bond orbital ought to be based on a quantum-mechanical theory which makes no reference to electron-pair bonds in its basis. Molecular orbital theories satisfy this type of condition insofar as each electron is treated as being free to move anywhere in the molecular framework.

4. The theory should be developed in such a way that the results can be interpreted in detail and used to support or discount qualitative hypotheses. For example, it is useful if the electronic charge distribution calculated from a wavefunction can be easily and realistically divided into contributions on individual atoms which may then be compared with qualitative discussions. As a rule, approximate quantum-mechanical treatments are more easily interpreted in this manner than complex, accurate wavefunctions in cases where the latter are available.

5. Finally, the theory should be sufficiently general to take account of all chemically effective electrons. Normally, this means all electrons in the valence shell. Extensive theories have been developed, of course, for the π electrons of conjugated planar systems, but those apply only to a limited class of molecules, and even then are subject to frequent uncertainty because of lack of knowledge about the remaining electrons which are not treated explicitly. The extension of quantum-mechanical techniques to apply to all valence electrons of a general three-dimensional molecule must be a major objective.

The theories which are the main topic of the remainder of this book attempt to provide general methods which are consistent with these conditions.   These are approximate self-consistent field methods and take explicit account of the electrostatic effects of ionic and polar groups.   They are simple enough to be applied to moderately large molecules (molecular weight up to about 300) using only modest amounts of computer time and can be applied extensively to series of organic and inorganic compounds in many configurations.   Once completely specified, such a method constitutes a mathematical model which simulates chemical behavior and which can be examined in quantitative detail at any stage.

It should be clear from the discussion in Chap. 2 that the most difficult and time-consuming part of LCAO self-consistent molecular orbital calculations is the evaluation and handling of a large number of electron repulsion integrals.   It is well known that many of these electron repulsion integrals have values near zero, especially those involving the overlap distribution $\phi_\mu(1)\phi_\nu(1)$, with $\mu \neq \nu$.   Thus, in developing approximate self-consistent field molecular orbital schemes, a useful approach is the systematic neglect of electron repulsion integrals having uniformly small values.   This is effected by means of the *zero-differential overlap approximation* [1], whereby electron repulsion integrals involving the overlap distributions are assumed negligibly small.   Under the zero-differential overlap approximation,

$$(\mu\nu|\lambda\sigma) = (\mu\mu|\lambda\lambda)\delta_{\mu\nu}\delta_{\lambda\sigma} \tag{3.1}$$

where δ_{ij} is the Kronecker delta.   In addition, the corresponding overlap integrals

$$S_{\mu\nu} = \int\phi_\mu(1)\phi_\nu(1)\,d\tau_1 \tag{3.2}$$

are neglected in the normalization of the molecular orbitals.   The core integrals

$$H_{\mu\nu} = \int\phi_\mu(1)\mathbf{H}^{\text{core}}\phi_\nu(1)\,d\tau_1 \tag{3.3}$$

which involve an overlap distribution are *not* neglected but may be treated in a semiempirical manner to accommodate the possible bonding effect of the overlap.   The various levels of approximate self-consistent field theory to be discussed differ mainly in the extent to which the zero-differential overlap approximation is invoked in electron repulsion integrals.

If the zero-differential overlap approximation is used for all atomic orbital pairs, the Roothaan equations (2.61) for the LCAO coefficients for a closed-shell molecule simplify to

$$\sum_{\nu} F_{\mu\nu} c_{\nu i} = \epsilon_i c_{\mu i} \tag{3.4}$$

where the elements of the Fock matrix $F_{\mu\nu}$ are now given by

$$F_{\mu\mu} = H_{\mu\mu} - \tfrac{1}{2} P_{\mu\mu} (\mu\mu|\mu\mu) + \sum_{\lambda} P_{\lambda\lambda} (\mu\mu|\lambda\lambda) \tag{3.5}$$

and

$$F_{\mu\nu} = H_{\mu\nu} - \tfrac{1}{2} P_{\mu\nu} (\mu\mu|\nu\nu) \qquad \mu \neq \nu \tag{3.6}$$

These approximations greatly simplify the computation of wave-functions, largely because they eliminate many of the difficult two-electron integrals. In particular, all three- and four-center integrals become zero. Although individually they may introduce considerable error, there is some consistency between these approximations, and the neglect of the overlap integral $S_{\mu\nu}$ in the normalization involving the associated charge distribution $\phi_\mu \phi_\nu$ is consistent with the neglect of electron repulsion integrals involving a similar $\phi_\mu \phi_\nu$ distribution. In the succeeding sections we shall describe the various levels at which zero-differential overlap approximations can be made.

3.2 INVARIANT LEVELS OF APPROXIMATION [2]

An important aspect of LCAO molecular orbitals is their behavior under transformations of the set of basis functions ϕ_μ. If a molecular orbital ψ_i can be written as a linear combination of the atomic orbitals ϕ_μ

$$\psi_i = \sum_{\mu} c_{\mu i} \phi_\mu \tag{3.7}$$

then ψ_i can also be written as a linear combination of another basis set ϕ'_α if these are linear combinations of the original ϕ_μ,

$$\phi'_\alpha = \sum_{\mu\alpha} t_{\mu\alpha} \phi_\mu \tag{3.8}$$

Here $t_{\mu\alpha}$ is any nonsingular square matrix (i.e., with nonzero determinant). In fact, the whole calculation could be formulated in terms of the set ϕ'_α to begin with, and the final set of *molecular* orbitals would be the same.

Let us suppose that the original set ϕ_μ is a set of s, p, d, . . . atomic orbitals centered on the various nuclei in the molecule. Then we may classify possible transformations in order of increasing complexity in the following manner:

1. Transformations which only mix together orbitals on the same atom
   which have the same principal and azimuthal quantum numbers
   n and l. For example, such a transformation might mix the
   three orbitals $2px$, $2py$, and $2pz$, or the five $3d$ functions. A
   particularly important transformation of this kind is rotation of
   the cartesian axes used to define the atomic orbitals.
2. Transformations which mix *any* atomic orbitals on the same atom.
   If different azimuthal quantum numbers l are involved, the resulting orbitals ϕ'_α are usually known as *atomic hybrid orbitals*. For a
   carbon atom, for example, the four atomic orbitals $2s$, $2px$, $2py$,
   $2pz$ may be replaced by four sp^3 hybrids along tetrahedral directions. The same molecular orbital can be expressed as a linear
   combination of either set.
3. Transformations which mix atomic orbitals centered on different
   atoms. These lead to a nonatomic basis set. One important
   example of this type is the transformation of atomic orbitals to
   group orbitals which belong to one of the symmetry species of
   the molecular point group.

We have already noted that the full calculation of the LCAO
molecular orbitals will give the same total wavefunction and calculated molecular properties whether or not transformations such as
these are applied to the basis set ϕ_μ. However, if we are dealing with
approximations to the full Roothaan equations, it becomes important
to study whether this invariance still applies. The next step, therefore, is to examine the zero-differential overlap approximation under
these transformations.

The zero-differential overlap approximation will be used for
atomic orbitals only, where it is most appropriate. The differential
overlap $\phi_\mu\phi_\nu$ involving two atomic orbitals may be *monatomic* or
diatomic, depending on whether ϕ_μ and ϕ_ν are on the same or different
atoms. Clearly the intra-atomic transformations of types 1 and 2
will transform a diatomic differential overlap $\phi_\mu\phi_\nu$ into another
diatomic type $\phi'_\alpha\phi'_\beta$. Thus, if the diatomic differential overlap is
systematically neglected for any pair of atoms, it will automatically
be neglected for the orbitals obtained after such transformations.
The approximation may then be said to be invariant to such
transformations.

For the monatomic differential overlap $\phi_\mu\phi_\nu$ involving the product of two different orbitals on the same atom, the situation is less

simple. Consider, for example, a rotation of $45°$ about the z axis, leading to new cartesian coordinates

$$x' = 2^{-\frac{1}{2}}(x + y)$$
$$y' = 2^{-\frac{1}{2}}(-x + y)$$

(3.9)

Then the product of $2px$ and $2py$ atomic orbitals referred to the new axes is given by

$$(2px')(2py') = \frac{1}{2}[(2py)^2 - (2px)^2]$$

(3.10)

Thus the differential overlap $\phi_\mu\phi_\nu$ for one set of axes corresponds to something involving only squared quantities $\phi_\mu{}^2$ for the other axes. Clearly, the approximation is not invariant to rotation unless the right-hand side of Eq. (3.10) is also neglected.

To find the effects of the transformation generally, we need to know the way in which the various integrals transform. Under the transformation of Eq. (3.8), the overlap matrix, the core hamiltonian, and the two-electron integrals become

$$S'_{\alpha\beta} = \sum_{\mu\nu} t_{\mu\alpha}t_{\nu\beta}S_{\mu\nu}$$

(3.11)

$$H'_{\alpha\beta} = \sum_{\mu\nu} t_{\mu\alpha}t_{\nu\beta}H_{\mu\nu}$$

(3.12)

and

$$(\alpha\beta|\gamma\delta)' = \sum_{\mu\nu\lambda\sigma} t_{\mu\alpha}t_{\nu\beta}t_{\lambda\gamma}t_{\sigma\delta}(\mu\nu|\lambda\sigma)$$

(3.13)

Approximate LCAOSCF computations will only be invariant insofar as they satisfy these transformation conditions. We shall require invariance under all transformations of types 1 and 2. Invariance with respect to rotation of local axes is an essential feature, especially for molecules of low symmetry where there is no unique choice. Invariance to hybridization is less essential, but it is desirable as it is sometimes convenient to interpret molecular orbitals in these terms.

In the following sections we shall consider various ways in which the zero-differential overlap approximation can be applied in a manner invariant under transformations of types 1 and 2. These methods differ mainly in the degree of approximation involved.

3.3 COMPLETE NEGLECT OF DIFFERENTIAL OVERLAP (CNDO) [2, 3]

The most elementary theory retaining the main features of electron repulsion is the complete neglect of differential overlap method (CNDO) introduced by Pople, Santry, and Segal [2]. Only valence electrons are treated explicitly, the inner shells being treated as part of a rigid core, so that they modify the nuclear potential in the one-electron part of the hamiltonian. The atomic orbital basis set ϕ_μ is then a valence set (1s for hydrogen, 2s, 2px, 2py, 2pz for carbon, nitrogen, etc.).

The basic approximation is that the zero-differential overlap approximation is used for *all* products of different atomic orbitals $\phi_\mu\phi_\nu$ so that the simplified Eqs. (3.4) to (3.6) apply. However, we have already noted that, by itself, this is not invariant to rotation of the axes. To restore rotational invariance, we make the additional approximation of making the remaining two-electron integrals depend only on the nature of the atoms A and B to which ϕ_μ and ϕ_λ belong and not on the actual type of orbital. Thus

$$(\mu\mu|\lambda\lambda) = \gamma_{AB} \begin{cases} \text{all } \mu \text{ on atom A} \\ \text{all } \lambda \text{ on atom B} \end{cases} \tag{3.14}$$

γ_{AB} is then an average electrostatic repulsion between any electron on A and any electron on B. For large interatomic distances R_{AB}, γ_{AB} will be approximately equal to R_{AB}^{-1}.

To prove that zero-differential overlap, together with Eq. (3.14), leads to integrals which transform according to Eq. (3.13), we first consider a local transformation on atom A,

$$\phi'_\alpha = \sum_\mu^A t_{\mu\alpha}\phi_\mu \tag{3.15}$$

If the original atomic orbitals are normalized and orthogonal, the new set will have the same property provided that $t_{\mu\alpha}$ is an orthogonal matrix. (This is always true for a simple rotation of axes.) If the old orbitals ϕ_μ and ϕ_ν on atom A transform into new orbitals ϕ'_α and ϕ'_β and if ϕ_λ and ϕ_σ are two orbitals on another atom B, then the general electron repulsion integral (remaining after neglecting diatomic differential overlap) is given by

$$(\alpha\beta|\lambda\sigma) = \sum_{\mu\nu}^A t_{\mu\alpha}t_{\nu\beta}(\mu\nu|\lambda\sigma) \tag{3.16}$$

Now if the additional condition of Eq. (3.1) applies for the old basis set, the integral $(\mu\nu|\lambda\sigma)$ will vanish unless $\mu = \nu$ and $\lambda = \sigma$. If both these conditions are satisfied, the integral is γ_{AB} and Eq. (3.16) becomes

$$(\alpha\beta|\lambda\sigma) = \gamma_{AB}\delta_{\lambda\sigma}\sum_\mu^A t_{\mu\alpha}t_{\mu\beta} = \gamma_{AB}\delta_{\lambda\sigma}\delta_{\alpha\beta} \tag{3.17}$$

using properties of an orthogonal matrix. If a local transformation is now applied to the orbitals ϕ_λ and ϕ_σ of B, giving ϕ'_γ and ϕ'_δ, a similar argument applies and we obtain finally

$$(\alpha\beta|\gamma\delta) = \gamma_{AB}\delta_{\alpha\beta}\delta_{\gamma\delta} \qquad (3.18)$$

Thus the same result would have been obtained if the approximations had been applied directly to the new set of orbitals. These approximations are therefore equivalent to the complete neglect of differential overlap for all sets of orthonormal atomic orbitals.

Using Eq. (3.14), the CNDO expressions for the Fock hamiltonian matrix elements given in Eqs. (3.4) and (3.6) now simplify to

$$F_{\mu\mu} = H_{\mu\mu} - \tfrac{1}{2}P_{\mu\mu}\gamma_{AA} + \sum_B P_{BB}\gamma_{AB} \qquad \phi_\mu \text{ on } A \qquad (3.19)$$

and   *all orbitals not μ*
                                 includes orbitals on A

$$F_{\mu\nu} = H_{\mu\nu} - \tfrac{1}{2}P_{\mu\nu}\gamma_{AB} \qquad \phi_\mu \text{ on } A, \ \phi_\nu \text{ on } B \qquad (3.20)$$

Here we have used the symbol P_{BB} for the total electron density associated with atom B,

$$P_{BB} = \sum_\lambda^B P_{\lambda\lambda} \qquad (3.21)$$

where the summation is over all atomic orbitals on B.

The next step is to apply a related series of approximations to the matrix elements $H_{\mu\nu}$ of the core hamiltonian operator,

$$\mathbf{H} = -\tfrac{1}{2}\nabla^2 - \sum_B \mathbf{V}_B \qquad (3.22)$$

where $-\mathbf{V}_B$ is the potential due to the nucleus and inner shells of atom B. The diagonal matrix elements $H_{\mu\mu}$ are conveniently separated into one- and two-center contributions. If ϕ_μ is on atom A, we write

$$H_{\mu\mu} = U_{\mu\mu} - \sum_{B(\neq A)} (\mu|\mathbf{V}_B|\mu) \qquad (3.23)$$

where $U_{\mu\mu}$ is the one-center term

$$U_{\mu\mu} = (\mu|-\tfrac{1}{2}\nabla^2 - \mathbf{V}_A|\mu) \qquad (3.24)$$

and is essentially an atomic quantity (the energy of ϕ_μ in the bare field of the core of its own atom). $U_{\mu\mu}$ is obtained semiempirically from atomic data by methods to be discussed in the following sections. The remaining terms in Eq. (3.23) give the electrostatic interaction of an electron in ϕ_μ with the cores of other atoms B. We shall consider approximations for these terms shortly.

Next we consider the off-diagonal core matrix elements $H_{\mu\nu}$ between different atomic orbitals ϕ_μ and ϕ_ν on the same atom A. This may again be separated into two parts analogously to (3.23),

$$H_{\mu\nu} = U_{\mu\nu} - \sum_{B(\neq A)} (\mu|\mathbf{V}_B|\nu) \qquad \phi_\mu, \phi_\nu \text{ on A} \qquad (3.25)$$

where again $U_{\mu\nu}$ is the one-electron matrix element using only the local core hamiltonian. If ϕ_μ, ϕ_ν are functions of the s, p, d, . . . type, $U_{\mu\nu}$ is zero by symmetry. On the other hand, if a hybrid basis is used, this is no longer so. However, we shall restrict ourselves to s, p, d, . . . sets in the following development. The remaining terms in Eq. (3.25) represent the interaction of the distribution $\phi_\mu\phi_\nu$ with cores of other atoms.

In the CNDO method, the two-center terms $(\mu|\mathbf{V}_B|\mu)$ and $(\mu|\mathbf{V}_B|\nu)$ in Eqs. (3.23) and (3.25) have to be approximated in a manner which is consistent with the way the two-electron integrals are treated. Thus, neglect of monatomic differential overlap $\phi_\mu\phi_\nu$ ($\mu \neq \nu$) on atom A means that $(\mu|\mathbf{V}_B|\nu)$ is taken to be zero. Further, the invariance conditions also require that the diagonal elements $(\mu|\mathbf{V}_B|\mu)$ are the same for all ϕ_μ on A [for reasons comparable to those already given for replacing $(\mu\mu|\nu\nu)$ by γ_{AB}]. Consequently, we shall write

$$(\mu|\mathbf{V}_B|\mu) = V_{AB} \qquad (3.26)$$

where $-V_{AB}$ is the interaction of *any* valence electron on atom A with the core of atom B. It should be noted that the matrix V_{AB} is not necessarily symmetric. However, for large internuclear distances R_{AB}, it is approximately equal to R_{AB}^{-1}.

As a result of these approximations, we now have

$$H_{\mu\mu} = U_{\mu\mu} - \sum_{B(\neq A)} V_{AB} \qquad \phi_\mu \text{ on A} \qquad (3.27)$$

$$H_{\mu\nu} = 0 \qquad \phi_\mu \neq \phi_\nu, \text{ both on A} \qquad (3.28)$$

To complete the specification of the calculation, we need the off-diagonal core matrix elements $H_{\mu\nu}$, where ϕ_μ and ϕ_ν are on different atoms A and B. As discussed previously, we do not neglect differential overlap here, since these elements take account of the basic bonding capacity of the overlap between the orbitals. However, we may separate the cores of atoms A and B and write

$$H_{\mu\nu} = (\mu|-\tfrac{1}{2}\nabla^2 - \mathbf{V}_A - \mathbf{V}_B|\nu) - \sum_{C(\neq A,B)} (\mu|\mathbf{V}_C|\nu) \qquad (3.29)$$

where the second part gives the interaction of the distribution with the cores of third atoms C. These integrals will be neglected, since they are comparable to three-center, two-electron integrals which have already been omitted. The first part of Eq. (3.29) then depends only on the local environment and is a measure of the possible lowering of energy levels by an electron being in the electrostatic field of two atoms simultaneously. It is commonly referred to as a *resonance integral* and denoted by the symbol $\beta_{\mu\nu}$.

In the CNDO method, the resonance integrals $\beta_{\mu\nu}$ are handled in a semiempirical manner. However, this has to be done in a manner which satisfies the required invariance conditions. This will be done by assuming that $\beta_{\mu\nu}$ is proportional to the overlap integral

$$H_{\mu\nu} = \beta_{\mu\nu} = \beta_{AB}{}^0 S_{\mu\nu} \tag{3.30}$$

This assumption is not unreasonable since the bonding capacity of the overlap will increase as the overlap increases. Approximations of this sort have frequently been used in independent electron calculations, following the original suggestion by Mulliken [4]. For the calculations to be invariant under transformations of the atomic basis sets, it is required that the proportionality factor between $H_{\mu\nu}$ and $S_{\mu\nu}$ is the same for all atomic orbitals. This is necessary since $S_{\mu\nu}$ itself transforms correctly. The constant is written $\beta_{AB}{}^0$ and will be chosen to depend only on the nature of the atoms A and B. It could depend on the AB distance without altering the invariance, but this possible flexibility has not been used in CNDO schemes thus far. The numerical choice of β_{AB} values will be discussed in the following section.

This completes the basic approximations of the CNDO method. It is useful to recapitulate them at this point. In summary, they are:

Approximation 1: Replacing the overlap matrix by the unit matrix in the Roothaan equations and neglecting the overlap integrals $S_{\mu\nu}$ in normalizing the molecular orbitals

Approximation 2: Neglecting differential overlap in all two-electron integrals so that

$$(\mu\nu|\lambda\sigma) = \delta_{\mu\nu}\delta_{\lambda\sigma}(\mu\mu|\lambda\lambda) \tag{3.31}$$

Approximation 3: Reducing the remaining set of coulomb-type integrals to one value per atom pair,

$$(\mu\mu|\lambda\lambda) = \gamma_{AB} \qquad \phi_\mu \text{ on A, } \phi_\lambda \text{ on B} \tag{3.32}$$

Approximation 4: Neglecting monatomic differential overlap (in an invariant manner) in the interaction integrals involving the cores of other atoms

$$(\mu|\mathbf{V}_B|\nu) = \delta_{\mu\nu}V_{AB} \tag{3.33}$$

Approximation 5: Taking diatomic off-diagonal core matrix elements to be proportional to the corresponding overlap integrals

$$H_{\mu\nu} = \beta_{AB}{}^0 S_{\mu\nu} \qquad \phi_\mu \text{ on A, } \phi_\nu \text{ on B} \tag{3.34}$$

Using all these approximations, the matrix elements of the Fock hamiltonian reduce to the following simple form (ϕ_μ belonging to atom A and ϕ_ν to atom B):

$$F_{\mu\mu} = U_{\mu\mu} + (P_{AA} - \tfrac{1}{2}P_{\mu\mu})\gamma_{AA} + \sum_{B(\neq A)} (P_{BB}\gamma_{AB} - V_{AB}) \tag{3.35}$$

$$F_{\mu\nu} = \beta_{AB}{}^0 S_{\mu\nu} - \tfrac{1}{2}P_{\mu\nu}\gamma_{AB} \qquad \mu \neq \nu \tag{3.36}$$

The off-diagonal expression, Eq. (3.36), applies even if ϕ_μ and ϕ_ν are both on the same atom A, when $S_{\mu\nu} = 0$ and γ_{AB} is replaced by γ_{AA}.

The expression given in Eq. (3.35) for the diagonal matrix element can be rearranged in the form

$$F_{\mu\mu} = U_{\mu\mu} + (P_{AA} - \tfrac{1}{2}P_{\mu\mu})\gamma_{AA}$$
$$+ \sum_{B(\neq A)} [-Q_B\gamma_{AB} + (Z_B\gamma_{AB} - V_{AB})] \tag{3.37}$$

where Q_B is the net charge on atom B,

$$Q_B = Z_B - P_{BB} \tag{3.38}$$

The two-center terms in Eq. (3.37) are then easily interpreted. $-Q_B\gamma_{AB}$ represents the effect of the potential due to the total charge on atom B (and will vanish if this atom is neutral in the molecular environment). The quantity $Z_B\gamma_{AB} - V_{AB}$ represents the difference between the potentials due to the valence electrons and core of the neutral atom B. Following Goeppert-Mayer and Sklar [5], such a term is usually referred to as a *penetration integral*.

Once a set of CNDO coefficients $c_{\mu i}$ and a corresponding density matrix $P_{\mu\nu}$ have been obtained, the total energy can be found from

$$\mathcal{E}_{total} = \tfrac{1}{2} \sum_{\mu\nu} P_{\mu\nu}(H_{\mu\nu} + F_{\mu\nu}) + \sum_{A<B} Z_A Z_B R_{AB}{}^{-1} \tag{3.39}$$

using the appropriate expressions for $H_{\mu\nu}$ and $F_{\mu\nu}$.

One useful feature of a CNDO calculation is that every term in the total energy expression is associated with one or two atoms, so that an *energy breakdown* into monatomic and diatomic contributions is possible

$$\mathcal{E}_{total} = \sum_A \mathcal{E}_A + \sum_{A<B} \mathcal{E}_{AB} \tag{3.40}$$

The detailed expressions for $\mathcal{E}_A$ and $\mathcal{E}_{AB}$ are

$$\mathcal{E}_A = \sum_\mu^A P_{\mu\mu} U_{\mu\mu} + \tfrac{1}{2} \sum_\mu^A \sum_\nu^A (P_{\mu\mu} P_{\nu\nu} - \tfrac{1}{2} P_{\mu\nu}{}^2) \tag{3.41}$$

and

$$\mathcal{E}_{AB} = \sum_\mu^A \sum_\nu^B (2 P_{\mu\nu} \beta_{\mu\nu} - \tfrac{1}{2} P_{\mu\nu}{}^2 \gamma_{AB})$$
$$+ (Z_A Z_B R_{AB}{}^{-1} - P_{AA} V_{AB} - P_{BB} V_{BA} + P_{AA} P_{BB} \gamma_{AB}) \tag{3.42}$$

For large intermolecular separations, the potential integrals V_{AB}, V_{BA}, and γ_{AB} all approximate to $R_{AB}{}^{-1}$ so that the last group of terms in Eq. (3.42) becomes $Q_A Q_B R_{AB}{}^{-1}$. This shows that the theory takes proper account of the electrostatic interaction between charged atoms in a molecule.

The CNDO method is easily extended to open shells of electrons if a single-determinant wavefunction is used with different molecular orbitals for α and β electrons. This is the unrestricted molecular orbital type of function described in Sec. 2.5. As indicated there, if the number of α electrons exceeds the β electrons by one, this gives a component of the doublet state of a free radical with one unpaired electron. If there are two extra α electrons, the wavefunction corresponds to a component of the lowest triplet state.

Recapitulating from Sec. 2.5, two sets of molecular orbitals are used,

$$\psi_i{}^\alpha = \sum_\mu c_{\mu i}{}^\alpha \phi_\mu \qquad \psi_i{}^\beta = \sum_\mu c_{\mu i}{}^\beta \phi_\mu \tag{3.43}$$

and there are corresponding density matrices

$$P_{\mu\nu}{}^\alpha = \sum_i^{occ} c_{\mu i}{}^\alpha c_{\nu i}{}^\alpha \qquad P_{\mu\nu}{}^\beta = \sum_i^{occ} c_{\mu i}{}^\beta c_{\nu i}{}^\beta \tag{3.44}$$

The total density matrix $P_{\mu\nu}$ and the spin density matrix $\rho_{\mu\nu}^{spin}$ are given by

$$P_{\mu\nu} = P_{\mu\nu}{}^\alpha + P_{\mu\nu}{}^\beta \tag{3.45}$$

and

$$\rho_{\mu\nu}^{spin} = P_{\mu\nu}{}^\alpha - P_{\mu\nu}{}^\beta \tag{3.46}$$

The LCAO coefficients $c_{\mu i}{}^\alpha$ and $c_{\mu i}{}^\beta$ satisfy the general equations (2.93), and the elements of the two Fock matrices $F_{\mu\nu}{}^\alpha$ and $F_{\mu\nu}{}^\beta$ can be easily simplified by the general CNDO approximations used for closed shells in the previous section. The results are

$$F_{\mu\mu}{}^\alpha = U_{\mu\mu} + (P_{AA} - P_{\mu\mu}{}^\alpha)\gamma_{AA} + \sum_{B(\neq A)} (P_{AA}\gamma_{AB} - V_{AB}) \tag{3.47}$$

$$F_{\mu\nu}{}^\alpha = \beta_{AB}{}^0 S_{\mu\nu} - P_{\mu\nu}{}^\alpha \gamma_{AB} \qquad \mu \neq \nu \tag{3.48}$$

and corresponding expressions for the β matrix. Equations (3.47) and (3.48) reduce to Eqs. (3.35) and (3.36) if α and β orbitals are identical. The total energy, using the unrestricted wavefunction, is

$$\mathcal{E}_{total} = \frac{1}{2} \sum_{\mu\nu} [P_{\mu\nu}{}^{\alpha}(H_{\mu\nu} + F_{\mu\nu}{}^{\alpha}) + P_{\mu\nu}{}^{\beta}(H_{\mu\nu} + F_{\mu\nu}{}^{\beta})]$$

$$+ \sum_{A<B} \frac{Z_A Z_B}{R_{AB}} \quad (3.49)$$

and again this can be split into monatomic and diatomic parts as in Eq. (3.40). Full expressions for $\mathcal{E}_A$ and $\mathcal{E}_{AB}$ are

$$\mathcal{E}_A = \sum_{\mu}^{A} P_{\mu\mu} U_{\mu\mu}$$

$$+ \frac{1}{2} \sum_{\mu}^{A} \sum_{\nu}^{A} (P_{\mu\mu}P_{\nu\nu} - P_{\mu\nu}{}^{\alpha}P_{\mu\nu}{}^{\alpha} - P_{\mu\nu}{}^{\beta}P_{\mu\nu}{}^{\beta})\gamma_{AA} \quad (3.50)$$

and

$$\mathcal{E}_{AB} = \sum_{\mu}^{A} \sum_{\nu}^{B} [2P_{\mu\nu}\beta_{\mu\nu} - (P_{\mu\nu}{}^{\alpha})^2\gamma_{AB} - (P_{\mu\nu}{}^{\beta})^2\gamma_{AB}]$$

$$+ (Z_A Z_B R_{AB}{}^{-1} - P_{AA}V_{AB} - P_{BB}V_{BA} + P_{AA}P_{BB}\gamma_{AB}) \quad (3.51)$$

3.4 THE CNDO/1 PARAMETERIZATION [3]

A full specification of a CNDO calculation requires values for the overlap integrals $S_{\mu\nu}$, the core hamiltonian elements $U_{\mu\mu}$, V_{AB}, the electron repulsion integrals γ_{AB} and the bonding parameters $\beta_{AB}{}^{0}$. Two procedures for obtaining these have been proposed which will be referred to as CNDO/1 and CNDO/2. The second type is rather more successful and has been more widely applied. However, we shall describe CNDO/1 first as this was the original formulation.

The CNDO/1 method can be used for atoms up to fluorine. The basis set ϕ_μ consists of Slater-type atomic orbitals for the valence shell ($1s$ for hydrogen and $2s$, $2px$, $2py$, $2pz$ for lithium to fluorine). Exponents are chosen according to Slater's rules except that for hydrogen we use a value of 1.2, close to the optimum value for this constant in an LCAO calculation for the hydrogen molecule. It should be noted that the Slater $2s$ functions are nodeless and are not orthogonal to the inner-shell orbitals. However, since inner-shell electrons are not treated explicitly, no complications result.

The overlap integrals $S_{\mu\nu}$ are calculated explicitly using formulas discussed in Appendix B. The electron repulsion integral γ_{AB}, which represents an average interaction between electrons in valence atomic orbitals on atoms A and B, is calculated as the two-center coulomb integral involving valence s functions,

$$\gamma_{AB} = \int\int s_A{}^2(1)(r_{12})^{-1}s_B{}^2(2)\ d\tau_1\ d\tau_2 \qquad (3.52)$$

The evaluation of these is also discussed in Appendix B. The parameter V_{AB}, representing the interaction between a valence electron on atom A with the core (nucleus and inner-shell electrons) of another atom B, is also calculated using the A valence s orbital s_A. Further, the B core is treated as a point charge at the B nucleus. Thus, we take

$$V_{AB} = Z_B\int s_A{}^2(1)(r_{1B})^{-1}\ d\tau_1 \qquad (3.53)$$

where Z_B is the core charge of B and r_{1B} is the distance of electron 1 from the B nucleus. Integrals of this type can be handled by the same method as overlaps.

The $U_{\mu\mu}$ are atomic matrix elements of the one-electron hamiltonian, i.e., kinetic energy plus core potential of the atom to which ϕ_μ belongs. These could be calculated from atomic orbitals, but in view of the importance of accommodating in the theory the relative energies of $2s$ and $2p$ electrons, and the difficulty in reproducing this without an adequate treatment of inner shells, it is preferable to obtain these parameters from observed atomic energy levels. At the level of approximation used in CNDO theory, the energy of an atomic core and valence electrons for an atom or ion X (Li to F) with an electronic configuration $(2s)^m(2p)^n$ is given by

$$E(X,2s^m2p^n) = mU_{2s,2s} + nU_{2p,2p}$$
$$+ \tfrac{1}{2}(m + n)(m + n - 1)\gamma_{AA} \qquad (3.54)$$

since all electron-electron repulsion integrals are equal to γ_{AA}. In general, there will be several states arising from the configuration $2s^m2p^n$, but in this level of approximation, the states are all degenerate due to the neglect of atomic exchange integrals. In making use of experimental data to calculate $U_{\mu\mu}$, it is therefore necessary to either arbitrarily select the state to which Eq. (3.54) refers or consider an average energy of all the states arising from the same configuration. The latter is clearly the preferable choice, and one takes a multiplicity weighted average of all the states involved. For the carbon atom, for example, the configuration $2s^22p^2$ gives rise to a ^3P, ^1D, and ^1S state, and thus we take

$$E(C,2s^2,2p^2) = \tfrac{3}{5}E(C,{}^3P) + \tfrac{1}{3}E(C,{}^1D) + \tfrac{1}{15}E(C,{}^1S) \qquad (3.55)$$

The core integrals $U_{2s,2s}$ and $U_{2p,2p}$ can be related to ionization potentials or electron affinities referred to these states. We may, for example, write an expression analogous to Eq. (3.54) for the energy of the atomic cation X^+ formed on ionization of a $2p$ electron. Thus,

$$E(X^+, 2s^m 2p^{n-1}) = mU_{2s,2s} + (n-1)U_{2p,2p}$$
$$+ \tfrac{1}{2}(m+n-1)(m+n-2)\gamma_{AA} \quad (3.56)$$

The atomic ionization potentials from $2s$ and $2p$ orbitals are then given by

$$I_s(X, 2s^m, 2p^n) = E(X^+, 2s^{m-1} 2s^n) - E(X, 2s^m 2p^n)$$
$$= -U_{2s,2s} - (m+n-1)\gamma_{XX} \quad (3.57)$$
$$I_p(X, 2s^m, 2p^n) = E(X^+, 2s^m 2p^{n-1}) - E(X, 2s^m 2p^n)$$
$$= -U_{2p,2p} - (m+n-1)\gamma_{XX} \quad (3.58)$$

Equations (3.57) and (3.58) relate the atomic ionization potentials to the U and γ parameters. Since we have already specified a theoretical procedure for calculating the γ integrals, these equations can be used to estimate the $U_{\mu\mu}$ from the experimental values of I_s and I_p. This is the procedure followed in CNDO/1. The only exception is for the $1s$ orbital of hydrogen, where the U value is taken to be -13.06 ev, the theoretical value for $\zeta = 1.2$ rather than the experimental value. The complete set of numerical values is given in Table 3.1.

The only remaining quantities required for a complete specification of the calculation are the bonding parameters β_{AB}^0. To reduce the amount of empirical parameterization, these are assumed to have the form

$$\beta_{AB}^0 = \tfrac{1}{2}(\beta_A^0 + \beta_B^0) \quad (3.59)$$

Here β_A^0 depends only on the nature of the atom A, so only a single semiempirical parameter is selected for each element. The values used are given in Table 3.2 and are selected to give the best overall

Table 3.1 "Average" ionization potentials (electron volts) used to fix $U_{\mu\mu}$ in CNDO/1

Atom	H	Li	Be	B	C	N	O	F
1s	13.06							
2s	...	5.39	9.32	14.05	19.44	25.58	32.38	40.20
2p	...	3.54	5.96†	8.30	10.67	13.19	15.85	18.66

† Obtained from the excited configuration Be$(2s2p)$.

Table 3.2   Bonding parameters $\beta_A{}^0$ (electron volts)

Atom	H	Li	Be	B	C	N	O	F
$-\beta_A{}^0$	9	9	13	17	21	25	31	39

fit with accurate LCAOSCF calculations using a minimal basis set. The details of this comparison are described below.

Given a complete set of parameters specified in this way, the LCAOSCF equations may be solved by a series of steps comparable to those used in the full calculations described in Sec. 2.4:

1. An initial guess is made at the molecular orbital coefficients. This is best done by a "Hückel-type" calculation in which the diagonal elements $F_{\mu\mu}$ are replaced by the appropriate ionization potentials, Eq. (3.57) or (3.58), and the off-diagonal elements $F_{\mu\nu}$ are replaced by $\beta_{AB}{}^0 S_{\mu\nu}$.
2. Electrons are assigned in pairs to the molecular orbitals with lowest energies (i.e., lowest eigenvalues of $F_{\mu\nu}$).
3. The density matrix $P_{\mu\nu}$ is calculated from the coefficients of the occupied molecular orbitals and then used to form a new Fock matrix $F_{\mu\nu}$.
4. Diagonalization of the $F_{\mu\nu}$ matrix then leads to a new set of coefficients $c_{\mu i}$.
5. Steps 2, 3, and 4 are repeated until self-consistency is achieved. This may be done by comparing coefficients, but this is not altogether satisfactory, since these are not uniquely defined if the Fock matrix has degenerate eigenvalues (as in molecules with n-fold rotation axes where n is greater than 2). A better procedure is to test for convergence on the density matrix, as by requiring the root-mean-square change to be less than some specified parameter δ. Thus, the process is terminated if

$$\left[\sum_\mu \sum_\nu (P_{\mu\nu} - P'_{\mu\nu})^2\right]^{1/2} < \delta \qquad (3.60)$$

A value of 10^{-4} for δ is sufficient for most applications. Lower values can be used, although more self-consistent cycles will be needed. A lower limit on δ will, of course, be imposed by the details of the computational equipment used. A third possibility is to examine the change in the calculated electronic energy. If this differs by less than some specified amount Δ in successive cycles, the cyclic process can be stopped.

We now turn to the comparison of the CNDO/1 theory with *ab initio* minimal basis calculations for small molecules. As mentioned above, this is used to calibrate the bonding parameters $\beta_A{}^0$. However, the coefficients obtained by the accurate methods are based on normalization of molecular orbitals using correct overlap integrals, whereas the CNDO coefficients will be normalized neglecting overlap. To make a comparison more realistic, it is necessary to cast the accurate results into a different form.

Under the assumption of neglect of overlap, the original Roothaan equation

$$\mathbf{F'C'} = \mathbf{SC'E'} \tag{3.61}$$

becomes

$$\mathbf{FC} = \mathbf{CE} \tag{3.62}$$

which is the form used in the CNDO treatment. The full equations become comparable to Eq. (3.62), however, if the transformation

$$\mathbf{C} = \mathbf{S}^{\frac{1}{2}}\mathbf{C'} \tag{3.63}$$

is applied. Equation (3.61) then becomes (after premultiplication by $\mathbf{S}^{-\frac{1}{2}}$)

$$(\mathbf{S}^{-\frac{1}{2}}\mathbf{F'S}^{-\frac{1}{2}})\mathbf{C} = \mathbf{CE} \tag{3.64}$$

The transformation given in Eq. (3.63) is equivalent to replacing the original basis of atomic orbitals ϕ' by a set of orbitals ϕ orthogonalized by the procedure first proposed for molecules by Löwdin [6]. Thus

$$\phi = \phi'\mathbf{S}^{-\frac{1}{2}} \tag{3.65}$$

As ϕ is the closest set of orthogonal orbitals (in the least-squares sense) to the original atomic orbitals ϕ', it is appropriate to compare the coefficients of the CNDO calculations with those of the reference calculation after multiplication by the matrix $\mathbf{S}^{\frac{1}{2}}$ according to Eq. (3.63).

The actual values of the bonding parameters $\beta_A{}^0$ (Table 3.2) were chosen by comparison with reference calculations on diatomic molecules. Table 3.3 shows typical results for the OH and BH systems. These have molecular orbital configurations

$$\begin{aligned} &\text{BH:} \quad (1\sigma)^2(2\sigma)^2(3\sigma)^2 \\ &\text{OH:} \quad (1\sigma)^2(2\sigma)^2(3\sigma)^2(1\pi)^3 \end{aligned} \tag{3.66}$$

The 1σ orbital is closely identified with the inner shell of the heavy atom and is not treated in the CNDO calculation. This molecular orbital (and the small coefficients of the $1s$ atomic orbital in the higher

Table 3.3 Eigenvectors and orbital energies

OH ($r_{OH} = 1.8342$ a.u.)

	CNDO				Reference a			
	$2s$	$2p$	$1s_H$	ϵ_i(a.u.)	$2s$	$2p$	$1s_H$	ϵ_i(a.u.)
2σ	0.9114	0.0697	0.4056	−1.3484	0.8894	0.1277	0.4381	−1.2256
3σ	−0.3102	0.7640	0.5658	−0.7086	−0.3669	0.7719	0.5190	−0.5265
4σ	−0.2704	−0.6415	0.7179	0.3524	−0.2725	−0.6228	0.7334	0.4733

BH ($r_{BH} = 2.39$ a.u.)

	CNDO				References b, c, d			
	$2s$	$2p$	$1s_H$	ϵ_i(a.u.)	$2s$	$2p$	$1s_H$	ϵ_i(a.u.)
2σ	0.6701	0.3281	0.6658	−0.7660	0.6690	0.3211	0.6695	−0.6475
3σ	−0.6582	0.6772	0.3288	−0.4404	−0.6471	0.6953	0.3128	−0.3459
4σ	0.3430	0.6586	−0.6698	0.3487	0.3656	0.6430	−0.6723	0.4673

a M. Krauss, *J. Chem. Phys.*, **28**:1021 (1958).
b The calculations of Ransil (Ref. *d*, Table III) employ nonorthogonal 1s and 2s Slater orbitals. Since we regard the 1s electrons as part of the molecular core, these calculations were transformed to an orthogonal basis by $C_{i\cdot1s} = C'_{i\cdot1s} + \lambda C'_{i\cdot2s}$, $C_{i\cdot2s} = (1 - \lambda^2)^{1/2}C'_{i\cdot2s}$, where C' are the Ransil coefficients, $\lambda = \int\phi_{1s}\phi_{2s}d\tau$,
c Slater LCAO-MO calculation.
d B. J. Ransil, *Rev. Mod. Phys.*, **32**:245 (1960).

molecular orbitals from the reference calculations) is omitted in Table 3.3.   The remaining atomic orbital functions are $2s$, $2p\sigma$, and $2p\pi$ on the heavy atom and $1s_H$ on the hydrogen.   The 1π molecular orbitals have to be identical with the $2p\pi$ atomic orbitals in this approximation. The remaining molecular orbitals 2σ, 3σ, and an unoccupied one 4σ are linear combinations of $2s$, $2p\sigma$, and $1s_H$, and these are the coefficients listed in the table.   The OH radical is not a closed-shell system, of course, but a rough calculation can be carried out by localizing the $2p$ electrons and taking their coulomb interactions into proper account with the appropriate γ_{AB} integral.

The overall agreement between the CNDO/1 coefficients and those obtained from the reference calculations is fairly good.   The CNDO/1 orbital energies ϵ_i are consistently more negative than those obtained by the full calculations, but the differences $(\epsilon_j - \epsilon_i)$ are well reproduced.   These conclusions are valid over a wider range of comparisons as reported in the original publication.   In addition, fairly good agreement was obtained in a similar comparison for HCN using the β parameters selected for diatomic molecules.   This provides some check on the use of diatomic calibration for the application of the theory to larger polyatomic systems.

A number of detailed studies of polyatomic molecules using the CNDO/1 method were reported in Ref. [3].   However, these will not be described here as improved versions of the techniques are now available.

3.5   THE CNDO/2 PARAMETERIZATION [7]

The second version of the CNDO method differs from CNDO/1 in the way it handles penetration integrals and the one-center atomic core integrals.   The modifications were made to correct certain evident deficiencies of the earlier method and lead to a more satisfactory scheme for the calculation of molecular properties.

If CNDO/1 calculations are carried out as a function of distance for diatomic molecules, it is found that the predicted equilibrium distance is much too small and the dissociation energy correspondingly too large.   Detailed breakdown of the total energy using Eqs. (3.41) and (3.42) indicates that this is primarily due to a "penetration" effect in which electrons in an orbital on one atom penetrate the shell of another leading to a net attraction.   Mathematically this is described by the penetration integrals $(Z_B\gamma_{AB} - V_{AB})$ appearing in Eq. (3.37).

These penetration terms give rise to calculated bonding energies even when the bond orders connecting two atoms are zero. Thus, if the energy of the first triplet state ($^3\Sigma_u{}^+$) of H_2 with the electronic configuration $(1\sigma_g)(1\sigma_u)$ is calculated by the CNDO/1 method, the theoretical interaction energy is

$$E_{AB} = \gamma_{AB} - 2V_{AB} + R_{AB}{}^{-1} \qquad (3.67)$$

If γ_{AB} and V_{AB} are calculated using Slater orbitals with effective charge 1.2 (as specified by CNDO/1), E_{AB} has a minimum of 0.637 ev at a distance of 0.85 Å, whereas accurate calculations show this state to be repulsive (except for weak van der Walls attraction at large distances).

In the CNDO/2 method this deficiency is corrected in the simplest possible way by neglecting the penetration integrals. Thus the electron-core potential integrals V_{AB} are no longer evaluated separately but are related to the electron repulsion integrals by

$$V_{AB} = Z_B\gamma_{AB} \qquad (3.68)$$

The core-core repulsion energies, however, will still be taken to be equal to $Z_AZ_BR_{AB}{}^{-1}$. With this change, the H_2 triplet interaction energy, Eq. (3.67), becomes

$$E_{AB} = R_{AB}{}^{-1} - \gamma_{AB} \qquad (3.69)$$

and is repulsive at all distances.

No really satisfactory theoretical justification for this neglect of penetration can be given, but it does appear to compensate errors of the opposite sign introduced by the neglect of overlap integrals. We shall see in the next chapter that the CNDO/2 method (and the closely related INDO method) does predict equilibrium bondlengths quite well.

The second change in CNDO/2 concerns the way that the local core matrix element $U_{\mu\mu}$ is estimated from atomic data. In CNDO/1, this was obtained from the ionization potential I_μ of the appropriate average atomic state by the relation

$$-I_\mu = U_{\mu\mu} + (Z_A - 1)\gamma_{AA} \qquad (3.70)$$

the atomic orbital ϕ_μ belonging to atom A. An alternative procedure would have been to use atomic electron affinities A_μ for which the corresponding relation is

$$-A_\mu = U_{\mu\mu} + Z_A\gamma_{AA} \qquad (3.71)$$

In a comprehensive molecular orbital theory, we wish to be able to account satisfactorily for the tendency of an atomic orbital both to acquire and lose electrons, so that the new procedure adopted in CNDO/2 is to use the average of Eqs. (3.70) and (3.71).

$$-\tfrac{1}{2}(I_\mu + A_\mu) = U_{\mu\mu} + (Z_A - \tfrac{1}{2})\gamma_{AA} \qquad (3.72)$$

Using Eqs. (3.35), (3.36), (3.68), and (3.72), the basic equations for the Fock matrix in the CNDO/2 method can now be written

$$F_{\mu\mu} = -\tfrac{1}{2}(I_\mu + A_\mu) + [(P_{AA} - Z_A) - \tfrac{1}{2}(P_{\mu\mu} - 1)]\gamma_{AA}$$
$$+ \sum_{B(\neq A)} (P_{BB} - Z_B)\gamma_{AB} \qquad (3.73)$$
$$F_{\mu\nu} = \beta_{AB}{}^0 S_{\mu\nu} - \tfrac{1}{2}P_{\mu\nu}\gamma_{AB} \qquad (3.74)$$

This form for $F_{\mu\mu}$ shows up the self-consistent character of the theory in a very simple manner. The first term is a fundamental electronegativity for the atomic orbital, closely related to the scale introduced by Mulliken [8]. The remaining terms show how this is modified by the charge distribution in the actual molecular environment. The diagonal element $F_{\mu\mu}$ reduces to $-\tfrac{1}{2}(I_\mu + A_\mu)$ if the orbital ϕ_μ contains one electron ($P_{\mu\mu} = 1$) and if all atoms have zero net charge ($P_{AA} = Z_A$, $P_{BB} = Z_B$).

In relating the molecular theory to Mulliken-type atomic electronegativities $\tfrac{1}{2}(I_\mu + A_\mu)$ rather than the ionization potentials I_μ, the CNDO/2 method departs somewhat from a calibration on full a priori minimal basis calculations on diatomics. This is because Slater orbitals (using Slater rules for effective screening constants) give a poorer account of atomic electron affinities than of ionization potentials. Since an atomic calculation with Slater orbitals underestimates the electron affinity of fluorine, for example, a CNDO/1 molecular calculation will underestimate the electron-attracting power of fluorine orbitals. This deficiency is corrected in CNDO/2, and we shall see in the next chapter that the new method gives a better description of polarity.

The numerical values used for the electronegativities $-\tfrac{1}{2}(I_\mu + A_\mu)$ are listed in Table 3.4. Since the energies of monatomic negative ions are less well known than those of the positive ions, these values

Table 3.4 Matrix elements from atomic data (electron volts)

	H	Li	Be	B	C	N	O	F
$\tfrac{1}{2}(I_s + A_s)$	7.176	3.106	5.946	9.594	14.051	19.316	25.390	32.272
$\tfrac{1}{2}(I_p + A_p)$		1.258	2.563	4.001	5.572	7.275	9.111	11.080

involve some assumptions, details of which are given in Ref. [7]. However, the broad features of the theory are not highly sensitive to choice of these parameters.

Other features of the CNDO/2 method are the same as CNDO/1. Slater atomic orbitals are used to calculate the overlap integrals (with an effective charge of 1.2 for hydrogen) and the γ_{AB} are obtained theoretically from valence s orbitals. The parameters $\beta_A{}^0$ are identical with those used in CNDO/1. The detailed numerical calculations can be carried out using the computer program listed in Appendix A, starting from the charges and cartesian coordinates of the nuclei, total net charge, and spin multiplicity. Initial estimates of the LCAO coefficients may be obtained by a Hückel-type theory using matrix elements

$$F_{\mu\mu}{}^{(0)} = -\tfrac{1}{2}(I_\mu + A_\mu) \tag{3.75}$$
$$F_{\mu\nu}{}^{(0)} = \beta_{AB}{}^0 S_{\mu\nu} \qquad \mu \neq \nu \tag{3.76}$$

and the final solution is approached by an iterative scheme as described in Sec. 3.4. If the spin multiplicity is unity (a singlet ground state), this is based on the F-matrix elements of Eqs. (3.73) and (3.74).

For higher multiplicities (doublets, triplets, etc.), an unrestricted calculation is required and the corresponding expressions are

$$F_{\mu\mu}{}^\alpha = -\tfrac{1}{2}(I_\mu + A_\mu) + [(P_{AA} - Z_A) - (P_{\mu\mu}{}^\alpha - \tfrac{1}{2})]\gamma_{AA}$$
$$+ \sum_{B(\neq A)} (P_{BB} - Z_B)\gamma_{AB} \tag{3.77}$$

and

$$F_{\mu\nu}{}^\alpha = \beta_{AB}{}^0 S_{\mu\nu} - P_{\mu\nu}{}^\alpha \gamma_{AB} \tag{3.78}$$

with similar expressions for $F_{\mu\mu}{}^\beta$ and $F_{\mu\nu}{}^\beta$. Computational details for the unrestricted procedure require little elaboration. Each self-consistent cycle consists of diagonalization of both F-matrices using the $P_{\mu\nu}{}^\alpha$ and $P_{\mu\nu}{}^\beta$ density matrices from the previous cycle. The procedure can be terminated either on the basis of the root-mean-square change in the density matrices P^α and P^β or on the basis of the energy change.

The extension of the CNDO methods to heavier atoms presents a number of difficulties. In the first place, fewer satisfactory sets of a priori calculations for calibration exist. Secondly, a satisfactory description of the valence electronic structure of heavier atoms is likely to require $3d$ atomic orbitals in the basis set and the corresponding atomic energy levels required to obtain electronegativities are mostly unavailable. Nevertheless, a preliminary extension of the CNDO/2 method to the second-row elements sodium to chlorine has been made by Santry and Segal [9].

Santry and Segal consider three possible basis sets for a second-row atom referred to as sp, spd, and spd'. The sp set consists of $3s$ and $3p$ functions only and is analogous to the calculations on first-row atoms. The spd set also includes five $3d$ atomic orbitals with the same radial part as the $3s$ and $3p$ functions, while spd' has d functions which are more diffuse. The orbital exponents adopted are those collected in Table 1.5. The spd' calculations involve a number of modifications to the equations of the previous section and will not be described in detail here. Only the sp and spd type can be carried out with the program given in Appendix A.

The sp and spd calculations are based on the CNDO/2 Eq. (3.73) or (3.74) with new values for the parameters. Table 3.5 gives the values used for the atomic electronegativities. The bonding parameters β_{AB}^0 are approximated by

$$\beta_{AB}^0 = \tfrac{1}{2}K\,(\beta_A^0 + \beta_B^0) \tag{3.79}$$

where β_A^0 for second-row elements are estimated from the corresponding first-row values β_C^0 by the proportionality relation

$$\beta_A^0 = \beta_C^0 \,\frac{U_{3s,3s}(A) + U_{3p,3p}(A)}{U_{2s,2s}(C) + U_{2p,2p}(C)} \tag{3.80}$$

This leads to the values listed in Table 3.5. An additional constant K is introduced into Eq. (3.79) which is given the value 0.75 if either A or B is a second-row element (and unity otherwise). This empirical modification is found to improve the overall performance of the theory and partially corrects the inadequacy of Eq. (3.80).

All other details of the theory are the same as for the first-row calculations. The sp and spd type of calculations differ only by the omission of $3d$ functions from the basis set in sp.

Table 3.5 CNDO parameters for second-row elements (electron volts)

	Na	Mg	Ae	Si	P	S	Cl
$\tfrac{1}{2}(I_s + A_s)$	2.804	5.125	7.771	10.033	14.033	17.650	21.591
$\tfrac{1}{2}(I_p + A_p)$	1.302	2.052	2.995	4.133	5.464	6.989	8.708
$\tfrac{1}{2}(I_d + A_d)$	0.150	0.162	0.224	0.337	0.500	0.713	0.977
$-\beta_A^0$	7.720	9.447	11.301	13.065	15.070	18.150	22.330

3.6 INTERMEDIATE NEGLECT OF DIFFERENTIAL OVERLAP (INDO) [10]

The complete neglect of differential overlap (CNDO) approximation discussed in previous sections introduces electron-electron repulsions in the simplest possible manner. It does not make adequate allowance, however, for the different interactions that actually take place between two electrons with parallel or antiparallel spins, particularly if they are on the same atom. We have already seen, in Chap. 2, that the anti-symmetry of a complete wavefunction requires that electrons of parallel spin may not occupy the same small region of space and that, consequently, two electrons in different atomic orbitals on the same atom will have a smaller average repulsion energy if they have parallel spins. Mathematically, this difference shows up as a two-electron exchange integral of the type

$$(\mu\nu|\mu\nu) = \iint \phi_\mu(1)\phi_\mu(2) \frac{1}{r_{12}} \phi_\nu(1)\phi_\nu(2) \, d\tau_1 \, d\tau_2 \qquad \mu \neq \nu \qquad (3.81)$$

where ϕ_μ and ϕ_ν are on the same atom. In CNDO theory such integrals are neglected, and all interactions between two electrons on atom A are replaced by γ_{AA} irrespective of their spin. As a result, CNDO calculations are frequently unable to give an account of the separation of states arising from the same configuration. Two examples are the ^3P, ^1D, and ^1S states from the configuration $(1s)^2(2s)^2(2p)^2$ of the carbon atom and the $^3\Sigma^-$ and $^1\Delta$ states of the NH radical. Also, when applied to the NH triplet state or to aromatic free radicals, the CNDO method cannot lead to any spin density in σ orbitals as do the full unrestricted calculations described in Sec. 2.6. All such effects are closely associated with electron interaction integrals of the exchange type.

To take some account of exchange terms, the simplest procedure (which retains rotational invariance) is to retain *monatomic differential overlap, but only in one-center integrals.* This is less approximate than CNDO but not as accurate a theory as one which retains monatomic differential overlap completely (see Sec. 3.7). It is referred to as the method of *intermediate neglect of differential overlap* (INDO). The version of the method described here was introduced by Pople, Beveridge, and Dobosh [10]. A closely related method was also put forward by Dixon [11]. We shall see in the following chapter that the INDO method is a substantial improvement over CNDO/2 in any problem where electron spin distribution is important. At the same time, the additional computation required is negligible.

The INDO and CNDO/2 methods are closely related, for the basic approximations are the same except for monatomic terms. The general expressions for the unrestricted F-matrix elements without approximations for the one-center integrals are then

$$F_{\mu\mu}{}^{\alpha} = U_{\mu\mu} + \sum_{\lambda\sigma}^{A} [P_{\lambda\sigma}(\mu\mu|\lambda\sigma) - P_{\lambda\sigma}{}^{\alpha}(\mu\lambda|\mu\sigma)]$$
$$+ \sum_{B(\neq A)} (P_{BB} - Z_B)\gamma_{AB} \qquad \mu \text{ on atom A} \quad (3.82)$$

$$F_{\mu\nu}{}^{\alpha} = U_{\mu\nu} + \sum_{\lambda\sigma}^{A} [P_{\lambda\sigma}(\mu\nu|\lambda\sigma) - P_{\lambda\sigma}{}^{\alpha}(\mu\lambda|\nu\sigma)]$$
$$\mu \neq \nu, \text{ both on atom A} \quad (3.83)$$

$$F_{\mu\nu}{}^{\alpha} = \tfrac{1}{2}(\beta_A{}^0 + \beta_B{}^0)S_{\mu\nu} - P_{\mu\nu}{}^{\alpha}\gamma_{AB}$$
$$\mu \text{ on atom A, } \nu \text{ on atom B} \quad (3.84)$$

The $F_{\mu\nu}{}^{\beta}$ elements have similar form. Corresponding expressions for the closed-shell matrix elements follow by putting $P_{\mu\nu}{}^{\alpha} = P_{\mu\nu}{}^{\beta} = \tfrac{1}{2}P_{\mu\nu}$.

If an s, p, d, . . . basis set is used (no hybrids), many of the one-center integrals vanish by symmetry. Since there is only one atomic orbital of each symmetry s, px, py, pz in the basis set, all off-diagonal core elements vanish. Further, the only nonvanishing types of one-center, two-electron integrals are $(\mu\mu|\mu\mu)$, $(\mu\mu|\nu\nu)$, and $(\mu\nu|\mu\nu)$, with $\mu \neq \nu$. Consequently (3.82) and (3.83) reduce to

$$F_{\mu\mu}{}^{\alpha} = U_{\mu\mu} + \sum_{\lambda}^{A} [P_{\lambda\lambda}(\mu\mu|\lambda\lambda) - P_{\lambda\lambda}{}^{\alpha}(\mu\lambda|\mu\lambda)]$$
$$+ \sum_{B(\neq A)} (P_{BB} - Z_B)\lambda_{AB} \qquad \mu \text{ on atom A} \quad (3.85)$$

and

$$F_{\mu\nu}{}^{\alpha} = (2P_{\mu\nu} - P_{\mu\nu}{}^{\alpha})(\mu\nu|\mu\nu) - P_{\mu\nu}{}^{\alpha}(\mu\mu|\nu\nu) \quad (3.86)$$

It now only remains to specify the one-center integrals. We deal with the two-electron integrals first. Using the notation of Slater, and assuming $2s$ and $2p$ orbitals to have the same radial parts, we may write the nonvanishing integrals

$$(ss|ss) = (ss|xx) = F^0 = \gamma_{AA} \qquad (3.87)$$
$$(sx|sx) = \tfrac{1}{3}G^1 \qquad (3.88)$$
$$(xy|xy) = \tfrac{3}{25}F^2 \qquad (3.89)$$
$$(xx|xx) = F^0 + \tfrac{4}{25}F^2 \qquad (3.90)$$
$$(xx|yy) = F^0 - \tfrac{2}{25}F^2 \qquad (3.91)$$

and similar expressions for $(ss|zz)$, etc. The Slater-Condon parameters [12] F^0, G^1, and F^2 are two-electron integrals involving the radial parts of the atomic orbitals. We may note that if F^2 is given a non-

Table 3.6　Empirical values for G^1 and F^2

Element	G^1	F^2
Li	0.092012	0.049865
Be	0.1407	0.089125
B	0.199265	0.13041
C	0.267708	0.17372
N	0.346029	0.219055
O	0.43423	0.266415
F	0.532305	0.31580

zero value, Eqs. (3.90) and (3.91) show that the interaction between electrons in different p orbitals are distinguished.

In order to make the theory as close as possible to CNDO/2, the integral F^0 (or γ_{AA}) is again evaluated theoretically from Slater atomic orbitals. The values for G^1 and F^2, on the other hand, are chosen semiempirically. The values are listed in Table 3.6 and correspond to those given by Slater [12] to give best fits with experimental atomic energy levels.

Values for the monatomic core integrals $U_{\mu\mu}$ are again found semiempirically by subtracting electron interaction terms from the mean of the ionization potential I and electron affinity A of appropriate average atomic states. However, details differ somewhat from the CNDO method because of the F^1 and F^2 constants. The energy of the average states of X associated with the configuration $(2s)^m(2p)^n$ may be written at this level of approximation

$$E(X,2s^m,2p^n) = mU_{2s,2s} + nU_{2p,2p} + \tfrac{1}{2}(m + n)(m + n - 1)F^0$$
$$- \tfrac{1}{6}mnG^1 - \tfrac{1}{25}n(n - 1)F^2 \quad (3.92)$$

Defining I and A as the differences between appropriate energies of this type, we can deduce the following relations between the orbital electronegativities and the core integrals $U_{\mu\mu}$.

Hydrogen:
$$-\tfrac{1}{2}(I + A)_s = U_{ss} + \tfrac{1}{2}\gamma_{HH} \quad (3.93)$$

Lithium:
$$-\tfrac{1}{2}(I + A)_s = U_{ss} + \tfrac{1}{2}F^0 \quad (3.94)$$
$$-\tfrac{1}{2}(I + A)_p = U_{pp} + \tfrac{1}{2}F^0 - (\tfrac{1}{12})G^1 \quad (3.95)$$

Beryllium:

$$-\tfrac{1}{2}(I + A)_s = U_{ss} + \tfrac{3}{2}F^0 - \tfrac{1}{12}G^1 \tag{3.96}$$
$$-\tfrac{1}{2}(I + A)_p = U_{pp} + \tfrac{3}{2}F^0 - \tfrac{1}{4}G^1 \tag{3.97}$$

Boron to fluorine:

$$-\tfrac{1}{2}(I + A)_s = U_{ss} + (Z_A - \tfrac{1}{2})F^0 - \tfrac{1}{6}(Z_A - \tfrac{3}{2})G^1 \tag{3.98}$$
$$-\tfrac{1}{2}(I + A)_p = U_{pp} + (Z_A - \tfrac{1}{2})F^0 - \tfrac{1}{3}G^1$$
$$\qquad\qquad\qquad\qquad - \tfrac{2}{25}(Z_A - \tfrac{5}{2})F^2 \tag{3.99}$$

where Z_A is the core charge of atom A. Values used for $\tfrac{1}{2}(I + A)$ are given in Table 3.4, and values of U_{ss} and U_{pp} can be deduced. This completes the specification of the method. All other details are the same as in CNDO/2, to which this method reduces if the one-center exchange integrals G^1 and F^2 are omitted. INDO calculations can be carried out for first-row elements using the program listed in Appendix A.

3.7 NEGLECT OF DIATOMIC DIFFERENTIAL OVERLAP (NDDO) [2]

The next level of invariant approximate self-consistent field theory features neglect of differential overlap only for atomic orbitals on different atoms. The principal extra feature at this level of approximation is the retention of dipole-dipole interactions, since integrals of the type $(s_A p_A | s_B p_B)$, roughly proportional to R^{-3}, are included. These integrals may be calculated directly from given atomic orbitals or, if chosen empirically, must satisfy the invariance condition, Eq. (3.13), if the transformation is between orbitals on the same atom. The matrix elements of the Hartree-Fock hamiltonian operator at the NDDO level of approximation are

$$F_{\mu\nu} = H_{\mu\nu} + \sum_{B} \sum_{\lambda\sigma}^{B} P_{\lambda\sigma}(\mu\nu|\lambda\sigma) - \tfrac{1}{2}\sum_{\lambda\sigma}^{A} P_{\lambda\sigma}(\mu\sigma|\nu\lambda)\ \mu,\ \nu\ \text{both on A}$$
$$F_{\mu\nu} = H_{\mu\nu} - \tfrac{1}{2}\sum_{\sigma}^{A}\sum_{\gamma}^{B} P_{\lambda\sigma}(\mu\sigma|\nu\lambda) \qquad \mu\ \text{on A},\ \nu\ \text{on B} \tag{3.100}$$

Calculations at this level of approximation have been implemented by Sustmann et al. [13].

REFERENCES

1. Parr, R. G.: *J. Chem. Phys.*, **20**:239 (1952).
2. Pople, J. A., D. P. Santry, and G. A. Segal: *J. Chem. Phys.*, **43**:S129 (1965).
3. Pople, J. A., and G. A. Segal, *J. Chem. Phys.*, **43**:S136 (1965).

4. Mulliken, R. S.: *J. Phys. Chem.*, **56**:295 (1952).
5. Goeppert-Mayer, M., and A. L. Sklar: *J. Chem. Phys.*, **6**:645 (1938).
6. Löwdin, P. O.: *J. Chem. Phys.*, **18**:365 (1950).
7. Pople, J. A., and G. A. Segal: *J. Chem. Phys.*, **44**:3289 (1966).
8. Mulliken, R. S.: *J. Chem. Phys.*, **2**:782 (1934).
9. Santry, D. P., and G. A. Segal: *J. Chem. Phys.*, **47**:158 (1967).
10. Pople, J. A., D. L. Beveridge, and P. A. Dobosh, *J. Chem. Phys.*, **47**:2026 (1967).
11. Dixon, R. N.: *Mol. Phys.*, **12**:83 (1967).
12. Slater, J. C.: "Quantum Theory of Atomic Structure," McGraw-Hill Book Company, vol. 1, pp. 339–342, New York, 1960.
13. R. Sustmann, J. E. Williams, M. J. S. Dewar, L. C. Allen, P. von R. Schleyer, *J. Am. Chem. Soc.*, **91**:5350 (1969).

4
Applications of Approximate Molecular Orbital Theory

4.1 INTRODUCTION

In the previous chapters, the basic principles of molecular orbital theory were presented, leading up to the specification of the various forms of approximate molecular orbital theory acceptable from the point of view of invariance criteria. This chapter deals with the various applications of invariant CNDO and INDO molecular orbital theory reported to date, including consideration of molecular geometries, electronic charge distributions, electron-spin–nuclear-spin interactions, and nuclear-spin–nuclear-spin interactions. This is followed by a survey of other methods and applications in the recent scientific literature.

4.2 MOLECULAR GEOMETRIES AND ELECTRONIC CHARGE DISTRIBUTIONS

In this section, we consider the calculation of equilibrium molecular geometries and electronic charge distributions by means of the approximate self-consistent field methods introduced in the preceding chapter.

The *equilibrium molecular geometry* of a molecule is defined as the geometry corresponding to an absolute minimum in the total energy of the system. The theoretical calculation of the equilibrium geometry for a molecule involves systematically minimizing the total energy of the system with respect to all independent internal displacement coordinates of the molecule. The *binding energy* of a molecule is then the difference between the total energy of the molecule at equilibrium geometry and the sum of the atomic energies of the component atoms.

While the position of the absolute minimum in the total energy of the system is specified by the equilibrium geometry, the shape of the potential curve in this region is reflected in the various force constants characteristic of each of the normal modes of vibration of the system [1]. The theoretical nature of the force constants is revealed by expanding the total energy of the system E in a Taylor series about the minimum energy E_0 in terms of the atomic displacements characteristic of each of the normal coordinates Q_i,

$$E = E_0 + \tfrac{1}{2} \sum_i \frac{\partial^2 E}{\partial Q_i{}^2} Q_i{}^2 + \cdots \tag{4.1}$$

Here the terms linear in Q_i have vanished by definition of an energy minimum. The coefficients $\partial^2 E / \partial Q_i{}^2$ of the term quadratic in Q_i are directly proportional to the curvature of the potential function experienced by the system on the displacement of atoms as specified by Q_i and define the force constants of the system. Force constants may be calculated quantum mechanically by evaluating the total energy of the system at several points along a normal coordinate and fitting the values to a polynomial. The coefficients of the quadratic term, with appropriate units, are the calculated force constants. Experimentally, force constants are deduced from the vibrational frequency of the characteristic normal mode as obtained from an analysis of the infrared or Raman absorption spectra of the molecule.

The electronic charge distribution $\rho(\mathbf{R})$ at any point $\mathbf{R}$ in a molecule is calculated as the expectation value of the charge density operator $\sum_i \delta(\mathbf{R} - \mathbf{r}_i)$, which is just a summation of Dirac delta functions. This is a simple one-electron operator, and matrix elements are evaluated in a manner analogous to that developed for the core hamiltonian operator in Chap. 2. Proceeding in this manner for a spin-unrestricted single determinant wavefunction,

$$\rho(\mathbf{R}) = \langle \Psi \mid \sum_i \delta(\mathbf{R} - \mathbf{r}_i) \mid \Psi \rangle$$
$$= \sum_{\mu\nu} (P_{\mu\nu}{}^\alpha + P_{\mu\nu}{}^\beta) \, \phi_\mu(\mathbf{R}) \phi_\nu(\mathbf{R}) \tag{4.2}$$

where the $P_{\mu\nu}{}^\alpha$ and $P_{\mu\nu}{}^\beta$ are density matrix elements defined in Eq. (2.89). The interpretation of the density matrices in terms of molecular electronic structure is accomplished by means of a population analysis [2]. For LCAO molecular orbital wavefunctions calculated with the zero-differential overlap approximation, the diagonal elements $P_{\mu\mu}{}^\alpha$ and $P_{\mu\mu}{}^\beta$ give the α and β electron populations of atomic orbital ϕ_μ. The summation of electron populations of all atomic orbitals centered on a given atom A is the gross electron population of atom A, P_{AA},

$$P_{AA} = \sum_\mu^A (P_{\mu\mu}{}^\alpha + P_{\mu\mu}{}^\beta) \tag{4.3}$$

The corresponding quantities for a spin-restricted wavefunction are a special case of Eqs. (4.2) and (4.3) for $P_{\mu\mu}{}^\alpha = P_{\mu\mu}{}^\beta$. Another useful quantity is the net atomic charge ΔP_{AA},

$$\Delta P_{AA} = Z_A - P_{AA} \tag{4.4}$$

where Z_A is the core charge. This gives a quantitative measure of the charge transferred from neutral atoms on molecule formation.

A molecular property closely related to the charge distribution in the molecule is the electric dipole moment $\mathbf{\mu}$. In calculations carried out on the CNDO and INDO level of approximation, dipole moments are calculated as the sum of two contributions [3],

$$\mathbf{\mu} - \mathbf{\mu}_{chg} + \mathbf{\mu}_{hyb} \tag{4.5}$$

The first contribution, $\mathbf{\mu}_{chg}$, is obtained from the net charges located at the nuclear positions,

$$\mathbf{\mu}_{chg} = 2.5416 \sum_A \Delta P_{AA} \mathbf{R}_A \text{ debyes} \tag{4.6}$$

where $\mathbf{R}_A$ is the position vector of nucleus A and ΔP_{AA} is the net atomic charge defined in Eq. (4.4). The second contribution $\mathbf{\mu}_{hyb}$ is essentially a hybridization term and measures the contribution due to the displacement of charge away from the center of the nuclear position. This effect is proportional to the off-diagonal density matrix elements $P_{2s_A 2p_A}$ between $2s$ and $2p$ atomic orbitals centered on atom A, a typical component being

$$(\mathbf{\mu}_{hyb})_x = -14.674 \sum_A^* \zeta_A^{-1} P_{2s_A 2p_{xA}} \text{ debyes} \tag{4.7}$$

Here ζ_A is the orbital exponent of valence orbitals centered on atom A, and the asterisk on the summation indicates that the sum is restricted to atoms other than hydrogen. It should be noted that dipole integrals involving the product of two atomic orbitals on the same atom are used explicitly in the calculation of the electric dipole moment, even though analogous electron repulsion integrals are neglected in calculations by CNDO theory (but not INDO theory).

The square of the derivative of the dipole moment with respect to a displacement of atoms in the manner of a normal vibration of the system is also a quantity of interest, it being proportional to the intensity of the infrared absorption band characteristic of the normal vibration.

With the molecular properties to be considered in this section thus defined, we proceed now to a survey of the results of approximate molecular orbital calculations on these properties. For diatomic molecules, the results are summarized in Tables 4.1. Generally

Table 4.1a

Molecule	CNDO		INDO		Obs.[†]
	Configuration	State	Configuration	State	
H_2	$1\sigma_g^2$	$^1\Sigma_g^+$	$1\sigma_g^2$	$^1\Sigma_g^+$	$^1\Sigma_g^+$
Li_2	$2\sigma_g^2$	$^1\Sigma_g^+$	$2\sigma_g^2$	$^1\Sigma_g^+$	$^1\Sigma_g^+$
B_2	$2\sigma_g^2 1\pi_u^3 2\sigma_u$	$^3\Pi_g$	$2\sigma_g^2 1\pi_u^3 2\sigma_u$	$^3\Pi_g$	$^3\Sigma_g^-$
C_2	$2\sigma_g^2 1\pi_u^4 2\sigma_u^2$	$^1\Sigma_g^+$	$2\sigma_g^2 1\pi_u^4 2\sigma_u^2$	$^1\Sigma_g^+$	$^1\Sigma_g^+$ ‡
N_2^+	$2\sigma_g^2 2\sigma_u^2 1\pi_u^4 3\sigma_g$	$^2\Sigma_g^+$	$2\sigma_g^2 2\sigma_u^2 1\pi_u^4 3\sigma_g$	$^2\Sigma_g^+$	$^2\Sigma_g^+$
N_2	$2\sigma_g^2 2\sigma_u^2 1\pi_u^4 3\sigma_g^2$	$^1\Sigma_g^+$	$2\sigma_g^2 2\sigma_u^2 1\pi_u^4 3\sigma_g^2$	$^1\Sigma_g^+$	$^1\Sigma_g^+$
O_2^+	$2\sigma_g^2 2\sigma_u^2 1\pi_u^4 3\sigma_g^2 1\pi_g$	$^2\Pi_g$	$2\sigma_g^2 2\sigma_u^2 1\pi_u^4 3\sigma_g^2 1\pi_g$	$^2\Pi_g$	$^2\Pi_g$
O_2	$2\sigma_g^2 2\sigma_u^2 3\sigma_g^2 1\pi_u^4 1\pi_g^2$	$^3\Sigma_g^-$	$2\sigma_g^2 2\sigma_u^2 3\sigma_g^2 1\pi_u^4 1\pi_g^2$	$^3\Sigma_g^-$	$^3\Sigma_g^-$
F_2	$2\sigma_g^2 2\sigma_u^2 1\pi_u^4 3\sigma_g^2 1\pi_g^4$	$^1\Sigma_g^+$	$2\sigma_g^2 2\sigma_u^2 1\pi_u^4 3\sigma_g^2 1\pi_g^4$	$^1\Sigma_g^+$	$^1\Sigma_g^+$
LiH	$2\sigma^2$	$^1\Sigma^+$	$2\sigma^2$	$^1\Sigma^+$	$^1\Sigma^+$
BeH	$2\sigma^2 3\sigma$	$^2\Sigma^+$	$2\sigma^2 3\sigma$	$^2\Sigma^+$	$^2\Sigma^+$
BH	$2\sigma^2 3\sigma^2$	$^1\Sigma^+$	$2\sigma^2 3\sigma^2$	$^1\Sigma^+$	$^1\Sigma^+$
CH	$2\sigma^2 3\sigma^2 1\pi$	$^2\Pi_r$	$2\sigma^2 3\sigma^2 1\pi$	$^2\Pi_r$	$^2\Pi_r$
NH	$2\sigma^2 3\sigma^2 1\pi^2$	$^3\Sigma^-$	$2\sigma^2 3\sigma^2 1\pi^2$	$^3\Sigma^-$	$^3\Sigma^-$
OH	$2\sigma^2 3\sigma^2 1\pi^3$	$^2\Pi_i$	$2\sigma^2 3\sigma^2 1\pi^3$	$^2\Pi_i$	$^2\Pi_i$
FH	$2\sigma^2 3\sigma^2 1\pi^4$	$^1\Sigma^+$	$2\sigma^2 3\sigma^2 1\pi^4$	$^1\Sigma^+$	$^1\Sigma^+$
BF	$3\sigma^2 4\sigma^2 1\pi^4 5\sigma^2$	$^1\Sigma^+$	$3\sigma^2 4\sigma^2 1\pi^4 5\sigma^2$	$^1\Sigma^+$	$^1\Sigma^+$
LiF	$3\sigma^2 1\pi^4 4\sigma^2$	$^1\Sigma^+$	$3\sigma^2 1\pi^4 4\sigma^2$	$^1\Sigma^+$	$(^1\Sigma^+)$
BeF	$3\sigma^2 4\sigma^2 1\pi^4 5\sigma$	$^2\Sigma^+$	$3\sigma^2 4\sigma^2 1\pi^4 5\sigma$	$^2\Sigma^+$	$^2\Sigma^+$
BeO	$3\sigma^2 4\sigma^2 1\pi^4$	$^1\Sigma^+$	$3\sigma^2 4\sigma^2 1\pi^4$	$^1\Sigma^+$	$^1\Sigma^+$
BO	$3\sigma^2 4\sigma^2 1\pi^4 5\sigma$	$^2\Sigma^+$	$3\sigma^2 4\sigma^2 1\pi^4 5\sigma$	$^2\Sigma^+$	$^2\Sigma^+$
CO	$3\sigma^2 4\sigma^2 1\pi^4 5\sigma^2$	$^1\Sigma^+$	$3\sigma^2 4\sigma^2 1\pi^4 5\sigma^2$	$^1\Sigma^+$	$^1\Sigma^+$
NO	$3\sigma^2 4\sigma^2 1\pi^4 5\sigma^2 6\sigma$	$^2\Sigma^+$	$3\sigma^2 4\sigma^2 1\pi^4 5\sigma^2 6\sigma$	$^2\Sigma^+$	$^2\Pi_{1/2}$
BN	$3\sigma^2 1\pi^4 4\sigma 5\sigma$	$^3\Sigma^+$	$3\sigma^2 1\pi^4 4\sigma 5\sigma$	$^3\Sigma^+$	$^3\Pi$
CN	$3\sigma^2 1\pi^4 4\sigma^2 5\sigma$	$^2\Sigma^+$	$3\sigma^2 1\pi^4 4\sigma^2 5\sigma$	$^2\Sigma^+$	$^2\Sigma^+$

† G. Herzberg, "Diatomic Molecules," D. Van Nostrand Company, Inc., Princeton, N.J., 1950, except where noted.

‡ Ballik and Ramsey, *J. Chem. Phys.*, **31**:1128 (1959).

Table 4.1b

A—B	Equilibrium bond length[a] (Å) CNDO	INDO	Obs.	Force constant[a] (mdyn/Å) CNDO	INDO	Obs.	Binding energy[b] De (ev) CNDO	INDO	Obs.	Ionization potential[b] (ev) CNDO	INDO	Obs.	(ZA − PAA) CNDO	INDO	Dipole moment, A⁻B⁺ positive (debyes) CNDO	INDO	Obs.	SCF
H₂	0.746	0.746	0.742	10.4	10.4	5.7	5.37	5.37	4.75	20.82	20.82	15.426						
Li₂	2.179	2.134	2.672	0.84	0.85	0.25	14.71	14.40	1.05	14.09	13.88	4.96						
B₂	1.278	1.278	1.589	17.83	17.93	3.5	24.43	24.68	3.66[a]	13.47	14.66	12.0						
C₂	1.146	1.148	1.242	36.31	36.3	12.2	27.30	26.55	6.36	17.59	17.23							
N₂⁺	1.127	1.147	1.116	50.3	50.5	20.1	2.40	2.21	8.90	34.08	33.28							
N₂	1.140	1.100	1.094	52.2	50.3	23.0	25.49	20.21	8.84	18.51	16.32	15.58						
O₂⁺	1.095	1.140	1.123	66.3	64.8	16.6	2.52	2.72	6.76	31.91	31.20	38.0						
O₂	1.132	1.128	1.207	56.8	54.5	11.8	17.44	15.37	5.21	14.85	14.98	12.075						
F₂	1.119	1.128	1.435	56.7	53.8	3.60	14.62	12.85	1.64	19.19	18.32	15.7						
LiH	1.573	1.572	1.595	1.95	1.94	1.03	5.90	5.71	2.52	13.21	13.02	6.5	+0.27	+0.29	−6.16	−6.20	−5.882[d]	−6.002[i]
BeH	1.324	1.323	1.343	5.02	5.03	2.26	7.07	7.43	2.52	13.02	13.24	8.6	+0.14	+0.14	−0.67	−0.64		−0.282[i]
BH	1.194	1.204	1.233	8.60	8.30	3.0	10.01	9.37	3.58	9.44	11.81	9.7	+0.08	+0.08	−2.13	−1.84		−1.773[i]
CH	1.108	1.118	1.120	12.07	11.65	4.5	9.61	8.62	3.64	13.28	13.60	10.64	−0.01	−0.01	1.87	1.69	1.46[e]	1.570[i]
NH	1.061	1.070	1.038	14.64	14.05	5.6	8.26	6.89	3.90	13.57	17.14	13.10	−0.08	−0.09	1.76	1.68		1.627[i]
OH	1.026	1.033	0.971	17.02	16.39	7.8	6.77	6.30	4.56	16.83	18.01	13.36	−0.17	−0.18	1.86	1.79	1.660[f]	1.780[i]
FH	1.000	1.006	0.917	19.12	18.64	9.6	12.25	11.57	6.11	18.85	19.96	15.77	−0.23	−0.27	1.78	1.98	1.8195[g]	1.942[i]
BF	1.404	1.408	1.262	17.01	17.28	7.94	1.85	1.83	4.38	21.14	11.67		+0.15	+0.15	−1.31	−0.86		+1.04[k]
LiF	2.161	2.162	1.51	1.97	1.94		35.94	35.49	5.99[c]	14.59	10.58		+0.56	+0.58	−7.90	−7.86	−6.6[h]	−6.297[i]
BeF	1.671	1.670	1.361	7.50	7.38	5.8	7.52	6.11	5.48	11.97	14.19		−0.33	−0.66	−2.03	1.96		
BeO	1.463	1.474	1.331	28.92	17.30	7.5	15.22	14.75	4.69	10.58	14.22	6.0	−0.40	−0.39	−6.19	−5.67		−7.29[m]
BO	1.297	1.300	1.205	25.54	25.26	13.6	22.17	19.82	9.22	14.88	15.56	7.0	+0.19	+0.19	−1.80	−1.63		
CO	1.191	1.196	1.128	41.34	40.46	19.0	20.00	16.12	11.22	18.03	12.34	14.013	+0.08	+0.07	−0.64	−0.60	0.112[i]	−0.181[k]
NO	1.152	1.159	1.151	50.89	48.95	15.9	17.11	13.36	6.62	14.22	13.38	9.25	+0.05	+0.04	−0.15	−0.17		
BN	1.268	1.269	1.281	26.55	26.70	8.3		13.36	5.09	12.64	13.38		+0.05	+0.03	−0.36	−0.50		
CN	1.169	1.174	1.172	40.63	38.88	16.3	23.53	21.58	7.63	15.94	15.56	14.2	0.05	0.05	0.85	0.63		

[a] G. Herzberg, "Diatomic Molecules," D. Van Nostrand Company, Inc., Princeton, N.J., 1950.
[b] P. G. Wilkinson, Astrophys. J., **138**:778 (1963), except where noted otherwise.
[c] A. G. Gaydon, "Dissociation Energies," rev. ed. 1953.
[d] L. Wharton, L. P. Gold, and W. Klemperer, J. Chem. Phys., **33**:1255 (1960).
[e] D. H. Phelps and F. W. Dalby, Phys. Rev. Letters, **16**:3 (1966).
[f] F. X. Powell and D. R. Lide, Jr., J. Chem. Phys., **42**:4201 (1965).
[g] R. Weiss, Phys. Rev. **131**:659 (1963).
[h] Quoted in B. J. Ransil, Rev. Mod. Phys. **32**:239 (1960).
[i] B. Rosenblum, A. H. Nethercot, Jr., and C. H. Townes, Phys. Rev., **109**:400 (1958).
[j] P. E. Cade and W. N. Huo, J. Chem. Phys., **45**:1063 (1966).
[k] W. F. Huo, J. Chem. Phys., **43**:624 (1965).
[l] A. D. McLean, J. Chem. Phys., **39**:2653 (1963).
[m] M. Yoshimine, J. Chem. Phys., **40**:2970 (1964).

speaking, the equilibrium bondlengths and dipole moments are well accommodated, and the results of CNDO and INDO calculations are quite similar. The correlations for stretching force constants, binding energies, and ionization potentials are not very good, with the binding and ionization energies consistently too large. The complete results are presented in order to give a quantitative idea of what one may expect from a molecular orbital theory at this level of approximation.

Turning now to polyatomic molecules, calculations on the CNDO and INDO level of approximation have been carried out for a series of AB_2 and AB_3 molecules, and the equilibrium bond angles have been calculated for assumed bondlengths.

The results of CNDO/2 calculations [3] on a number of AB_2 molecules are collected in Table 4.2. For the AH_2 molecules, the calculations always order the valence-shell molecular orbitals $2a_1 < 1b_2 < 4a_1 < 1b_1 < 3a_1$ with respect to orbital energies. In linear AH_2 molecules, the $3a_1$ and $1b_1$ become a degenerate $1\pi_u$ pair, concentrated entirely on the central atom with the ordering then denoted $2\sigma_g < 1\sigma_u < 1\pi_u < 3\sigma_g$. Electronic configurations for a given AH_2 molecule follow by filling these orbitals according to an aufbau principle. Of particular interest are the two Renner molecules BH_2 and NH_2. BH_2 is a free radical with ground state $^3A_1$ and low-lying excited state $^2B_1$ arising from the configurations $(2a_1)^2(1b_2)^2(3a_1)$ and $(2a_1)^2(1b_2)^2(1b_1)$, respectively. In the linear form, these two states each correlate with one of the Renner half-states which together form the doubly degenerate $^2\Pi$ state. By appropriate specification of occupied molecular orbitals, it is possible to obtain spin-unrestricted molecular orbital wavefunctions for both $^2A_1$ and $^2B_1$ states, and it was found that the $^2A_1$ state was below the $^2B_1$. The total energy of the system is presented as a function of B—A—B bond angle in Fig. 4.1. The equilibrium geometry of the ground state $^2A_1$ is bent, and the equilibrium geometry of the excited state is linear $^2\Pi$. Analogous considerations apply to the NH_2 radicals, where the two low-lying states are $^2B_1$ and $^2A_1$, arising from the configurations $(2a_1)^2(1b_2)^2(3a_1)^2(1b_1)$ and $(2a_1)^2(1b_2)^2(3a_1)$ $(1b_1)^2$, respectively. The calculations predict both states to be bent, with $^2B_1$ lowest in energy and having a smaller B—A—B bond angle as shown in Fig. 4.2. The equilibrium angle for the upper state was calculated to be 145.1° with a barrier height of 1,103 cm^{-1}. Early experimental work [5] suggested that the upper state is linear, but a recent reconsideration of these data gave an equilibrium angle of 144° ± 5° and a barrier height of 777 ± 100 cm^{-1}. (For complete references to experimental work, see Table 4.2 and Ref. [3].)

The water molecule has the closed-shell configuration $(2a_1)^2(1b_2)^2$

No. of valence electrons	Molecule	State	Valence electronic configuration	B—A—B angle calc.	B—A—B angle obs.	Dipole moment calc.,[aa] (debyes)	Dipole moment obs.,[aa] (debyes)	Bending force constant calc., (mdyn/Å)	Bending force constant obs., (mdyn/Å)	P_{BB}	$r_e{}^a$, (Å)
4	BeH₂	$^1\Sigma_g^+$	$2\sigma_g^2 1\sigma_u$	180.0	…	0	…	0.07	…	1.144	1.343[g]
5	BH₂	$^2A_1$	$2a_1^2 1b_2^2 3a_1$	136.6	…	0.51	…	0.27	…	1.040	1.180[z]
5	BH₂	$^2\Pi_u$	$2\sigma_g^2 1\sigma_u^2 1\pi_u$	180.0	…	…	…	0.23	…	1.015	1.180[z]
6	CH₂	$^1A_1$	$2a_1^2 1b_2^2 3a_1^2$	108.6	103.2[b]	2.26	…	0.69	…	0.991	1.094[z]
6	CH₂	$^3B_1$	$2a_1^2 1b_2^2 3a_1 1b_1$	141.4	180[a]	0.75	…	0.38	…	0.937	1.094[z]
7	NH₂	$^2B_1$	$2a_1^2 1b_2^2 3a_1^2 1b_1$	107.3	103.3[c]	2.16	…	0.81	…	0.917	1.024
7	NH₂	$^2A_1$	$2a_1^2 1b_2^2 3a_1 1b_1^2$	145.1	144[d]	0.87	…	0.34	…	0.849	1.024[z]
8	OH₂⁺	$^2B_1$	$2a_1^2 1b_2^2 3a_1^2 1b_1$	118.7	…	…	…	0.52	…	0.591	0.960[z]
8	OH₂	$^1A_1$	$2a_1^2 1b_2^2 3a_1^2 1b_1^2$	107.1	104.45[c]	2.08	1.8[v]	0.95[e]	0.69[f]	0.856	0.960[z]
9	FH₂	$^2\Sigma_g^+$	$2\sigma_g^2 1\sigma_u^2 1\pi_u^4 3\sigma_g$	180.0	…	0	…	0.19	…	0.968	0.920[z]
15	BO₂	$^2\Pi_i$	$2\sigma_g^2 3\sigma_g^2 1\pi_u^4 4\sigma_g^2 3\sigma_u^2 1\pi_g^3$	180.0	180[A]	…	…	0.36	0.26[g]	6.134	1.250[g]
15	CO₂⁺	$^2\Pi_i$	$3\sigma_g^2 2\sigma_u^2 4\sigma_g^2 1\pi_u^4 3\sigma_u^2 1\pi_g^3$	180.0	180[A]	0	…	0.44	…	5.823	1.176[z]
16	CO₂	$^1\Sigma_g^+$	$2\sigma_g^2 3\sigma_g^2 1\pi_u^4 4\sigma_g^2 3\sigma_u^2 1\pi_g^4$	180.0	180[f]	0	…	0.58	0.57[f]	6.266	1.162
16	BeF₂	$^1\Sigma_g^+$	$2\sigma_g^2 3\sigma_g^2 1\pi_u^4 4\sigma_g^2 3\sigma_u^2 1\pi_g^4$	180.0	180[i]	…	…	0.12	0.73[i]	7.271	1.360[z]
16	NO₂⁺	$^1\Sigma_g^+$	$3\sigma_g^2 2\sigma_u^2 4\sigma_g^2 1\pi_u^4 3\sigma_u^2 1\pi_g^4$	180.0	180[k]	0	…	0.44	0.42[i]	5.883	1.154
17	CO₂⁻	$^2A_1$	$3a_1^2 2b_2^2 4a_1^2 5a_1^2 1b_1^2 3b_2^2 4b_2^2 1a_2^2 6a_1$	142.3	134[m]	0.75	…	0.73	…	6.528	1.200[z]
17	NO₂	$^2A_1$	$3a_1^2 2b_2^2 4a_1^2 5a_1^2 1b_1^2 3b_2^2 4b_2^2 1a_2^2 6a_1$	137.7	132[n]	0.05	±0.4[o]	0.66	0.40[p]	6.204	1.200
17	BF₂	$^2A_1$	$3a_1^2 2b_2^2 4a_1^2 5a_1^2 1b_1^2 3b_2^2 4b_2^2 5a_1^2 1a_2^2 6a_1$	124.6	…	…	…	0.62	(0.58)[q]	7.162	1.300[z]
18	NO₂⁻	$^1A_1$	$3a_1^2 2b_2^2 4a_1^2 5a_1^2 1b_1^2 3b_2^2 4b_2^2 6a_1^2 1a_2^2$	118.3	115.4[r]	−1.26	…	1.13	1.75[s]	6.543	1.236
18	O₃	$^1A_1$	$3a_1^2 2b_2^2 4a_1^2 5a_1^2 1b_1^2 3b_2^2 4b_2^2 6a_1^2 1a_2^2$	114.0	116.8	0.53	±0.58[t]	0.76	1.28[f]	6.152	1.278[z]
18	CF₂	$^1A_1$	$3a_1^2 2b_2^2 4a_1^2 5a_1^2 1b_1^2 3b_2^2 4b_2^2 5a_1^2 1a_2^2$	104.6	(100 or 108)[u]	…	…	1.09	(1.28)[q]	7.145	1.320[z]
19	NF₂	$^2B_1$	$3a_1^2 2b_2^2 4a_1^2 1b_1^2 5a_1^2 3b_2^2 1a_2^2 4b_2^2 6a_1^2 2b_1$	102.5	104.2[v]	−0.12	…	0.97	…	7.113	1.350
20	OF₂	$^1A_1$	$3a_1^2 2b_2^2 4a_1^2 1b_1^2 5a_1^2 3b_2^2 1a_2^2 4b_2^2 6a_1^2 2b_1^2$	99.2	103.8[w]	−0.21	±0.297[x]	0.71	0.55[f]	7.060	1.410

a "Tables of Interatomic Distances and Configurations in Molecules and Ions," The Chemical Society, London, 1965.

b G. Herzberg, *Proc. Roy. Soc. (London)*, **A262**:291 (1961).

c K. Dressler and D. A. Ramsay, *Phil. Trans. Roy. Soc. London*, **A251**:553 (1959).

d R. N. Dixon, *Mol. Phys.*, **9**:357 (1965).

e D. W. Posener and M. W. P. Strandberg, *Phys. Rev.*, **95**:374 (1954).

f G. Herzberg, "Infrared and Raman Spectra," D. Van Nostrand Company, Inc., Princeton, N.J., 1945.

g A. Sommer, D. White, M. J. Linevsky, and D. E. Mann, *J. Chem. Phys.*, **38**:87 (1963).

h D. A. Ramsay, *Advan. Spectry.*, **1**:1 (1959).

i L. Brewer, G. R. Somayajulu, and E. Bracket, *Chem. Rev.*, **63**:111 (1963).

j A. Buchler and W. Klemperer, *J. Chem. Phys.*, **29**:121 (1958).

k J. W. M. Steeman and C. H. Macgillavry, *Acta Cryst.*, **7**:402 (1954).

l R. Teranishi and J. C. Decius, *J. Chem. Phys.*, **22**:896 (1954).

m D. W. Ovenall and D. H. Whiffen, *Mol. Phys.*, **4**:135 (1961).

n S. Claesson, J. Donohue, and V. Schomaker, *J. Chem. Phys.*, **16**:207 (1948).

o C. T. Zahn, *Z. Physik*, **33**:686 (1932).

p L. C. Hisatsune, J. P. Devlin, and S. Califano, *Spectrochim. Acta*, **16**:450 (1960).

q G. Nagarajan, *Australian J. Chem.*, **16**:717 (1963).

r G. B. Carpenter, *Acta Cryst.*, **8**:852 (1955).

s R. H. Weston, Jr., and T. F. Brodasky, *J. Chem. Phys.*, **27**:683 (1957).

t R. H. Hughes, *J. Chem. Phys.*, **21**:959 (1953).

u D. E. Milligan, D. G. Mann, and M. E. Jacox, *J. Chem. Phys.*, **41**:1199 (1964).

v M. D. Harmony and R. J. Myers, *J. Chem. Phys.*, **35**:1129 (1961).

w J. A. Ibers and V. Schomaker, *J. Phys. Chem.*, **57**:699 (1953).

x L. Pierce, R. Jackson, and N. DiCianni, *J. Chem. Phys.*, **35**:2240 (1961).

y A. L. McClellan, "Tables of Experimental Dipole Moments," W. H. Freeman and Company, San Francisco, 1963.

z Assumed average bondlength.

aa Dipole moment + in the direction A⁻B⁺.

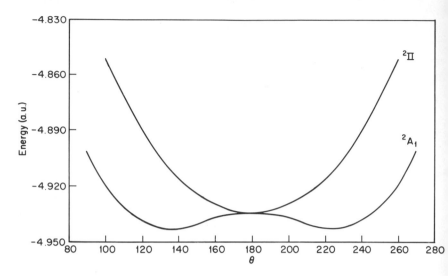

Fig. 4.1   Total energy as a function of H—B—H bond angle θ in BH_2.

$(3a_1)^2(1b_1)^2$ leading to a $^1A_1$ state, and the calculations predict that a bent molecule with a bond angle of the correct order of magnitude. In this case, the breakdown of the total energy into monatomic and diatomic parts using Eqs. (3.40) to (3.42) has been carried out.   The results (relative to corresponding quantities for the linear form) are

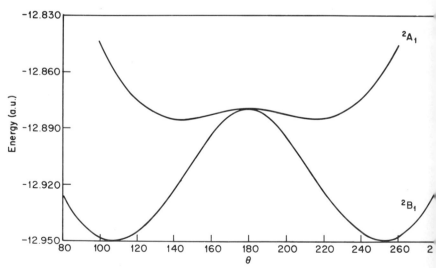

Fig. 4.2   Total energy as a function of H—N—H bond angle θ in NH_2.

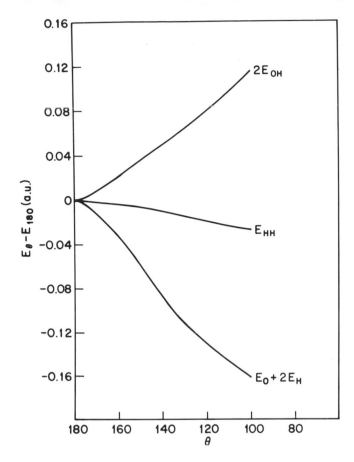

Fig. 4.3 Energy components as a function of H—O—H bond angle θ in H_2O.

shown in Fig. 4.3.　From this diagram, it is clear that the monatomic parts of the energy decrease as the molecule bends away from the linear form, but this is partly offset by a rise in the oxygen-hydrogen diatomic part.　This corresponds to the accepted qualitative picture. As the molecule deviates from linearity, the population of the oxygen $2s$ orbital increases (one of the lone pairs acquiring s character), and this is the primary "driving force" causing the molecule to be bent. On the other hand, the oxygen-hydrogen bonding energy is weaker in the bent molecule, primarily because the overlap between digonal hybrids and hydrogen (in the linear form) is more effective than overlap involving hybrids with more p character (in the bent form).　According

Table 4.3 Summary of results for AB₃ molecules

No. of valence electrons	Molecule	State	Electronic configuration	B—A—B angle calc.	B—A—B angle obs.	Dipole moment calc.,[n] (debyes)	Dipole moment obs.,[n] (debyes)	Bending force constant calc.,[o] (mdyn/Å)	Bending force constant obs.,[o] (mdyn/Å)	P_{BB}	r_a[a], Å
6	BH₃	¹A₁′	$(2a_1')^2(1e')^4$	120.0	⋯	0	⋯	0.73	⋯	1.066	1.180[m]
7	CH₃	²A₂″	$(2a_1')^2(1e')^4(1a_2'')$	120.0	(120)[b]	0	⋯	0.27	⋯	0.968	1.094
8	OH₃⁺	¹A₁	$(2a_1')^2(1e')^4(3a_1)^2$	113.9	117[c]	⋯	⋯	0.70	⋯	0.630	0.960
8	NH₃	¹A₁	$(2a_1)^2(1e)^4(3a_1)^2$	106.7	106.6[d]	2.08	1.47[c]	0.95	0.6[f]	0.924	1.020[m]
9	OH₃	²A₁	$(2a_1)^2(2e')^4(1a_2'')^2(3a_1)$	120.0	⋯	0	⋯	1.09	⋯	0.966	0.970[m]
24	CO₃⁻	¹A₁′	$(3a_1')^2(2e')^4(4a_1')(1a_2')^2(3e')^4(1a_2')^2(1e'')^4(4e')^4$	120.0	120[g]	⋯	⋯	1.53	1.46[f]	6.796	1.313
24	BF₃	¹A₁′	$(3a_1')^2(2e')^4(1a_2')^2(4a_1')^2(3e')^4(1a_2')^2(1e'')^4(4e')^4$	120.0	120[h]	0	⋯	0.91	0.87[f]	7.233	1.300
24	NO₃⁻	¹A₁′	$(3a_1')^2(2e')^4(4a_1')^2(1a_2')^2(3e')^4(1a_2')^2(1e'')^4(4e')^4$	120.0	120[i]	⋯	⋯	1.48	1.47[f]	6.533	1.242
25	CF₃	²A₁	$(3a_1)^2(2e)^4(3e^4)(5a_1)^2(1a_2)^2(4e^4(5e)^46a_1$	113.5	111.1[i]	−0.17	⋯	1.61	⋯	7.162	1.320[m]
26	NF₃	¹A₁	$(3a_1)^2(3e')^4(4a_1)^2(5a_1)^2(3e)^4(4e)^4(1a_2)^2(5e)^46a_1^2$	104.0	102.5[k]	0.05	±0.23[l]	1.33	0.76[k]	7.112	1.370

[a] "Tables of Interatomic Distances and Configurations in Molecules and Ions," The Chemical Society, London, 1965.
[b] G. Herzberg, Proc. Roy. Soc. (London), A262:291 (1961).
[c] Y. K. Yoon and G. B. Carpenter, Acta Cryst., 12:17 (1959).
[d] A. Almenningen and O. Bastiansen, Acta Chem. Scand., 9:815 (1955).
[e] A. L. McClellan, "Tables of Experimental Dipole Moments," W. H. Freeman and Company, San Francisco, 1963.
[f] G. Herzberg, "Infrared and Raman Spectra," D. Van Nostrand Company, Inc., Princeton, N.J., 1945.
[g] N. Elliott, J. Am. Chem. Soc., 59:1380 (1937).
[h] A. H. Nielson, J. Chem. Phys., 22:659 (1954).
[i] E. Grison, K. Eriks, and J. L. DeVries, Acta Cryst., 3:290 (1950).
[j] R. W. Fessenden and R. H. Schuler, J. Chem. Phys., 43:2704 (1965).
[k] V. Schomaker and C. S. Lu, J. Am. Chem. Soc., 72:1182 (1950).
[l] S. N. Ghosh, J. Chem. Phys., 21:308 (1953).

[m] Assumed average bondlength.

[n] Dipole moment + in the direction A—B⁺.

[o] Relative to the angle of deviation from plane for planar molecules, otherwise relative to B—A—B angle.

to Fig. 4.3, there is some direct hydrogen-hydrogen bonding favoring the bent form, but this is not the main factor involved.

The calculations on H_2O^+ predict an opening of the H—O—H bond angle by about 12° on the ionization of water. This may be because the increased net charge on the hydrogen atoms leads to hydrogen-hydrogen repulsion.

Calculations on AB_2 molecules, where B is oxygen or fluorine, are also listed in Table 4.2, from which it is clear that the theory is fairly successful in predicting equilibrium bond angles along these series. This angle is strongly dependent on the number of valence electrons as noted by Walsh [6]. Dipole moments and bending force constants are in moderately good agreement with experimental values with the exception of BeF_2 which is calculated to have a much lower force constant than observed.

Calculations on some AH_3 and AB_3 molecules are summarized in Table 4.3, which again show good agreement with experimental bond angles where available. It is interesting to note that H_3O (assuming the same bondlengths as H_2O) is calculated to be planar so that, as in the AH_2 systems, the addition of an a_1 antibonding electron restores the more symmetrical configuration. At this level of approximation, CH_3 is calculated to be planar (experimental evidence suggests that this is probably so), while CF_3 is pyramidal consistent with the experimental findings.

A comparison of molecular properties calculated by CNDO theory and INDO theory is shown in Table 4.4. The equilibrium

Table 4.4a Comparison of CNDO and INDO calculated bond angles and dipole moments for AB_3 molecules

No. of valence electrons	Molecule	Equilibrium angle (BAB)		Dipole moment, debyes		Bond-length, Å
		$CNDO/2$	$INDO$	$CNDO/2$	$INDO$	
6	BH_3	120.0	120.0	0	0	1.180
7	CH_3	120.0	120.0	0	0	1.094
8	CH_3^+	113.9	120.0	...	...	0.960
	NH_3	106.7	109.7	2.08	1.90	1.020
9	H_3O	120.0	120.0	0	0	0.970
24	CO_3^-	120.0	120.0	...	...	1.313
	BF_3	120.0	120.0	0	0	1.300
	NO_3^-	120.0	120.0	...	...	1.243
25	CF_3	113.5	111.6	−0.17	−0.68	1.320
26	NF_3	104.0	101.0	0.05	−0.48	1.370

Table 4.4b Comparison of CNDO and INDO calculated bond angles and dipole moments for AB$_2$ molecules

No. of valence electrons	Molecule	Equilibrium angle (BAB)		Dipole moment, debyes		Bond-length, Å
		CNDO/2	INDO	CNDO/2	INDO	
4	BeH$_2$	180.0	180.0	0	0	1.343
5	BH$_2$	136.6	130.0	0.51	0.32	1.180
	BH$_2$	180.0	180.0	0	0	1.180
6	CH$_2$	108.6	107.2	2.26	2.17	1.094
	CH$_2$	141.4	132.4	0.75	0.53	1.094
7	NH$_2$	107.3	107.2	2.16	2.12	1.024
	NH$_2$	145.1	140.3	0.87	0.79	1.024
	OH$_2$$^+$	118.7	123.4	...	...	0.960
8	OH$_2$	107.1	108.6	2.08	2.14	0.960
9	FH$_2$	180.0	180.0	0	0	0.920
15	BO$_2$	180.0	180.0	0	0	1.250
	CO$_2$$^+$	180.0	180.0	...	...	1.176
16	CO$_2$	180.0	180.0	0	0	1.162
	BeF$_2$	180.0	180.0	0	0	1.360
	NO$_2$$^+$	180.0	180.0	...	...	1.154
17	CO$_2$$^-$	142.3	140.8	...	...	1.200
	NO$_2$	137.7	138.5	−0.75	−0.79	1.200
	BF$_2$	124.6	122.9	0.05	−0.29	1.300
18	NO$_2$$^-$	118.3	118.6	...	...	1.236
	O$_3$	114.0	115.5	−1.26	−1.09	1.278
	CF$_2$	104.6	103.6	0.53	0.26	1.320
19	NF$_2$	102.6	101.7	−0.12	−0.38	1.350
20	OF$_2$	99.2	99.0	−0.21	−0.40	1.410

bond angles calculated by the CNDO and INDO methods are all similar and both reproduce experimental trends well, and it is clear that the theoretical bond angles are generally insensitive to the inclusion of one-center exchange integrals. The principal difference between the two sets of calculations is observed in the calculations on methylene, CH$_2$. For the linear CH$_2$, the electronic configuration is $(2\sigma_g)^2(1\sigma_u)^2(1\pi_u)^2$ and leads to $^3\Sigma_g^-$, $^1\Delta_g$, and $^1\Sigma_g^+$ states. The CNDO method theory fails to predict any separation between these states due to the neglect of one-center exchange integrals. The effect is introduced by the INDO method, as shown in Fig. 4.4. It should be noted that both the triplet and the singlet states are predicted to be bent by INDO theory, whereas the experimental evidence is that the triple methylene is linear.

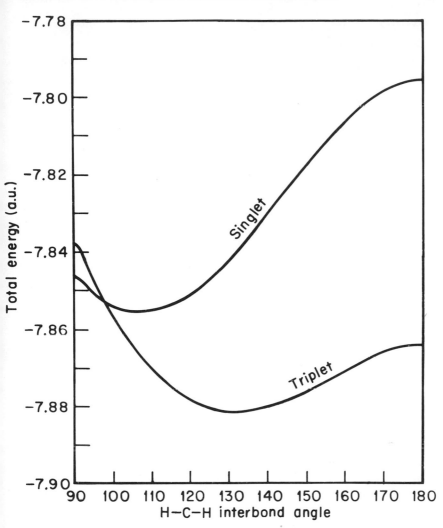

Fig. 4.4 Total energy as a function of H—C—H bond angle in CH_2.

Considering further the calculation of equilibrium molecular geometries for polyatomic molecules, a systematic study [7] has been made of molecules containing the atoms H, C, N, O, and F with INDO theory with only one or two polyvalent atoms (C, N, or O). If we denote polyvalent atoms by the symbols A, B and other atoms (H or F) by X, Y, the classes of molecules considered are AX_2, AXY, AX_3, AX_2Y, AX_4, AX_3Y, AX_2Y_2, XAB, X_2AB, $XAAX$, X_2ABX, X_2AAX_2,

X_3ABX, X_3ABX_2, and X_3AAX_3. The following constraints were placed on the nuclear configurations:

AX_2, AX_2Y_2:	C_{2v} symmetry
AX_3, AX_3Y:	C_{3v} symmetry
AX_2Y, X_2AB:	at least C_s symmetry
AX_4:	T_d
$XAAX$, X_2AAX_2:	at least C_2 symmetry
X_2ABY:	X_2AB fragment restricted to C_s symmetry; that is, the two XA bondlengths are assumed equal as are the two XAB bond angles
X_3ABY:	X_3AB fragment restricted to C_{3v} symmetry; that is, the three XA bondlengths, XAB angles, and XAX angles are assumed equal
X_3ABY_2:	X_3AB fragment restricted to C_{3v} symmetry as above; ABY_2 fragment restricted to at least C_s symmetry; that is, the two BY bondlengths are assumed equal as are the two ABY angles
X_3AAX_3:	X_3AA and AAX_3 fragments restricted to C_{3v} symmetry

For the first five groups of molecules listed above, the symmetry restrictions are simply those inherent in the molecules. All other degrees of freedom were varied to find the lowest calculated total energy. In principle, some further relaxation is possible in some molecules without altering overall molecular symmetry. For example, the three C—H bonds in methyl alcohol (class X_3ABY) may not have the same length; however, these possibilities were not considered in order to reduce the total amount of computation.

The calculations were performed by starting with an initial guess of the nuclear configuration and varying individual parameters (bondlengths and bond angles) in turn until a minimum in the total INDO energy was found. In most cases, bond angles were varied initially with steps of 1° and bondlengths with steps of 0.1 Å. After one complete cycle through all parameters, the step sizes were decreased by a factor of 10 for a second cycle. A third cycle was carried out in some cases. Calculated equilibrium geometries are given and compared with experimental data (when available) in Tables 4.5 to 4.15. The numbers in parentheses are values assumed in the experimental analysis.

AH₂, AHF, AF₂ molecules (Table 4.5)   The results shown in this table parallel those obtained previously when bondlengths were fixed at the experimental values and only the angles varied. When bondlengths are also varied in the calculation, good values are obtained except for OF and NF.

For the carbon compounds CH_2, CHF, and CF_2, all calculated bondlengths agree well with experiment, and the valence angles for the singlet states are also in good agreement. The bond angle in the triplet state of CH_2 is correctly predicted to be larger than that in the singlet; however, the INDO-optimized calculations still lead to a bent triplet form rather than the linear form suggested on the basis of spectroscopic evidence.

For the oxygen compounds, we may note that the experimental geometry of water is well reproduced. However, the theory incor-

Table 4.5   Calculated and experimental geometries for AH₂, AHF, and AF₂ molecules†

Molecule	R_{AH}, Å		R_{AF}, Å		Angle		Reference
	Calc.	Exptl.	Calc.	Exptl.	Calc.	Exptl.	
Singlet states:							
CH₂	1.17	1.12	...	...	106.0	103.2	a
CHF	1.13	(1.12)	1.30	1.31	105.7	101.8	b
CF₂	...	...	1.31	1.30	103.8	104.9	c
OH₂	1.03	0.98	...	...	104.7	104.3	d
OHF	1.04	...	1.18	...	106.9	...	
OF₂	...	...	1.18	1.41	106.6	103.3	e
Doublet states:							
NH₂	1.07	1.02	...	...	104.8	103.3	f
NHF	1.08	...	1.23	...	106.4	...	
NF₂	...	...	1.23	(1.37)	105.7	104.2	g
Triplet states:							
CH₂	1.10	1.04	...	...	131.8	180.0	a
CF₂	...	...	1.31	...	122.4	...	

† Values in parentheses were assumed in the experimental analysis.
a G. Herzberg, *Proc. Roy. Soc. (London)*, **A262**:291 (1961).
b A. J. Merer and D. N. Travis, *Can. J. Phys.*, **44**:1541 (1966).
c F. X. Powell and D. R. Lide, *J. Chem. Phys.*, **45**:1067 (1966).
d V. W. Laurie and D. R. Herschbach, *J. Chem. Phys.*, **37**:1687 (1962).
e L. Pierce, R. H. Jackson, and N. DiCianni, *J. Chem. Phys.*, **35**:2240 (1961).
f K. Dressler and D. A. Ramsay, *Phil. Trans. Roy. Soc. (London)*, **A251**:553 (1959).
g M. D. Harmony and R. J. Myers, *J. Chem. Phys.*, **35**:1129 (1961).

Table 4.6 Calculated and experimental geometries for AH_3, AH_2F, AHF_2, and AF_3 molecules

Molecule	R_{AH} Calc.	R_{AH} Exptl.	R_{AF} Calc.	R_{AF} Exptl.	θ_{HAH} Calc.	θ_{HAH} Exptl.	θ_{FAF} Calc.	θ_{FAF} Exptl.	θ_{HAF} Calc.	θ_{HAF} Exptl.	ϕ† Calc.	ϕ† Exptl.	Reference
NH_3	1.07	1.019	…	…	106.4	109.1	…	…	…	…	61.9	55.7	a
NH_2F	1.08	…	1.25	1.400	103.6	…	…	…	106.5	…	62.6	…	
NHF_2	1.09	1.026	1.25	1.371	…	…	104.6	102.9	105.2	99.8	64.6	74.1	b
NF_3	…	…	1.25	…	…	…	104.2	102.2	…	…	66.5	74.8	c
CH_3	1.11	1.079	…	…	119.0	120	…	…	…	…	17.2	0	d
CH_2F	1.11	…	1.32	…	119.6	…	…	…	114.4	…	34.8	…	
CHF_2	1.12	…	1.33	…	…	…	109.5	…	115.9	…	40.9	…	
CF_3	…	…	1.33	…	…	…	112.1	111.1	…	…	42.3	49.5	e

† $(180 - \phi)$ is the angle between the bond AY and the bisector of XAX for AX_2Y.

a O. Bastiansen and B. Beagly, *Acta Chem. Scand.*, **18**:2077 (1964).
b D. R. Lide, *J. Chem. Phys*, **38**:456 (1963).
c J. Sheridan and W. Gordy, *Phys. Rev.*, **79**:513 (1950).
d G. Herzberg, *Proc. Roy. Soc. (London)*, **A262**:291 (1961).
e R. W. Fessenden and R. H. Schuler, *J. Chem. Phys.*, **43**:2704 (1965).

rectly predicts the FOF angle in F_2O to be larger than the angle in water. This may be connected with the fact that INDO gives too small a value for the O—F bondlength. If experimental bondlengths are used, these two angles come out in the correct order. The calculated angle in OHF is probably also too large for similar reasons. The N—F bondlength in NF_2 is also probably underestimated in this theory, but for NH_2 and NF_2 the bond angles are given well and in the correct order.

AH_3, AH_2F, AHF_2, and AF_3 molecules (Table 4.6) The calculated geometries in this class of molecules are in overall agreement with the experimental data that are available. The N—F bondlength is again underestimated in NF_3. However, the theory correctly predicts that the HNH angle in NH_3 is larger than the corresponding angle in NF_3, although the difference is less than that observed experimentally. The intermediate molecules NH_2F and NHF_2 indicate that successive fluorine substitution on ammonia causes the molecule to become increasingly nonplanar.

The methyl radical is calculated to be slightly nonplanar by this method, but trifluoromethyl CF_3 is predicted to be much more so, in agreement with the experimental ESR evidence. Along the series, increasing fluorination leads to increasing deviation from the planar form. The theory of the hyperfine constants of these species has been discussed elsewhere [8].

CH_nF_{4-n} molecules (Table 4.7) This series of molecules shows a number of trends which are qualitatively reproduced by the theory.

Table 4.7   Calculated and experimental geometries for CH_nF_{4-n} molecules

Molecule	R_{CH}, Å		R_{CF}, Å		θ_{HCH}		θ_{FCF}		Reference
	Calc.	Exptl.	Calc.	Exptl.	Calc.	Exptl.	Calc.	Exptl.	
CH_4	1.116	1.093	...	...	109.5	109.5	...	...	a
CH_3F	1.120	1.105	1.348	1.385	109.8	109.9	...	...	b
CH_2F_2	1.130	(1.093)	1.345	1.36	111.1	(109.5)	105.7	108.5	c
CHF_3	1.124	1.098	1.342	1.332	...	...	107.2	108.8	d
CF_4	...	...	1.338	1.317	...	...	109.5	109.5	e

a H. C. Allen and E. K. Plyler, *J. Chem. Phys.*, **26**:972 (1957).
b C. C. Costain, *J. Chem. Phys.*, **29**:864 (1964).
c S. P. S. Porto, *N. Mol. Spec.*, **3**:248 (1958).
d S. N. Ghosh, R. Trambarulo, and W. Gordy, *J. Chem. Phys.*, **20**:605 (1952).
e C. W. W. Hoffmann and R. W. Livingston, *J. Chem. Phys.*, **21**:5656 (1953).

Table 4.8   Calculated and experimental geometries for XAB molecules

Molecule XAB	R_{AX}, Å		R_{AB}, Å		θ_{XAB}		Reference
	Calc.	Exptl.	Calc.	Exptl.	Calc.	Exptl.	
HCC	1.09	...	1.19	...	180	...	
HCN	1.09	1.063	1.18	1.155	180	180	a
HCO	1.11	1.08	1.22	1.198	131.2	119.5	b
HNO	1.09	1.063	1.19	1.212	111.2	108.6	c
HOO	1.05	...	1.19	...	110.7	...	
FCC	1.32	...	1.19	...	180	...	
FCN	1.32	1.262	1.18	1.159	180	180	a
FCO	1.32	...	1.23	...	129.4	...	
FNO	1.24	1.52	1.19	1.13	111.6	110	d
FOO	1.19	...	1.19	...	110.6	...	

[a] J. K. Tyler and J. Sheridan, *Trans. Faraday Soc.*, **59**:2661 (1963).
[b] D. A. Ramsey, *Advan. Spectry.*, **1**:1 (1959).
[c] F. W. Dalby, *Can. J. Phys.*, **36**:1336 (1958).
[d] R. L. Cook, *J. Chem. Phys.*, **42**:2927 (1965).

Experimentally, there is a marked decrease in CF bondlength with increasing fluorination. The INDO calculations do give such an effect but its magnitude is too small. There is also a tendency for the FCF angle to be less than the tetrahedral value in CH_2F_2 and CHF_3 which is also reproduced.

HAB and FAB molecules (Table 4.8)   Molecules of this type may be either linear or bent, and the correct configuration is given by the theory in all cases where there is experimental evidence. The ethynyl and fluoroethynyl radicals are both predicted to be linear as are HCN and FCN, the calculated bondlengths in the latter two molecules being also quite good. The formyl radical is correctly calculated to be nonlinear, whereas fluoroformyl is predicted to be slightly more bent. HNO and FNO are calculated to be strongly bent as observed, although the NF bondlength is underestimated. Only limited experimental evidence is available for the HOO and FOO radicals, both of which are predicted to be considerably bent in INDO theory.

H₂AB and F₂AB molecules (Table 4.9)   All the molecules listed in Table 4.9 are predicted to be planar. The calculated geometries for H_2CO and F_2CO agree quite well with experiment, the HCH angle being larger than FCF but significantly less than 120°. H_2CN and F_2CN are predicted to behave in a similar manner.

Table 4.9 Calculated and experimental geometries for X₂AB molecules

Molecule X₂AB	R_{AX}, Å		R_{AB}, Å		θ_{XAX}		ϕ†		θ_{XAB}		Reference
	Calc.	Exptl.	Calc.	Exptl.	Calc.	Exptl.	Calc.	Exptl.	Calc.	Exptl.	
H₂CN	1.12	...	1.26	...	113.3°	...	0.0°	...	123.3°	...	
H₂CO	1.12	1.1161	1.25	1.2078	115.0°	116.5	0.0°	0.0	122.5°	121.7	a
F₂CN	1.33	...	1.28	...	108.6°	...	0.0°	...	125.7°	...	
F₂CO	1.33	1.312	1.25	1.174	108.7°	108.0	0.0°	0.0	125.6°	126.0	b

† $(180 - \phi)$ is the angle which bond AB makes with the bisector of XAX.
ª K. Takagi and T. Oka, *J. Phys. Soc. Japan*, **18**:1174 (1963).
ᵇ V. W. Laurie, D. T. Pierce, and R. H. Jackson, *J. Chem. Phys.*, **37**:2995 (1962).

103

Table 4.10   Calculated and experimental geometries for XAAX molecules

| Molecule XAAX | R_{AA}, Å | | R_{AX}, Å | | θ_{AAX} | | θ_{XAAX}† | | Reference |
	Calc.	Exptl.	Calc.	Exptl.	Calc.	Exptl.	Calc.	Exptl.	
HCCH	1.20	1.2087	1.10	1.0566	180.0	180.0	...	...	a
HNNH	1.22	...	1.08	...	117.0	...	0.0	...	
HOOH	1.22	1.475	1.04	0.95	108.8	94.8	83.5	111.5	b
FCCF	1.19	...	1.32	...	180.0	...	...	...	
FNNF	1.22	1.214	1.25	1.384	116.0	114.5	0.0	0.0	c
FOOF	1.23	1.217	1.19	1.575	108.4	109.5	85.8°	87.5	d

† Dihedral angle between XAA planes, zero corresponding to the *cis* configuration.
a W. J. Lafferty, E. K. Plyler, and E. D. Tidwell, *J. Chem. Phys.*, **37**:1981 (1962).
b R. H. Hunt, R. A. Leacock, C. W. Peters, and K. T. Hecht, *J. Chem. Phys.*, **42**:1931 (1965).
c P. L. Kuczkowski and E. B. Wilson, Jr., *J. Chem. Phys.*, **39**:1030 (1963).
d R. H. Jackson, *J. Chem. Soc.*, **1962**:4585.

HAAH and FAAF molecules (Table 4.10)   Acetylene is correctly calculated to be linear, and difluoroacetylene is predicted to have the
same configuration.   The cis form of N_2F_2 is found to be more stable
than the trans as observed experimentally.   Although the relative
stabilities of the cis and trans rotamers of N_2H_2 have not been established experimentally, INDO predicts cis to be more stable.

The equilibrium geometry of hydrogen peroxide is correctly calculated to be nonplanar with barriers to internal rotation via either
the cis or trans configurations.   However, the O—O bondlength is
considerably underestimated, and the very small HOO angle observed
experimentally is not reproduced in the calculations.   The nature of
the theoretical potential curve for internal rotation (variation of the
dihedral angle θ_{XAAX}) is sensitive to the choice of the O—O bondlength
and the HOO angle.   If these two quantities are fixed at their experimentally observed values (rather than the values which give the lowest
INDO total energy), the minimum occurs in the trans configuration.

The molecular FOOF is also calculated to have a skew configuration, and the theoretical geometry is in good agreement with experiment.   However, it should be noted that the theory does not reproduce the marked shortening of the O—O bond that is reported on
going from HOOH to FOOF.   Nor does it reproduce the reported
lengthening of the OF bond on going from F_2O to FOOF.

H_2ABH and F_2ABF molecules (Table 4.11)   There are comparatively few
experimental data on this series of molecules.   The local geometries
of the CH_2 and CF_2 groups in H_2CCH, H_2CNH, F_2CCF, and F_2CNF

Table 4.11 Comparison of calculated and experimental geometries for X₂ABY molecules

Molecules	R_{XA}		R_{AB}		R_{BY}		XAB		ϕ†		ABY		ω‡		Reference
	Calc.	Exptl.	Calc.	Exptl.	Calc.	Exptl.	Calc.	Exptl.	Calc.	Exptl.	Calc.	Exptl.	Calc.	Exptl.	
H₂CCH	1.12	…	1.27	…	1.10	…	126.3	…	0.0	…	161.7	…	…	…	
H₂CNH	1.12	…	1.28	…	1.07	…	123.7	…	0.0	…	113.5	…	…	…	
H₂COH	1.11	…	1.34	…	1.04	…	116.4	…	32.1	…	109.0	…	91.9	…	
H₂NOH	1.08	1.02	1.28	1.41	1.04	0.96	110.2	106.0	55.1	65.1	111.8	103.0	0.0	0.0	a
F₂CCF	1.34	…	1.31	…	1.32	…	126.2	…	0.0	…	137.6	…	0.0	…	
F₂CNF	1.30	…	1.33	…	1.25	…	125.5	…	0.0	…	112.5	…	…	…	
F₂COF	1.36	…	1.33	…	1.19	…	113.7	…	44.7	…	109.9	…	88.3	…	
F₂NOF	1.26	…	1.29	…	1.19	…	107.2	…	61.3	…	111.3	…	0.0	…	

† $(180 - \phi)$ is the angle between the AB bond and the bisector of the XAX angle.

‡ ω is the dihedral angle defined such that a value of 0° corresponds to the bisector of the XAX angle eclipsing the BY bond.

a P. A. Giguère and I. D. Lew, *Can. J. Chem.*, **30**:948 (1952).

Table 4.12 Calculated and experimental geometries for X₂AAX₂ molecules

Molecule	R_{XA}, Å		R_{AA}, Å		θ_{XAA}		ϕ†		ω‡		Reference
	Calc.	Exptl.	Calc.	Exptl.	Calc.	Exptl.	Calc.	Exptl.	Calc.	Exptl.	
H₂CCH₂	1.11	1.086	1.31	1.337	124.3	121.3	0.0	0.0	0.0	0.0	a
H₂NNH₂	1.08	1.20	1.33	1.45	110.6	112.0	54.9	51.6	69.0	90–95	c, e
F₂CCF₂	1.34	1.30	1.33	1.33	125.5	123.0	0.0	0.0	0.0	0.0	b
F₂NNF₂	1.26	1.37	1.36	1.47	106.7	104.0	62.0	66.7	70.3	65.0	d

† $(180 - \phi)$ is the angle between the AA bond and the bisector of the XAX angle.
‡ ω is the dihedral angle defined as the angle between the planes bisecting the XAX angles.
[a] H. C. Allen and E. K. Plyler, *J. Am. Chem. Soc.*, **80**:2673 (1958).
[b] T. T. Brown and R. L. Livingston, *J. Am. Chem. Soc.*, **74**:6084 (1952).
[c] A. Y. Amaguali, I. Schishemia, T. Shimanoeshi, and S. Mezushemia, *Spectrochim. Acta*, **16**:1471 (1960).
[d] D. R. Lide and D. E. Maron, *J. Chem. Phys.*, **31**:1128 (1959).
[e] T. Kasuya and T. Kohima, *J. Phys. Soc. Japan*, **18**:364 (1963).

are predicted to be very similar to those in C_2H_4 and C_2F_4. On the other hand, the calculated CCH angle on the α carbon for the vinyl radical is predicted to open out considerably from the ethylene value. The corresponding CCF angle in C_2F_3 behaves in a similar, but less marked, manner. The only significant evidence about the structure of vinyl comes from the ESR data, and these appear to be consistent with a valence angle comparable with the ethylene value.

The H_2COH and F_2COF radicals are predicted to be nonplanar at the carbon atoms. As in other comparable systems, the fluorinated compound shows the effect more strongly. For both H_2NOH and F_2NOF, the theory predicts a cis-staggered ($\omega = 0$) configuration.

H_2AAH_2 and F_2AAF_2 molecules (Table 4.12) The experimental geometries of these molecules are well reproduced by the theory. The HCH and FCF in C_2H_4 and C_2F_4 are correctly calculated to be less than 120°, the FCF being the smaller. The carbon compounds are calculated to be planar, but the nitrogen compounds are not. Both N_2H_4 and N_2F_4 are predicted to have skew configurations with equilibrium dihedral angles in good agreement with experiment. Good agreement is also obtained for the NNH and NNF angles.

H_3COH, F_3COH, and F_3COF molecules (Table 4.13) Experimental data have only been found for methanol, for which agreement between theory and experiment is fairly good. It should be noted that the experimental data show a slight tilting of the CH_3 group relative to the CO axis. Deviations of this type are not allowed for in the present calculations.

H_3ABH_2 and F_3ABF_2 molecules (Table 4.14) The geometries of C_2H_5 and C_2F_5 are not known experimentally, but the predictions of INDO theory are seen to be similar to those for CH_3 and CF_3. Thus the α carbon is nearly planar in C_2H_5 but much less so in C_2F_5. The calculated geometry of methylamine is in good agreement with experiment, the nitrogen being nonplanar and the HNH bisector eclipsing one of the CH bonds. H_3CNF_2 and F_3CNF_2 are predicted to have similar structures, with fluorination of the nitrogen causing more deviation from planarity. Again, for these molecules, some tilting of CH_3 is found, but this was not allowed in the calculations.

C_2H_6 and C_2F_6 molecules (Table 4.15) Both these molecules are correctly predicted to be in the staggered configuration with HCH and FCF angles less than tetrahedral as observed.

Table 4.13 Calculated and experimental geometries for X₃ABY molecules

Molecule	R_{XA}, Å		R_{AB}, Å		R_{BY}, Å		θ_{XAX}		θ_{XAB}		θ_{ABY}		ω†		Reference
	Calc.	Exptl.	Calc.	Exptl.	Calc.	Exptl.	Calc.	Exptl.	Calc.	Exptl.	Calc.	Exptl.	Calc.	Exptl.	
H₃COH	1.12	(1.093)	1.37	1.434	1.04	0.937	108.2	109.5‡	110.7	109.5‡	107.3	105.9	180.0	180.0	a
F₃COH	1.34	…	1.36	…	1.04	…	107.3	…	111.5	…	109.4	…	180.0		
F₃COF	1.34	…	1.37	…	1.19	…	108.2	…	110.8	…	107.2	…	180.0		

† ω is the dihedral angle defined such that a value of 0° corresponds to the BY bond eclipsing an XA bond.
‡ Average of three values.
a E. V. Svash and D. M. Dennison, *J. Chem. Phys.*, **21**:1804 (1957).

Table 4.14 Calculated and experimental geometries for X₃ABY₂ molecules

Molecule	R_{XA}, Å		R_{AB}, Å		R_{BY}, Å		θ_{XAB}		θ_{XAX}		θ_{ABY}		ϕ†		ω‡		Reference
	Calc.	Exptl.	Calc.	Exptl.	Calc.	Exptl.	Calc.	Exptl.	Calc.	Exptl.	Calc.	Exptl.	Calc.	Exptl.	Calc.	Exptl.	
H₃CCH₂	1.13	…	1.42	…	1.11	…	112.4	…	106.4	…	123.0	…	4.3	…	0.0	…	
H₃CNH₂	1.12	(1.093)	1.40	1.474	1.07	1.011	111.8	(109.5)	107.0	(109.5)	111.1	112.3	53.0	51.0	0.0	0.0	a
F₃CCF₂	1.35	…	1.46	…	1.33	…	113.2	…	105.7	…	118.9	…	37.1	…	0.0	…	
H₃CNF₂	1.12	1.091	1.42	1.449	1.26	1.413	110.4	108.3	108.4	110.5	109.3	104.6	57.5	66.9	0.0	0.0	b
F₃CNF₂	1.35	…	1.44	…	1.27	…	111.8	…	107.1	…	107.2	…	60.8	…	0.0	…	

† (180 − φ) is the angle between the AB bond and the bisector of the YAY angle.
‡ ω is the dihedral angle such that a value of 0 corresponds to the bisector of the YBY angle eclipsing an AX bond.
a T. Nishikawa, T. Stoh, and K. Shimoda, *J. Chem. Phys.*, **23**:1735 (1955).
b L. Pierce, R. G. Hayes, and J. F. Bucher, *J. Chem. Phys.*, **46**:4352 (1967).

Table 4.15 Calculated and experimental geometries for X_3AAX_3 molecules

Molecule	R_{XA}, Å		R_{AA}, Å		θ_{XAX}		θ_{AAX}		ω†		Reference
	Calc.	Exptl.	Calc.	Exptl.	Calc.	Exptl.	Calc.	Exptl.	Calc.	Exptl.	
H_3CCH_3	1.12	1.108	1.46	1.536	106.6	108.8	112.2	110.1	180.0	180.0	a
F_3CCF_3	1.35	1.33	1.49	1.51	106.1	108.0	112.6	111.0	180.0	180.0	b

† The dihedral angle ω is defined such that a value of 0° corresponds to the eclipsical configuration.

[a] W. J. Lafferty and E. K. Plyler, *J. Chem. Phys.*, **37**:2688 (1962).

[b] D. A. Swish and I. L. Karle, *J. Chem. Phys.*, **23**:1499 (1955).

STANDARD GEOMETRICAL MODELS

The calculations discussed up to this point in this section have all involved some extent of energy minimization with respect to molecular geometry. Although this is a desirable feature, the procedure rapidly becomes impractical as the size of the molecules under consideration increases. An alternative procedure is to establish a set of *standard geometrical models* [9] for commonly occurring structural parameters in polyatomic molecules and assume these are close enough to the equilibrium parameters to give generally useful results for molecular properties.

For molecules without closed rings, the complete geometry can be defined by three types of information: (1) bondlengths for all bonds specified by the chemical formula, (2) bond angles specifying the complete stereogeometry of the neighboring atoms bonded to each atom in the molecule, and (3) dihedral angles specifying internal rotation about appropriate bonds. If rings are present, these quantities are not independent and an alternative type of specification will be needed in some cases.

In setting up rules for all these quantities, it will be convenient to use a notation Xn for an atom with elemental symbol X being bonded to n neighbors. Here n may be referred to as the connectivity of X. For example, the carbon atoms in ethane, ethylene, and acetylene will be described as C4, C3, and C2, respectively.

BONDLENGTHS

Four principal types of bond are distinguished—single, double, triple, and aromatic—the last for use in benzene-type rings. Dative (or partially dative) bonds will also be handled in certain special groups such as nitro. In all molecules discussed here, the assignment of bond type will be unambiguous. Numerical standard values used for lengths of bonds involving H, C, N, O, and F atoms are shown in Table 4.16. These are selected as suitable average values from available experimental data.

BOND ANGLES

Five types of local atomic geometry are distinguished. If the connectivity is 4, tetrahedral angles are used. For connectivity 3, the three bonds are either taken to be planar with bond angles of 120° or pyramidal with bond angles of 109.47° (the tetrahedral angle). Atoms with connectivity 2 are taken as linear (angle 180°) or bent (with a bond angle of 109.47°).

Table 4.16   Standard bondlengths

Bond	Length, Å	Bond	Length, Å
	Single bonds		
H—H	0.74	C3—N2	1.40
C4—H	1.09	C3—O2	1.36
C3—H	1.08	C3—F1	1.33
C2—H	1.06	C2—C2	1.38
N3—H	1.01	C2—N3	1.33
N2—H	0.99	C2—N2	1.33
O2—H	0.96	C2—O2	1.36
F1—H	0.92	C2—F1	1.30
C4—C4	1.54	N3—N3	1.45
C4—C3	1.52	N3—N2	1.45
C4—C2	1.46	N3—O2	1.36
C4—N3	1.47	N3—F1	1.36
C4—N2	1.47	N2—N2	1.45
C4—O2	1.43	N2—O2	1.41
C4—F1	1.36	N2—F1	1.36
C3—C3	1.46	O2—O2	1.48
C3—C2	1.45	O2—F1	1.42
C3—N3	1.40†	F1—F1	1.42
	Double bonds		
C3—C3	1.34	C2—O1	1.16
C3—C2	1.31	N3—O1	1.24‡
C3—N2	1.32	N2—N2	1.25
C3—O1	1.22	N2—O1	1.22
C2—C2	1.28	O1—O1	1.21
C2—N2	1.32		
	Triple bonds	Aromatic bonds	
C2—C2	1.20	C3—C3	1.40
C2—N1	1.16	C2—N2	1.34
N1—N1	1.10	N2—N2	1.35

† 1.32 used in N—C=O group.
‡ Partial double bonds in NO_2 and NO_3 groups.

The nature of the local atomic geometry frequently depends on the presence of unsaturation in a neighboring group. Although this cannot always be handled satisfactorily, some account can be taken by considering the total excess valence of the neighboring atoms (the excess valence being the normal valence minus the connectivity). In

Table 4.17   Standard atomic geometry and bond angles

Atom	Total excess valence of neighbors	Examples	Geometry	Bond angle degrees
C4	All values	CH_4	Tetrahedral	109.47
C3	All values	C_2H_4	Planar	120
C2	0, 1	CH_2, CHO	Bent	109.47
	2, 3, 4	CO_2, HCN	Linear	180
N4	All values	NH_4^+	Tetrahedral	109.47
N3	0	NH_3	Pyramidal	109.47
	1, 2, 3, 4	H_2N—CHO	Planar	120
N2	0, 1, 2	H_2CHN	Bent	109.47
	3, 4	HNC	Linear	180
O3	0	H_3O^+	Pyramidal	109.47
	1, 2, 3, 4		Planar	120
O2	All values	O_3, H_2O	Bent	109.47

allene, for example, the excess valence of the neighbors of the central atom is 2.

The rules adopted for selecting the atomic local geometry are given in Table 4.17. Inevitably, the model will give the incorrect type of geometry in some cases. For example, the equilibrium structure of the CF_3 radical is probably nonplanar, although taken as planar in the standard model. However, the rules given provide a broadly correct picture of the dependence of local geometry on the atomic arrangement.

These models as defined can only be used for cyclic compounds if no strain is involved. This will be true only if the bondlengths and bond angles are consistent with the cyclic structure. Benzene and chair cyclohexane rings belong to this category.

DIHEDRAL ANGLES

In an open-chain molecule, dihedral angles have to be specified for each bond joining atoms with connectivity greater than 1 (unless they are linear). Values of 0, 60, and 180° will be used for cis, gauche, and trans arrangements in accordance with usual nomenclature.

Rules used for dihedral angles are as follows: (1) staggered configurations are used for bonds connecting atoms with tetrahedral angles; (2) for bonds between tetrahedral and trigonal atoms, as in propene, one of the other bonds on the tetrahedral atom is in the trigonal plane, single bonds being trans where appropriate; (3) neighboring trigonal atoms are taken to be coplanar. These rules conform closely to most known data on equilibrium configurations.

With these conventions, one may proceed to the calculation of the cartesian coordinates of each of the atoms in the molecule, which is a necessary starting point for the molecular orbital calculations.

The CNDO/2 method has been used to calculate LCAO molecular orbitals, charge distributions, and electric dipole moments for a number of organic molecules using standard geometries described above [9]. The dipole-moment results are compared with available experimental values in Tables 4.18 and 4.19 using microwave data where possible. For directions, comparison is made for the angle between the dipolar axis and a particular bond. This involves some arbitrary selection, since the standard bond angles used in the calculation will differ from experimental bond angles determined by microwave spectral data. Figures 4.5 to 4.8 show the calculated net atomic charge densities for a selection of these molecules in units of 10^{-3} electron charges. (Owing to rounding errors and limitations of the method of computation, these numbers are subject to some uncertainty in the last figure.)

The general level of agreement between calculated and observed dipole moments is evidently good, few molecules being seriously in error. In Table 4.19 some calculated dipole directions are compared with the directions that would follow from a simple bond dipole additivity model. In almost all cases the deviation from the bond additive direction is calculated in the right sense. This overall level of agreement provides some general support for the validity of the calculated charge densities. We shall discuss some of these in detail and the bearing they have on theories of electron displacement.

HYDROCARBONS

The three simple nonpolar hydrocarbons—ethane, ethylene, and acetylene—show increasingly positive hydrogen atoms in line with the usual qualitative picture of more C^-—H^+ character as the s character of the bond increases. If the hydrogen atoms in any of these are replaced by substituents, we need to consider changes in charge relative to the parent molecule.

The paraffins, propane and 2-methylpropane, show small experimental dipole moments, but these are not interpreted by the theory (using the standard model) which gives vanishingly small calculated values.

Propene has a calculated dipole in good agreement with experiment, and it is clear from Fig. 4.5 that this arises from a considerable

Table 4.18 Dipole moments

Compound	Dipole moment, debyes	
	Calc.	Obs.
Hydrocarbons:		
Propane	0.00	0.083[a]
Propene	0.36	0.364[b]
Propyne	0.43	0.75[c,d]
2-Methylpropane	0.00	0.132[e]
2-Methylpropene	0.65	0.503[f]
2-Methyl-1,3-butadiene	0.25	0.292[g]
Toluene	0.21	0.43[h]
Fluorine compounds:		
Hydrogen fluoride	1.85	1.8195[i]
Methyl fluoride	1.66	1.855[j]
Methylene fluoride	1.90	1.96[k]
Fluoroform	1.66	1.645[l]
Ethyl fluoride	1.83	1.96[m]
1,1-Difluoroethane	2.23	2.30[n]
1,1,1-Trifluoroethane	2.18	2.32[o]
Fluoroethylene	1.51	1.427[p]
1,1-Difluoroethylene	1.02	1.37[q]
cis-1,2-Difluoroethylene	2.83	2.42[r]
Fluoroacetylene	1.04	0.75[s]
n-Propyl fluoride (trans)	1.84	2.05[t]
trans-1-Fluoropropene	1.67	1.85[u]
cis-1-Fluoropropene	1.59	1.46[v]
2-Fluoropropene	1.69	1.60[w]
3-Fluoropropene (s-cis)	1.83	1.765[x]
3,3,3-Trifluoropropene	2.34	2.45[y]
3,3,3-Trifluoropropyne	2.48	2.36[z]
2-Fluoro-1,3-butadiene	1.65	1.417[aa]
Fluorobenzene	1.66	1.66[bb]
Oxygen compounds:		
Water	2.10	1.846[cc]
Methanol	1.94	1.69[dd]
Dimethyl ether	1.83	1.30[ee]
Formaldehyde	1.98	2.339[l]
Acetaldehyde	2.53	2.68[ff]
Propionaldehyde	2.46	2.52[gg]
Acetyl acetylene	2.85	2.4[hh]
Acetone	2.90	2.90[ii]
Acrolein (s-trans)	2.63	3.11[jj]
Methyl vinyl ketone	2.92	3.16[kk]
Ketene	1.30	1.414[ll]
Methyl ketene	1.35	1.79[mm]
Formic acid	0.87	1.415[nn]
Phenol	1.73	1.55[h]

Table 4.18   Dipole moments (continued)

Compound	Dipole moment, debyes	
	Calc.	Obs.
Nitrogen compounds:		
Ammonia	1.97	1.468[oo]
Methylamine	1.86	1.326[pp]
Dimethylamine	1.76	1.03[qq]
Trimethylamine	1.68	0.612[rr]
Hydrogen cyanide	2.48	2.986[ss]
Methyl cyanide	3.05	3.92[c,d]
Mixed compounds:		
Nitrogen trifluoride	0.43	0.235[tt]
Difluoramine	2.13	1.93[uu]
Nitrous acid	2.27	1.85[vv]
Nitric acid	2.24	2.16[ww]
Cyano fluoride	1.55	1.68[xx]
Formyl fluoride	2.16	2.02[yy]
Carbonyl fluoride	1.42	0.951[zz]
Acetyl fluoride	2.84	2.96[aaa]
Acetyl cyanide	2.80	3.45[bbb]
Isocyanic acid	1.88	1.59[l,ccc]
Methyl isocyanate	1.80	2.81[ddd]
Formamide	3.79	3.71[eee]
Nitromethane	4.38	3.46[fff]
Nitrobenzene	5.33	4.28[ggg]

[a] R. D. Lide, *J. Chem. Phys.*, **33**:1514 (1960).

[b] D. R. Lide and D. E. Mann, *J. Chem. Phys.*, **27**:868 (1957).

[c] S. N. Ghosh, R. Trambarulo, and W. Gordy, *Phys. Rev.*, **87**: 172 (1952).

[d] S. N. Ghosh, R. Trambarulo, and W. Gordy, *J. Chem. Phys.*, **21**:308 (1953).

[e] D. R. Lide and D. E. Mann, *J. Chem. Phys.*, **29**:914 (1958).

[f] V. W. Laurie, *J. Chem. Phys.*, **34**:1516 (1961).

[g] D. R. Lide and M. Jen, *J. Chem. Phys.*, **40**:252 (1964).

[h] A. L. McClellan, "Tables of Experimental Dipole Moments," p. 251, W. H. Freeman and Company, San Francisco, 1963.

[i] R. Weiss, *Phys. Rev.*, **131**:659 (1963).

[j] M. Larkin and W. Gordy, *J. Chem. Phys.*, **38**:2329 (1963).

[k] D. R. Lide, *J. Am. Chem. Soc.*, **74**:3548 (1952).

[l] J. N. Shoolery and A. H. Sharbaugh, *Phys. Rev.*, **82**:95 (1951).

[m] J. Kraitchman and B. P. Dailey, *J. Chem. Phys.*, **23**:184 (1955).

[n] G. H. Kwei and D. R. Hershbach, *J. Chem. Phys.*, **32**:1270 (1960).

[o] R. G. Shulman, B. P. Dailey, and C. H. Townes, *Phys. Rev.*, **78**:145 (1950).

[p] A. M. Mirri, A. Guanieri, and P. Favero, *Nuovo Cimento*, **19**:1189 (1961).

[q] A. Roberts and W. F. Edgell, *J. Chem. Phys.*, **17**:742 (1949).

[r] V. W. Laurie, *J. Chem. Phys.*, **34**:291 (1961).

[t] E. Hirota, *J. Chem. Phys.*, **37**:283 (1962).

[u] S. Siegel, *J. Chem. Phys.*, **27**:989 (1957).

[v] R. A. Beaudet and E. B. Wilson, *J. Chem. Phys.*, **37**:1133 (1962).

[w] L. Pierce and J. M. O'Reilly, *J. Mol. Spectry.*, **3**:536 (1959).

[x] E. Hirota, *J. Chem. Phys.*, **42**:2071 (1965).

[y] J. J. Conradi and N. C. Li, *J. Am. Chem. Soc.*, **75**:1705 (1953).

[z] J. N. Shoolery, R. G. Shulman, W. F. Sheehan, Jr., V. Schomaker, and D. M. Yost, *J. Chem. Phys.*, **19**:1364 (1951).

[aa] D. R. Lide, *J. Chem. Phys.*, **37**:2074 (1962).

[bb] D. G. deKowalski, P. Koheritz, and H. Selen, *J. Chem. Phys.*, **31**:1438 (1959).

[cc] G. Birnbaum and S. K. Chatterjie, *J. Appl. Phys.*, **23**:220 (1952).

[dd] D. G. Burkhard and D. M. Dennison, *Phys. Rev.*, **84**:408 (1951).

[ee] L. G. Groves and S. Sugden, *J. Chem. Soc.*, 1779 (1937).

[ff] R. W. Kilb, C. C. Lin, and E. B. Wilson, Jr., *J. Chem. Phys.*, **31**:882 (1957).

[gg] S. S. Butcher and E. B. Wilson, Jr., *J. Chem. Phys.*, **40**:1671 (1964).

[hh] O. L. Streifvater and J. Sheridan, *Proc. Chem. Soc.*, **1963**: 368.

[ii] J. D. Swalen and C. C. Costain, *J. Chem. Phys.*, **31**:1562 (1959).

[jj] R. J. Wagner, J. Fine, J. W. Simmons, and J. H. Goldstein, *J. Chem. Phys.*, **26**:634 (1957).

[kk] P. D. Foster, V. M. Rao, and R. F. Curl, Jr., *J. Chem. Phys.*, **43**:1064 (1965).

[ll] H. R. Johnson and M. W. P. Strandberg, *J. Chem. Phys.*, **20**:687 (1952).

[mm] B. Bak, J. J. Christiansen, K. Kunstmann, L. Nygaard, and J. Rastrup-Andersen, *J. Chem. Phys.*, **45**:883 (1966).

[nn] H. Kim, R. Keller, and W. D. Gwinn, *J. Chem. Phys.*, **37**:2748 (1962).

[oo] D. K. Coles, W. E. Good, J. K. Bragg, and A. H. Sharbaugh, *Phys. Rev.*, **82**:877 (1951).

[pp] D. R. Lide, *J. Chem. Phys.*, **27**:343 (1957).

[qq] R. J. W. LeFevre and P. Russell, *Trans. Faraday Soc.*, **43**:374 (1947).

[rr] D. R. Lide, Jr., and D. E. Mann, *J. Chem. Phys.*, **28**:572 (1958).

[ss] B. N. Battacharya and W. Gordy, *Phys. Rev.*, **119**:144 (1960).

[tt] P. Kisliuk, *J. Chem. Phys.*, **22**:86 (1954).

[uu] D. R. Lide, Jr., *J. Chem. Phys.*, **38**:456 (1963).

[vv] A. P. Cox and R. L. Kuczkowski, *J. Am. Chem. Soc.*, **88**:5071 (1966).

[ww] D. J. Millen and J. R. Morton, *J. Chem. Soc.*, 1523 (1960).

[xx] J. Sheridan, J. K. Tyler, E. E. Aynsley, R. E. Dodd, and R. Little, *Nature*, **185**:96 (1960).

[yy] O. H. LeBlanc, V. W. Laurie, and W. D. Gwinn, *J. Chem. Phys.*, **33**:598 (1960).

[zz] V. W. Laurie and D. T. Pense, *J. Chem. Phys.*, **37**:2995 (1962).

[aaa] L. Pierce and L. C. Krisher, *J. Chem. Phys.*, **31**:875 (1959).

[bbb] L. C. Krisher and E. B. Wilson, Jr., *J. Chem. Phys.*, **31**:882 (1959).

[ccc] J. N. Shoolery, R. G. Shulman, and D. M. Yost, *J. Chem. Phys.*, **19**:250 (1951).

[ddd] R. F. Curl, Jr., V. M. Rao, K. V. L. N. Sastry, and J. A. Hodgeson, *J. Chem. Phys.*, **39**:3335 (1960).

[eee] R. J. Kurland and E. B. Wilson, Jr., *J. Chem. Phys.*, **27**:585 (1957).

[fff] E. Tannenbaum, R. J. Myers, and W. D. Gwinn, *J. Chem. Phys.*, **25**:42 (1956).

[ggg] R. J. W. LeFevre and P. Russell, *J. Chem. Soc.*, 491 (1936).

Table 4.19   Dipole-moment orientations

Molecule	Angle†	Calc.‡	Obs.§
Propene	from C=C toward C—C	-8.4 (0)	-22^b
Ethyl fluoride	from C—F toward C—C	-5.4 (0)	-7^m
1,1-Difluoroethane	from C—Me toward C—H	-131.9 (-125.3)	-133.7^n
Fluoroethylene	from C—F toward C=C	$+8.8$ (0)	$\approx 0^p$
n-Propyl fluoride (*trans*)	from C—F toward C—Et	-5.6 (0)	-10.6^t
cis-1-Fluoropropene	from C—F toward C=C	-2.5 (0)	-15.3^v
2-Fluoropropene	from C—F toward C=C	$+24.5$ (0)	$+6.2^w$
3-Fluoropropene (*s-cis*)	from C—F toward C—C	-0.8 (0)	$\pm 1.5^x$
2-Fluoro-1,3-butadiene	from C—F toward C=C	$+20.8$ (0)	$\pm 10-15^{aa}$
Acetaldehyde	from C=O toward C—C	-7.0 (0)	-14.2^{ff}
Propionaldehyde (*s-cis*)	from C=O toward C—C	-7.4 (0)	-17^{gg}
Acrolein (*s-trans*)	from C=O toward C—C	-7.8 (0)	$\pm 14^{ii}$
Methyl ketene	from C=C toward C—C	$+5.6$ (0)	-8^{mm}
Formic acid	from C=O toward C—O	-21.5	-42.4^{nn}
Difluoramine	from N—H toward bisector of N—F bonds	$+7.2$	-18.6^{uu}
Nitrous acid (*trans*)	from N=O toward N—O	$+10.3$	$+0.8^{vv}$
Formyl fluoride	from C=O toward C—F	$+38.2$	$+41.0^{yy}$
Acetyl fluoride	from C=O toward C—F	$+39.9$	$+43^{aaa}$
Acetyl cyanide	from C=O toward C—CN	$+59.3$	$+71^{bbb}$
Formamide	from C=O toward C—N	-16.8	-17.5^{eee}
Methyl amine	from C—N toward C—H	-65.0	-73.2^{pp}

† The convention used for direction is specification of an angle with a bond C—A in the sense of a rotation toward another bond C—B from the same atom C. If the angle is *positive* (and less than the ABC bond angle) the resulting direction lies *between* the bonds C—A and C—B.

‡ Values in parentheses correspond to a vector additive bond moment model with zero moments for all C—C and C—H bonds.

§ Superscripts refer to Table 4.18 references.

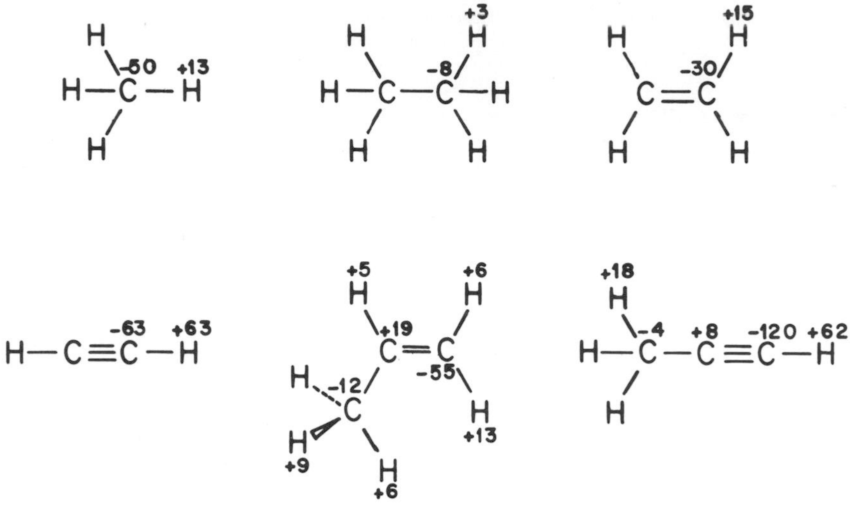

Fig. 4.5   Electron distribution in hydrocarbons (units of 10^{-3} electrons).

rearrangement of charge. However, if we consider the process of replacing one of the hydrogens in ethylene by a methyl group, the rearrangement of charge is mainly a "polarization" within the vinyl group rather than a net transfer of charge from methyl to vinyl. Thus the total vinyl charge in ethylene is -0.015, and this only changes to -0.012 in propene. The most significant change, however, is the redistribution of charge between the two carbon atoms in vinyl, the methyl group "driving" electrons away from the atom to which it is attached onto the β position. A further breakdown can be effected into charge distribution in π and σ atomic orbitals. The π electron charges on the vinyl carbons are

$$\text{Me}—\overset{0.972}{C_\alpha} = \overset{1.043}{C_\beta}$$

The corresponding figures are unity in ethylene, so that there is a small donation of π electrons from methyl to vinyl, but again the main effect is a redistribution within the vinyl group, the β position acquiring the greater electron density. In fact, most of the total redistribution between C_α and C_β occurs in the π system.

These theoretical results have some bearing on discussions of the role of hyperconjugation in determining the polarity of propene by means of a charge displacement of the type

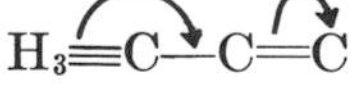

$$\text{H}_3 \equiv \text{C} \rightarrow \text{C} = \text{C}$$

Recently, Dewar [10] has argued that the dipole moment may alternatively be due to the polarity of the $C(sp^3)$—$C(sp^2)$ bond, this being more sensitive to hybridization changes than C—H bonds. The present calculations favor the hyperconjugative explanation insofar as the origin of the calculated moment lies mainly in the π orbitals. However, the polarity occurs without major charge migration into the double bond.

The origin of the dipole moment in methyl acetylene (the methyl end of the molecule being positive) can be interpreted in a similar manner. There is little overall charge transfer into the ethynyl group when hydrogen is replaced by methyl, but there is again a large redistribution between the α and β carbons. The π electron charges are

$$\overset{\text{1.968}\quad\text{2.066}}{\text{Me}\!-\!\text{C}_\alpha\!=\!\text{C}_\beta}$$

so the redistribution is again mainly associated with the π orbitals.

FLUORINE COMPOUNDS

The agreement between experimental dipole moments of fluorocarbons and those calculated by this model is very good, all the main effects being well reproduced. Examination of the atomic charge densities, however, reveals surprising features (Fig. 4.6). In methyl fluoride,

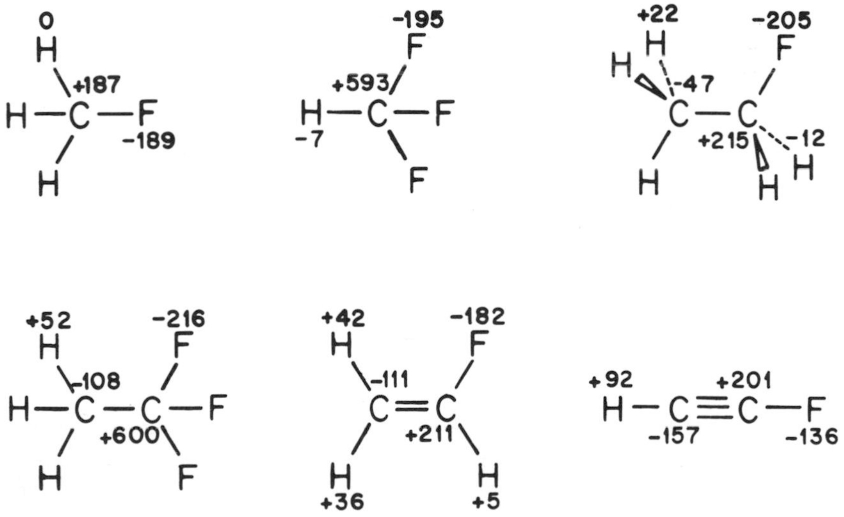

Fig. 4.6 Electron distribution in fluorocarbons (units of 10^{-2} electrons).

the main effect is a transfer of electrons from carbon to the more electronegative fluorine, but a secondary feature is that the hydrogens are slightly more negative than in methane.   This negative character of atoms separated by two bonds from the substituting fluorine is also apparent in fluoroform and becomes more evident for β carbon atoms as in ethyl fluoride and 1,1,1-trifluoroethane.

These results challenge the common interpretation of fluorine as an inductive-type substituent leading to positive character in a saturated hydrocarbon which diminishes steadily with the distance down the chain [11],

$$\overset{\delta-}{F} \leftarrow \overset{\delta+}{C} \leftarrow \overset{\delta\delta+}{C} \leftarrow \overset{\delta\delta\delta+}{C} \cdots$$

The calculations rather suggest that the induced charges *alternate* in a decaying manner, so that the β position is normally negative:

$$\overset{\delta-}{F} \leftarrow \overset{\delta+}{C} \leftarrow \overset{\delta\delta-}{C} \leftarrow \overset{\delta\delta+}{C}$$

Experimental dipole moments do not, of course, provide a direct test of these two charge distributions.   However, certain trends evident in the data are consistent with the alternating hypothesis. According to this, a fluorine substituent leads to a polarization of the hydrocarbon in which the atom 2 removed from the fluorine is relatively negative,

$$[(C \text{ or } H)^-\!\!-\!\!C^+]\!\!-\!\!F$$

This corresponds to a dipolar distribution in the hydrocarbon which is *opposed* to the primary dipole of the bond to fluorine.   For a CF_3 substituent, on the other hand, the alternating hypothesis predicts a charge distribution

$$[(C \text{ or } H)^+\!\!-\!\!C^-]\!\!-\!\!CF_3$$

leading to a hydrocarbon dipole which *reinforces* the primary moment. If we now compare the experimental dipole moments of HX and CH_3X, where X is F or CF_3, we find that CF_3 does have a considerably larger dipole when attached to CH_3 compared with H, but the two compounds with X fluorine have very similar moments, in spite of the fact that methyl is a larger polarizable group.

Another piece of evidence supporting the CNDO charge distributions of Fig. 4.6 is the fact that the experimental and calculated dipole directions in ethyl fluoride are *external* to the F—C—C angle (Table 4.19).   This is consistent with the alternating hypothesis which leads to an additional polarization in the methyl group $H_3^+\!\!-\!\!C^-$.

Some insight into the origin of the calculated charge alternation in fluoroparaffins may be obtained by breaking down the electron distribution of methyl fluoride into σ and π parts relative to the C—F bond. If this is the z axis, the population of the $2px$ atomic orbitals on carbon and fluorine and the corresponding hydrogen group orbital are

$$\overset{1.035}{H_3} \equiv \overset{0.986}{C} - \overset{1.979}{F}$$

The bond order between the carbon and fluorine π orbitals is 0.147. The fact that the fluorine figure is less than 2 implies a "back-donation" effect by the fluorine π lone pairs which could be represented by a valence structure

$$H_3{}^- = C = F^+$$

This leads to additional charge in the hydrogen π-type group orbital. In fact, this group orbital contains more electrons then in methane where the corresponding population is 1.002. In summary, fluorine behaves as a strong σ electron attractor, removing electrons from the carbon to which it is bonded; but it is also a weak π electron donor, and these electrons go to the hydrogens in methyl fluoride (or the β position in larger molecules). This type of back-donation has also been proposed in a theory of geminal proton-proton spin coupling constants [12].

Similar, but stronger, alternation effects are shown in the calculations on vinyl fluoride and ethynyl fluoride. In both cases, the β carbon acquires considerable negative charge, leading to a relatively small dipole moment. CF_3 substituents, on the other hand, lead to large dipoles (3,3,3-trifluoropropene and 3,3,3-trifluoropropyne). The small dipoles of vinyl fluoride and ethynyl fluoride are often attributed to π electron donation from a fluorine lone pair into the unsaturated group leading to a structure

$$\overset{\frown}{C} = C \overset{\frown}{\leftarrow} F$$

This suggestion is supported by the CNDO calculations on vinyl fluoride which give π densities

$$\overset{1.076}{C} \equiv \overset{0.973}{C} - \overset{1.951}{F}$$

Clearly, most of the increase in electron density on the β carbon is due to π electron donation from the fluorine. On the other hand, a CF_3 group polarizes the C=C in the opposite direction, leading to the large moment of 3,3,3-trifluoropropene.

OXYGEN COMPOUNDS

There is less satisfactory agreement between experimental and calculated dipole moments for the oxygen compounds listed in Table 4.18, but the theory does reproduce a number of significant trends.

The calculated values for water, alcohols, and ethers are too high, but the observed ordering

$$\mu(\text{H}_2\text{O}) > \mu(\text{MeOH}) > \mu(\text{Me}_2\text{O})$$

is correctly reproduced. According to the CNDO/2 charge distribution shown in Fig. 4.7, the reason why methyl alcohol has a lower moment than water is again charge alternation, two of the methyl hydrogens having a negative charge. This is also a result of back-donation from the π-type lone pair of the oxygen, for the population of the $2p\pi$ atomic orbital on oxygen (with a node in the oxygen valence plane) is 2.000, 1.976, and 1.951 for the series water, methyl alcohol, and methyl ether.

The observed decrease of moment along this series is rather larger than calculated. Part of the decrease may be due to the open-

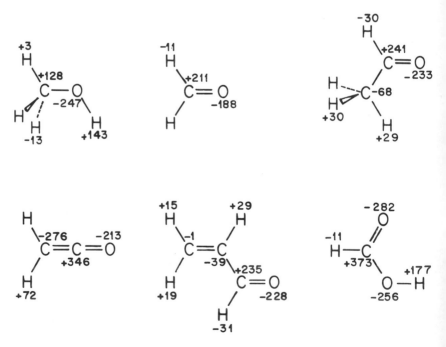

Fig. 4.7   Electron distribution in oxygen compounds (units of 10^{-3} electrons).

ing out of the bond angle in ethers.   However, this does not seem to be very important, for CNDO/2 calculations with experimental (rather than standard) bond angles give $\mu = 2.14$ debyes for water (angle 104.5°) and $\mu = 1.80$ debyes for methyl ether (angle 111.6°).

A corresponding series for the carbonyl group shows the opposite ordering of dipoles

$$\mu(H_2CO) < \mu[(CH_3)HCO] < \mu[(CH_3)_2CO]$$

and this is also reproduced by the calculations.   However, the theory incorrectly gives a dipole moment for formaldehyde less than that of water.   The increase in dipole moment of a carbonyl compound with methyl substituents is again consistent with an alternating charge effect

$$H_3{}^{\delta\delta+}$$
$$C^{\delta\delta-}$$
$$C^{\delta+}{=}O^{\delta-}$$

and this is reflected in the CNDO/2 atomic densities (Fig. 4.7).   The direction of the dipole in acetaldehyde is also consistent with this. The total charge on the oxygen increases from 6.188 in formaldehyde to 6.233 in acetaldehyde and 6.266 in acetone.   The population of the $2p$ oxygen atomic orbital has values 1.160, 1.208, and 1.241 along the same series, and so these changes are again mainly associated with the π system.   The corresponding charges on the $2p\pi$ atomic orbital of the carbonyl carbon are 0.840, 0.828, and 0.823.   These decreases are less than the oxygen π charge increases, and so there is a transfer of π electrons from CH_3 into the carbonyl group by hyperconjugation in this theory.   A similar π electron transfer is also noted in acrolein, although the calculated dipole moment for this molecule is rather too small.

The theory also predicts the observed low dipole moment of ketone compared with formaldehyde.   The CNDO/2 charge distribution in ketene (Fig. 4.7) clearly shows alternation due primarily to back-donation of the oxygen n electrons into the π atomic orbital of the methylene carbon atom.   (It should be noted that in ketene, the oxygen lone pair is in a π-type orbital with a node in the molecular plane.)

NITROGEN COMPOUNDS

The comparison between calculated and experimental dipoles for compounds containing nitrogen shows similar trends.   The experimental moments for ammonia and methylamines have the order

$$\mu(NH_3) > \mu(MeNM_2) > \mu(Me_2NH) > \mu(Me_3N)$$

and this progression is reproduced by the theory. As with corresponding oxygen compounds, the theory does not give the full magnitude of the decrease along the series. There is a slight opening of the angle in trimethylamine (from 107.1° in ammonia to 108.7°), but this is not sufficient to account completely for the very low dipole moment of this molecule.

The cyanide group —C≡N behaves in the opposite manner, having a *larger* dipole when attached to methyl instead of hydrogen. This effect is also reproduced by the theory, and the CNDO/2 densities shown in Fig. 4.8 suggest that this is associated with charge alternation. The total π densities on the carbon and nitrogen atoms in HCN and Me—CN are

$$\begin{array}{cc} 1.898 \quad 2.102 & \quad 1.882 \quad 2.170 \\ \text{H—} \ C \equiv N & \text{Me—} \ C \equiv N \end{array}$$

Comparison with the total atom densities (Fig. 4.8) again indicates that most of the rearrangement on methyl substitution is in the π system and that there is considerable hyperconjugation.

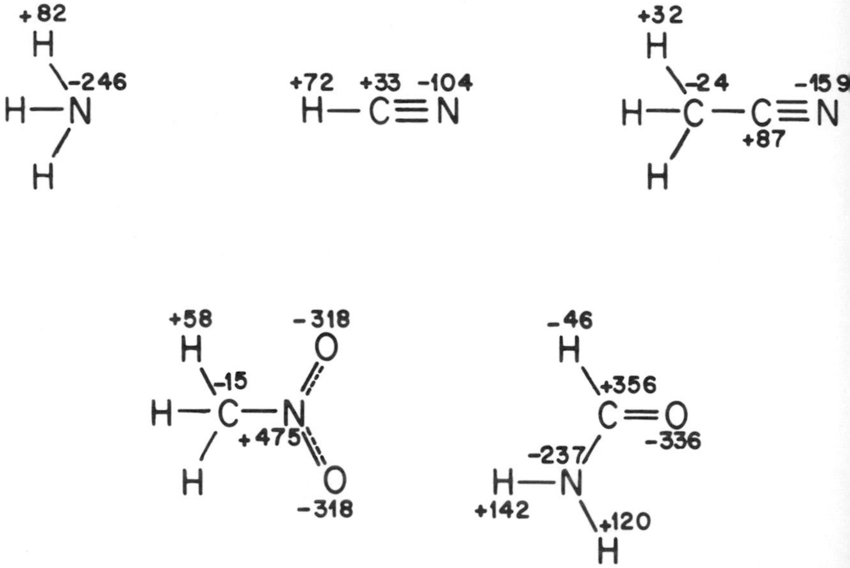

Fig. 4.8 Electron distribution in nitrogen and mixed compounds (units of 10^{-3} electrons).

MIXED COMPOUNDS

Dipole moments for a number of mixed compounds with nitrogen, oxygen, and fluorine are also given in Tables 4.18 and 4.19 including some that contain two groups already considered. Both magnitudes and directions are given fairly satisfactorily by the theory.

The high dipole moment of formamide is clearly due to the increased polarity of the carbonyl group when conjugated with the neighboring nitrogen. The charge in the π lone pair of nitrogen (the bonds to this atom being coplanar according to model A) is reduced from 2.00 in planar NH_3 to 1.82 in this molecule. The corresponding π bond order of the C—N single bond is 0.47 indicating a large amount of double-bond character.

The most important conclusion to be drawn from these calculations is that current qualitative theories of inductive charge displacement may need modification. The general pattern of charge distributions calculated by the molecular orbital method of this paper suggest a classification of substituents (attached to hydrocarbon fragments) in terms of the following two characteristic features:

1. Electrons may be withdrawn from or donated to the hydrocarbon fragment as a whole. According to the usual nomenclature, such substituents would be described as inductive $-I$ and $+I$ types, respectively.
2. The distribution of electrons remaining in the hydrocarbon fragments may be polarized so that electrons are drawn to or from the site of substitution. These two possibilities could be denoted by $-$ and $+$ superscripts, respectively, leading to four types of substituent $-I^-$, $-I^+$, $+I^-$, and $+I^+$.

The double-classification bases on these criteria are illustrated schematically in Fig. 4.9.

When the substituents dealt with are of the $-I$ type, this further subdivision is useful:

$-I^+$ type: F, OR, NR_2
$-I^-$ type: CF_3, RC=O, C   N, NO_2, COOR

In all these cases, the $-I^+$ substituents are those with the most electronegative atom directly attached to the hydrocarbon, while the $-I^-$ types have the electronegative atom one position removed. This is a consequence of the widespread charge alternation noted in Figs. 4.5 to 4.8.

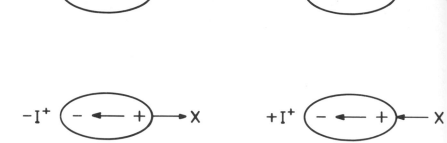

Fig. 4.9 Schematic representation of types of inductive substituent.

It may be noted that the $\pm$ superscript of this classification corresponds to the label used for a "mesomeric displacement" if the substituent is attached to an unsaturated system. Thus the usual charge-displacement diagram

$$\overset{\frown}{C}=\overset{\frown}{C}\overset{\frown}{-}X$$

for a $+M$ mesomeric substituent leads to a high-electron density on the carbon as shown for a $-I^+$ group in Fig. 4.9. The CNDO calculations confirm this behavior but also suggest that this feature of the $-I^+$ substituent and the consequent charge alternation apply even in saturated molecules. In both cases the alternation is associated with back-donation of lone pair electrons in molecular orbitals of π type relative to the C—X bond (that is, with a nodal plane through the C—X bond).

The application of CNDO theory to second-row atoms has been considered by Santry and Segal as discussed in Sec. 3.7, and calculations have been reported on a series of compounds containing such elements [13]. The results are summarized in Table 4.20, where a comparison of results of the sp, spd, and spd' basis sets is presented. The bond angles of second-row compounds are found to be accommodated with just s and p functions on the heavy atom. However, in all molecules considered, the inclusion of $3d$ orbitals causes a considerable redistribution of electrons among the orbitals of the second-row atom and has a significant effect on the dipole moment. A general description of the electronic structure of these compounds must include d orbital participation.

Table 4.20   Collected theoretical and experimental data for the second-row molecules

Negative dipole corresponds to A^+B^-, $A^+B_2^-$, A^+BC^-, $A^+B_3^-$, respectively.

Molecule	Experimental data			r_e, Å	spd			spd'			sp		
	Dipole, debyes	Bond angle	Force[t] constant, mdyn/Å × 10⁵		Dipole, debyes	Bond Angle	Force constant, mdyn/Å × 10⁵	Dipole, debyes	Bond angle	Force constant, mdyn/Å × 10⁵	Dipole, debyes	Bond angle	Force constant, mdyn/Å × 10⁵
NaCl	8.50[a]	…	…	2.361[a] (assumed)	−6.65	…	…	−6.20	…	…	−8.20	…	…
LiCl	8.20[b]	…	…	1.81	−3.82	…	…	−1.31	…	…	−5.10	…	…
FCl	0.88[c]	…	…	1.6281[u]	1.45	…	…	0.51	…	…	0.44	…	…
HCl	1.07[d]	…	…	1.27[v]	−0.59	…	…	−0.70	…	…	−2.10	…	…
H₂S	1.02[e]	93.3[l]	0.45	1.334[l]	−0.08	92.8	0.39	0.69	93.3	0.41	2.40	95.0	0.36
PH₃	0.55[f]	93.5[m]	0.33	1.4206[m]	−0.84	92.7	0.33	0.39	94.0	0.35	2.40	96.6	0.35
ClCN	2.80[e]	180[n]	0.20	ClC 1.63[n] CN 1.163[n]	−1.63	180	0.26	+2.96	Strongly bent	…	−1.00	180	0.34
CS₂	0	180[o]	0.23	1.554[o]	…	180	0.31	…	Strongly bent	…	…	180	1.00
COS	0.72[g]	180[p]	0.37	CO 1.161 CS 1.56[p]	1.48	180	0.20	Calculation nonconvergent			−2.48	180	0.36
SO₂	1.59[h]	119.5[q]	0.81	1.4321[q]	−2.23	141	0.39	0.09	116.9	0.63	−1.76	111	0.85
ClF₃	0.56[i]	87.5[r] planar	…	ClF 1.698[r] ClF' 1.598[r]	−0.77	88.8 planar	…	−0.62	87.3 planar	…	−0.13	79 planar	…
CS	1.97[j]	…	1.04	1.5349[w]	6.42	111°	…	2.57	…	…	−0.03	…	0.68
PF₃	1.025[k]	100[s] (assumed)	…	1.535[s]	−0.62		0.63	−2.11	101.25	0.63	−1.34	100.3	

[a] A. Hornig, M. Mandel, and M. L. Stitch, *Phys. Rev.*, **96**:629 (1954).
[b] M. T. Rogers and T. L. Brown, *J. Chem. Phys.*, **61**:366 (1957).
[c] D. A. Gilbert, A. Roberts, and P. A. Griswold, *Phys. Rev.*, **76**:1723 (1949).
[d] H. Braune and T. Asche, *Z. Physik. Chem.*, **B14**:18 (1931).
[e] C. H. Townes and A. L. Schawlow, "Microwave Spectroscopy," McGraw-Hill Book Company, New York, 1955.
[f] H. E. Watson, *Proc. Roy. Soc. (London)*, **A117**:43 (1927).
[g] R. G. Shulman and C. H. Townes, *Phys. Rev.*, **77**:421 (1950).
[h] G. F. Crable and W. V. Smith, *J. Chem. Phys.*, **19**:502 (1951).
[i] D. W. Magnuson, *J. Chem. Phys.*, **19**:1071 (1951).
[j] R. C. Mockler and G. R. Bird, *Phys. Rev.*, **98**:1837 (1955).
[k] R. G. Shulman, B. P. Daily, and C. H. Townes, *Phys. Rev.*, **78**:421 (1950).
[l] G. R. Bird and C. H. Townes, *Phys. Rev.*, **94**:1203 (1954).
[m] C. A. Burrus, A. Jacke, and W. Gordy, *Phys. Rev.*, **95**:700 (1954).
[n] A. G. Smith, H. Ring, W. V. Smith, and W. Gordy, *Phys. Rev.*, **74**:370 (1948).
[o] G. Herzberg, "Spectra of Diatomic Molecules," D. Van Nostrand Company, Inc., Princeton, N.J., 1950.
[p] T. W. Dakins, W. E. Good, and D. K. Coles, *Phys. Rev.*, **71**:640 (1947).
[q] D. Kivelson, *J. Chem. Phys.*, **22**:904 (1954).
[r] D. F. Smith, *J. Chem. Phys.*, **21**:609 (1953).
[s] V. Williams, J. Sheridan, and W. Gordy, *J. Chem. Phys.*, **20**:164 (1952).
[t] G. Herzberg, "Infrared and Raman Spectra," D. Van Nostrand Company, Inc., Princeton, N.J., 1945.
[u] D. A. Gilbert, A. Roberts, and P. A. Griswold, *Phys. Rev.*, **75**:1723 (1949).
[v] J. Pickworth and H. W. Thompson, *Proc. Roy. Soc. (London)*, **A218**:37 (1953).
[w] R. C. Mockler and G. R. Bird, *Phys. Rev.*, **98**:1837 (1955).

4.3 ELECTRON–SPIN–NUCLEAR–SPIN INTERACTIONS [14]

In the preceding section, calculations on the CNDO and INDO level of approximation were shown to give a reasonably satisfactory account of molecular geometry, electronic charge distributions, and dipole moments of a number of polyatomic organic and inorganic molecules. In this section, we consider applications to paramagnetic molecules, i.e., free radicals, radical cations, and radical anions. Here in addition to the *total* electronic charge distribution, which is the *sum* of the density of α and β electrons at any point in the system, it is possible to study the unpaired electron distribution, known as the spin density, which is essentially the *difference* in α electron density and β electron density at any point in the system.

The spin density at or near any magnetic nuclei in a paramagnetic molecule is related to the hyperfine interaction between electron and nuclear magnetic moments and is measured experimentally by the hyperfine coupling constants obtained from the electron spin resonance (ESR) spectrum. In an LCAO theory, the isotropic (orientationally averaged) part of the hyperfine coupling constants of a given magnetic nucleus reflects the unpaired electron population of s atomic orbitals centered on the nucleus, and the anisotropic part of the hyperfine coupling constants reflects the unpaired electron population of p or d orbitals of the atom. Since there are generally several magnetic nuclei in a paramagnetic organic molecule, it is possible to determine experimentally the spin density at several points in the system.

The isotropic hyperfine coupling constant a_N of magnetic nucleus N is related to the electronic wavefunction of the system Ψ by

$$a_N = \frac{4\pi}{3} g\beta\gamma_N h\langle S_z\rangle^{-1}\langle\Psi|\varrho^{spin}(\mathbf{R}_N)|\Psi\rangle \tag{4.8}$$

where g is the electronic g factor, β is the Bohr magneton, γ_N is the gyromagnetic ratio of nucleus N, and $\mathbf{R}_N$ is the position vector of nucleus N. The quantity $\rho^{spin}(\mathbf{R}_N)$ is the spin density operator evaluated at the nuclear position of atom N, defined as

$$\rho^{spin}(\mathbf{r}_N) = \sum_k 2\mathbf{s}_{zk}\delta(\mathbf{R}_N - \mathbf{r}_k) \tag{4.9}$$

where $\mathbf{r}_k$ is the position vector of the kth electron, $\mathbf{s}_{zk}$ is the component of the electron spin angular-momentum operator, and $\delta(\mathbf{r})$ is the Dirac delta function. With Ψ defined as in Eq. (2.78), the expectation value of the spin density operator becomes

$$\langle\Psi|\rho^{spin}(\mathbf{R}_N)|\Psi\rangle = \sum_{\mu\nu} \rho_{\mu\nu}{}^{spin}\phi_\mu(\mathbf{R})\phi_\nu(\mathbf{R}) \tag{4.10}$$

where $\rho_{\mu\nu}{}^{\text{spin}}$ is the unpaired electronic population,

$$\rho_{\mu\nu}{}^{\text{spin}} = P_{\mu\nu}{}^{\alpha} - P_{\mu\nu}{}^{\beta} \tag{4.11}$$

As discussed in Sec. 2.5, the matrix of elements $\rho_{\mu\nu}{}^{\text{spin}}$ is usually called the spin density matrix.

Electronic wavefunctions based on spin-unrestricted determinants of molecular orbitals are not in general eigenfunctions of the S^2 operator, and they contain contaminating contributions from states of higher multiplicity. An extensive study of the effect of the contaminating spin components on calculated isotropic hyperfine coupling constants has been carried out for calculations on the level of approximation considered herein [15]. It appears that no serious errors were introduced in hyperfine coupling constants by assuming that the effect of the contaminating spin components is negligible.

In the preceding section of this chapter, calculations on the CNDO and INDO levels of approximation were shown to be capable of accommodating electronic charge distribution in a satisfactory and generally useful manner. In the calculation of unpaired electron densities, the CNDO approximations are too extreme to give a proper account of the spin polarization contribution to the unpaired electron density. Here it is important to retain the one-center atomic exchange integrals as they introduce quantitatively the effect of Hund's rule, according to which electrons in different atomic orbitals on the same atom will have a lower repulsion energy if their spins are parallel. This type of interaction has important consequences on the unpaired electron distribution in the system, for it means that the attracting power of a particular atomic orbital for electrons of a particular spin will depend on the unpaired electron population of other orbitals on the same atom. In fact for π electron radicals (planar molecules with the odd electron occupying a molecular orbital of π symmetry), retention of one-center exchange integrals is necessary to introduce any spin density at all into the σ system, as required for a nonzero isotropic hyperfine coupling constant. In the INDO method, differential overlap is neglected in all *polycenter* interelectron repulsion integrals, but one-center atomic exchange integrals are retained. This is the lowest level of approximation that one may hope to accommodate hyperfine coupling phenomena *generally*, and thus calculations considered in this section are of the INDO type. It is important to note that *none* of the disposable parameters involved in the determination of the molecular orbitals is chosen on the basis of experimentally observed hyperfine coupling constants.

In order to evaluate Eq. (4.10) at a level of approximation commensurate with the approximations involved in integral evaluation in the wavefunction determination, we assume that all contributions to the summation are negligible unless both ϕ_μ and ϕ_ν are centered on atom N. Of the atomic functions centered on atom N, only s functions have nonvanishing densities at the nucleus and contribute to the isotropic hyperfine coupling constant. With these approximations, the expectation value of the spin density operator at the nucleus of atom N reduces to the single term

$$\langle\Psi|\rho^{\mathrm{spin}}(\mathbf{R}_N)|\Psi\rangle = \rho^{\mathrm{spin}}_{s_N s_N}|\phi_{s_N}(\mathbf{R}_N)|^2 \tag{4.12}$$

where $\rho^{\mathrm{spin}}_{s_N s_N}$ is the unpaired electronic population of the valence s orbital of atom N and $|\phi_{s_N}(\mathbf{R}_N)|^2$ is the density of the valence s orbital of atom N evaluated at the nucleus. Substituting Eq. (4.12) into Eq. (4.8), the final expression for the isotropic hyperfine coupling constant is

$$a_N = \left[\frac{4\pi}{3}\, g\beta\gamma_N\hbar\langle\mathbf{S}_z\rangle^{-1}|\phi_{s_N}(\mathbf{R}_N)|^2\right]\rho^{\mathrm{spin}}_{s_N s_N} \tag{4.13}$$

The quantity in brackets on the right-hand side of Eq. (4.13) is a constant for each type of magnetic nucleus to be considered. The quantities involved in this term are all fundamental constants with the exception of $|\phi_{s_N}(\mathbf{R}_N)|^2$ which involves some special consideration. The integrals calculated in the wavefunction determination were evaluated over Slater orbitals. In this analytical form for atomic functions, all radial nodes are collapsed to a point node at the nucleus, and thus spurious values for $|\phi_{s_N}(\mathbf{R}_N)|^2$ are obtained. Alternatively, one may evaluate this quantity using SCF atomic orbitals, but since the calculations were not carried out in this basis these are not strictly appropriate. The procedure adopted for determining $|\phi_{s_N}(\mathbf{R}_N)|^2$ involves recognizing the linear relation implied by Eq. (4.13) and selecting this quantity to give the best linear relation between the observed a_N and calculated $\rho^{\mathrm{spin}}_{s_N s_N}$ in a least-squares sense. This is the only disposable parameter involved which was selected on the basis of experimentally observed hyperfine coupling constants. The values adopted for $|\phi_{s_N}(\mathbf{R}_N)|^2$ for each magnetic nucleus considered are listed in Table 4.21 along with the statistics of the least-squares calculations involved.

INDO molecular orbital calculations have been carried out on a variety of molecules composed of first-row atoms, and ^{1}H, ^{13}C, ^{14}N, [17]O, and ^{19}F isotropic hyperfine coupling constants considered [14]. As with the study of charge distributions and dipole moments in the preceding section, standard bondlengths and bond angles were used for the molecular geometries. The standard models proposed previously are, however, not really suitable for radicals and radical ions,

Table 4.21 Analysis of linear relation† between observed a_N and calculated $\rho_{s_N s_N}^{spin}$

Nucleus	Number of data points	$\frac{4\pi}{3} g\beta\gamma h\langle S_z\rangle^{-1}\|\phi_{s_N}(\mathbf{R}_N)\|^2$, gauss	Standard deviation,‡ gauss	Correlation coefficient§	$\|\phi_{s_N}(\mathbf{R}_N)\|^2$, a.u.$^{-3}$
^{1}H	141	539.86	7.29	0.8797	0.338
^{13}C	26	820.10	23.78	0.9253	2.042
^{14}N	29	379.34	2.34	0.7561	3.292
^{17}O	5	−888.68	2.67	0.5188	41.082
^{19}F	9	44829.20	22.22	0.9224	29.840

† Constrained to origin.

‡ Calculated as $\sqrt{\Sigma(a - a^{calc})^2/(n-1)}$

§ Calculated as $(n\Sigma\rho a - \Sigma\rho\Sigma a)/\sqrt{[n\Sigma\rho^2 - (\Sigma\rho)^2][n\Sigma a^2 - (\Sigma a)^2]}$.

where it is frequently difficult to classify bonds by type (single, double, etc.). We shall, therefore, adopt for the present study a rather cruder scheme in which the internuclear distances chosen depend entirely on the nature of the two atoms involved. We shall henceforth refer to these geometries as model B, with those of the previous section being model A. The bondlengths for model B are listed in Table 4.22 with the rules for bond angles being the same as in model A.

Molecules chosen were generally those for which a reasonable knowledge of the molecular geometry could be inferred from chemical intuition, and molecules which required explicit consideration of several interconverting conformations were not included, with the exception of ethyl radical. Even with these limitations a number of exceptions to the standard model were necessary.

Using the values for $|\phi_{s_N}(\mathbf{R}_N)^2|$ listed in Table 4.21 and the $\rho_{s_N s_N}^{spin}$ computed from the INDO molecular orbitals for each molecule, isotropic hyperfine coupling constants a_N were calculated for each atomic nucleus in each compound. A comparison of the calculated a_N with observed values is presented for ^{1}H, ^{13}C, ^{14}N, ^{17}O, and ^{19}F in Tables 4.23 to 4.27. In preparing these tables, assignments were made

Table 4.22 Standard bondlengths (model B)

	H	C	N	O	F
H	0.74	1.08	1.00	0.96	0.92
C		1.40	1.37	1.36	1.35
N			1.35	1.30	1.36
O				1.48	1.42
F					1.42

Table 4.23   Observed and calculated isotropic hyperfine coupling constants for ^{1}H

Radical	Atom	A calc., gauss	A exptl., gauss
Methyl		-22.4	$(-)23.04^a$
Fluoromethyl^{mm}		-7.8	$(-)21.10^b$
Difluoromethyl^{mm}		21.9	$(+)22.20^b$
Ethyl^{nn}	CH_2	-20.4	$(-)22.38^a$
	CH_3	27.6	$(+)26.87^a$
Vinyl	α	17.1	$(+)13.40^a$
	$\beta1$	55.1	$(+)65.00^a$
	$\beta2$	21.2	$(+)37.00^a$
Formyl		74.9	$(+)137.00^c$
Ethynyl		32.7	$(+)16.10^d$
Allyl	1	-14.6	$(-)13.93^a$
	$1'$	-14.9	$(-)14.83^a$
	2	6.9	$(+)4.06^a$
Phenyl	2	18.7	$(+)19.50^c$
	3	6.1	$(+)6.50^c$
	4	3.9	
Cyclopentadienyl^{oo}		-4.8	$(-)5.60^f$
Tropyl^{oo}		-3.2	$(-)3.95^g$
Benzyl	$-CH_2$	-17.0	$(-)16.35^h$
	2	-6.4	$(-)5.14^h$
	3	3.6	$(+)1.75^h$
	4	-5.6	$(-)6.14^h$
Phenoxy	2	-4.1	$(-)6.60^i$
	3	2.2	$(+)1.96^i$
	4	-3.4	$(-)10.40^i$
Cyclohexadienyl^{oo}	$CH_2{}^{pp}$	97.6	$(+)47.71^a$
	2	-11.1	$(-)8.99^a$
	3	5.1	$(+)2.65^a$
	4	-9.8	$(-)13.04^a$
Perinaphthenyl	1	-7.5	$(-)7.30^j$
	2	4.3	$(+)2.80^j$
Benzene$^-$		-3.6	$(-)3.75^k$
Cyclooctatetraene^{-oo}		-2.6	$(-)3.21^l$
trans-Butadiene$^-$	1	-9.8	$(-)7.62^m$
	$1'$	-10.3	$(-)7.62^m$
	2	-0.8	$(-)2.79^m$
Naphthalene$^-$	1	-5.3	$(-)4.90^n$
	2	-0.9	$(-)1.83^n$
Anthracene$^-$	1	-2.7	$(-)2.74^o$
	2	-0.6	$(-)1.51^o$
	9	-6.8	$(-)5.34^o$
Anthracene$^+$	1	-2.9	$(-)3.08^p$
	2	-0.6	$(-)1.38^p$
	9	-6.6	$(-)6.49^p$
Phenanthrene$^-$	1	-4.6	$(-)3.60^q$
	2	2.1	$(+)0.72^q$
	3	-3.8	$(-)2.88^q$
	4	0.6	$(+)0.32^q$
	9	-5.0	$(-)4.32^q$

Table 4.23   Observed and calculated isotropic hyperfine coupling constants for ^{1}H (continued)

Radical	Atom	A calc., gauss	A exptl., gauss
Pyrene$^-$	1	-5.5	$(-)4.75^r$
	2	2.5	$(+)1.09^r$
	4	-1.9	$(-)2.08^r$
Stilbene$^-$	1	-3.7	$(-)1.90^s$
	2	2.0	$(+)0.86^s$
	3	-3.9	$(-)3.80^s$
	4	1.9	$(+)0.32^r$
	5	-3.4	$(-)2.96^s$
	7	-5.2	$(-)4.36^s$
Biphenylene$^-$	1	0.2	$(+)0.21^t$
	2	-2.1	$(-)2.86^t$
Azulene^{-oo}	1	0	$(+)0.27^u$
	2	-3.0	$(-)3.95^u$
	4	-7.0	$(-)6.22^u$
	5	3.9	$(+)1.34^u$
	6	-9.4	$(-)8.82^u$
Fluoranthrene^{-oo}	1	-4.4	$(-)3.90^v$
	2	2.2	$(+)1.30^v$
	3	-6.4	$(-)5.20^v$
	7	0.2	
	8	-0.9	
Benzonitrile^{-qq}	2	-3.3	$(-)3.63^w$
	3	1.1	$(+)0.30^w$
	4	-8.0	$(-)8.42^w$
Phthalonitrile^{-qq}	3	1.5	$(+)0.33^x$
	4	-4.0	$(-)4.24^x$
Isophthalonitrile^{-qq}	2	1.5	$(+)0.08^w$
	4	-7.6	$(-)8.29^w$
	5	2.6	$(+)1.44^w$
Terephthalonitrile^{-qq}		-1.0	$(-)1.59^w$
1,2,4,5-Tetracyanobenzene^{-qq}		2.2	$(+)1.11^w$
p-Nitrobenzonitrile$^{-qq,rr}$	2	1.8	$(+)0.76^y$
	3	-3.5	$(-)3.12^y$
Nitrobenzene^{-rr}	2	-3.6	$(-)3.39^z$
	3	1.9	$(+)1.09^z$
	4	-3.8	$(-)3.97^z$
m-Dinitrobenzene^{-rr}	2	0.4	$(+)3.11^{aa}$
	4	-7.8	$(-)4.19^{aa}$
	5	3.2	$(+)1.08^{aa}$
p-Dinitrobenzene^{-rr}		-1.0	$(-)1.12^{aa}$
m-Fluoronitrobenzene^{-rr}	2	-3.7	$(-)3.30^{bb}$
	4	-3.7	$(-)3.30^{bb}$
	5	1.8	$(+)1.10^{bb}$
	6	-3.4	$(-)3.00^{bb}$
p-Fluoronitrobenzene^{-rr}	2	-3.8	$(-)3.56^y$
	3	2.2	$(+)1.16^y$
3,5-Difluoronitrobenzene^{-rr}	2	-3.5	$(-)3.26^{cc}$
	4	-3.6	$(-)3.98^{cc}$

Table 4.23   Observed and calculated isotropic hyperfine coupling constants for ^{1}H (continued)

Radical	Atom	A calc., gauss	A exptl., gauss
o-Benzosemiquinone$^-$	3	-1.9	$(-)3.65^{dd}$
	4	0.2	$(+)0.95^{dd}$
p-Benzosemiquinone$^-$		-0.9	$(-)2.37^{ee}$
2,5-Dioxo-1,4-semiquinone$-$		2.4	$(+)0.79^{ff}$
1,4-Naphthosemiquinone$^-$	2	-1.0	$(-)3.23^{ee}$
	5	0.6	$(+)0.65^{ee}$
	6	-0.1	$(-)0.51^{ee}$
9,10-Anthrasemiquinone$^-$	1	0.8	$(+)0.96^{ee}$
	2	-0.2	$(-)0.55^{ee}$
Pyrazine$^-$		-2.0	$(-)2.64^{gg}$
N,N-Dihydropyrazine$^+$	NH	-10.1	$(-)8.30^{hh}$
	CH	-2.1	$(-)3.26^{hh}$
Pyridazine$^-$	3	1.1	$(+)0.16^{gg}$
	4	-3.6	$(-)6.47^{gg}$
s-Tetrazine$^-$		2.5	$(+)0.21^{gg}$
1,5-Diazanaphthalene$^-$	2	-0.6	$(-)1.69^{ii}$
	3	-1.5	$(-)2.95^{ii}$
	4	-3.8	$(-)5.77^{ii}$
Phthalazine$^-$	1	-6.4	$(-)5.91^{gg}$
	5	-5.2	$(-)4.64^{gg}$
	6	-0.9	$(-)2.14^{gg}$
Quinoxaline$^-$	2	-1.8	$(-)2.32^{jj}$
	5	-2.0	$(-)3.32^{jj}$
	6	0.4	$(-)1.00^{jj}$
Dihydroquinoxaline$^+$	1	-9.8	$(-)7.17^{kk}$
	2	-2.3	$(-)3.99^{kk}$
	5	-0.5	$(-)0.78^{kk}$
	6	-0.7	$(-)1.38^{kk}$
Phenazine$^-$	1	-1.7	$(-)1.93^{jj}$
	2	-0.4	$(-)1.61^{jj}$
1,4,5,8-Tetraazaanthracene$^-$	2	-1.0	$(-)2.73^{jj}$
	9	-4.4	$(-)3.96^{jj}$
p-Nitrobenzaldehyde^{-ss}	2	-0.6	$(-)1.23^{y}$
	3	-0.4	$(-)0.44^{y}$
	5	-0.4	$(-)0.44^{y}$
	6	-0.6	$(-)2.37^{y}$
	CHO	1.4	$(+)3.10^{y}$
p-Cyanobenzaldehyde$^{-ss,qq}$	3	1.2	$(+)0.19^{ll}$
	2	-2.5	$(-)2.73^{ll}$
	6	-2.5	$(-)3.14^{ll}$
	5	1.3	$(+)0.71^{ll}$
	CHO	-1.8	$(-)5.56^{ll}$
4-Cyanopyridine^{-qq}	2	-1.3	$(-)1.40^{w}$
	3	-1.5	$(-)2.62^{w}$

Table 4.23   Observed and calculated isotropic hyperfine coupling constants for ^1H (continued)

^{a} See Ref. [17].
^{b} R. W. Fessenden and R. H. Schuler, *J. Chem. Phys.*, **43**:2704 (1965).
^{c} F. J. Adrian, E. L. Cochran, and V. A. Bowers, *J. Chem. Phys.*, **36**:1661 (1962).
^{d} E. L. Cochran, F. J. Adrian, and V. A. Bowers, *J. Chem. Phys.*, **40**:213 (1964).
^{e} J. E. Bennett, B. Mile, and A. Thomas, *Proc. Roy. Soc. (London)*, **293A**:246 (1966).
^{f} S. Ohnishi and I. Nitta, *J. Chem. Phys.*, **39**:2848 (1963).
^{g} D. E. Wood and H. M. McConnell, *J. Chem. Phys.*, **37**:1150 (1962).
^{h} A. Carrington and I. C. P. Smith, *Mol. Phys.*, **9**:137 (1965).
^{i} T. J. Stone and W. A. Waters, *Proc. Chem. Soc.*, **1962**:253.
^{j} P. B. Sogo, M. Nakazaki, and M. Calvin, *J. Chem. Phys.*, **26**:1343 (1957).
^{k} T. R. Tuttle, Jr., and S. I. Weissman, *J. Am. Chem. Soc.*, **80**:5342 (1958).
^{l} T. J. Katz and H. L. Stevens, *J. Chem. Phys.*, **32**:1873 (1960).
^{m} D. H. Levy and R. J. Myers, *J. Chem. Phys.*, **41**:1062 (1964).
^{n} A. Carrington, F. Dravnieks, and M. C. R. Symons, *J. Chem. Soc.*, **1959**:947.
^{o} See Ref. [22].
^{p} I. C. Lewis and L. S. Singer, *J. Chem. Phys.*, **43**:2712 (1965).
^{q} S. H. Glarum and L. C. Snyder, *J. Chem. Phys.*, **36**:2989 (1962).
^{r} G. J. Hoijtink, J. Townsend, and S. I. Weissman, *J. Chem. Phys.*, **34**:507 (1961).
^{s} R. Chang and C. S. Johnson, Jr., *J. Chem. Phys.*, **41**:3273 (1964).
^{t} A. Carrington and J. dos Santos-Veiga, *Mol. Phys.*, **5**:285 (1962).
^{u} I. Bernal, P. H. Rieger, and G. K. Fraenkel, *J. Chem. Phys.*, **37**:1489 (1962).
^{v} E. DeBoer and S. I. Weissman, *J. Am. Chem. Soc.*, **80**:4549 (1958).
^{w} P. H. Rieger, I. Bernal, W. H. Reinmuth, and G. K. Fraenkel, *J. Am. Chem. Soc.*, **85**:683 (1963).
^{x} A. Carrington and P. F. Todd, *Mol. Phys.*, **6**:161 (1963).
^{y} A. H. Maki and D. H. Geske, *J. Am. Chem. Soc.*, **83**:1852, 3532 (1961).
^{z} D. H. Geske and A. H. Maki, *J. Am. Chem. Soc.*, **82**:2671 (1960).
^{aa} A. H. Maki and D. H. Geske, *J. Chem. Phys.*, **33**:825 (1960).
^{bb} P. B. Ayscough, F. P. Sargent, and R. Wilson, *J. Chem. Soc.*, **1963**:5418.
^{cc} M. Kaplan, J. R. Bolton, and G. K. Fraenkel, *J. Chem. Phys.*, **42**:955 (1965).
^{dd} B. Venkataremen, B. G. Segal, and G. K. Fraenkel, *J. Chem. Phys.*, **30**:1006 (1959).
^{ee} G. Vincow and G. K. Fraenkel, *J. Chem. Phys.*, **34**:1333 (1964).
^{ff} D. C. Reitz, F. Dravnieks, and J. E. Wertz, *J. Chem. Phys.*, **33**:1880 (1960).
^{gg} E. W. Stone and A. H. Maki, *J. Chem. Phys.*, **39**:1635 (1963).
^{hh} J. R. Bolton, A. Carrington, and J. dos Santos-Veiga, *Mol. Phys.*, **5**:465 (1962).
^{ii} J. C. M. Henning, *J. Chem. Phys.*, **44**:2139 (1966).
^{jj} A. Carrington and J. dos Santos-Veiga, *Mol. Phys.*, **5**:21 (1962).
^{kk} B. L. Barton and G. K. Fraenkel, *J. Chem. Phys.*, **41**:1455 (1964).
^{ll} P. H. Rieger and G. K. Fraenkel, *J. Chem. Phys.*, **37**:2813 (1962).
^{mm} Calculated equilibrium bond angles (Ref. [10]).
^{nn} Free rotation of methyl group simulated (Ref. [4]).
^{oo} Ring(s) assumed to be regular polygon.
^{pp} HCH angle 109.5°.
^{qq} C—N bondlength 1.16.
^{rr} N—O bondlength 1.24.
^{ss} C—O bondlength 1.36 and O cis to H_2.

Table 4.24 Observed and calculated isotropic hyperfine coupling constants for ^{13}C

Radical	Atom	A calc., gauss	A exptl., gauss
Methyl		45.0	(+)38.34[a]
Fluoromethyl		92.7	(+)54.80[b]
Difluoromethyl		145.1	(+)148.80[b]
Trifluoromethyl		184.6	(+)271.60[b]
Ethyl	—CH$_3$	−12.4	(−)13.57[b]
	—CH$_2$	39.9	(+)39.07[a]
Vinyl	α	178.0	(+)107.57[a]
	β	−14.5	(−)8.55[a]
Ethynyl	1	−2.5	
	2	342.8	
Allyl	1	28.0	
	2	−16.6	
Phenyl	1	151.3	
	2	−4.8	
	3	10.7	
	4	−2.6	
Cyclopentadienyl		4.1	
Tropyl		3.5	
Benzyl	1	−12.3	
	2	11.7	
	3	−8.5	
	4	10.5	
	—CH$_2$	32.6	
Phenoxy	1	−10.7	
	2	7.0	
	3	−5.5	
	4	6.3	
Cyclohexadienyl	2	17.9	
	3	−13.7	
	4	17.8	
	—CH$_2$	−17.6	
Perinaphthenyl	1	13.9	
	2	−10.3	
	4	−9.3	
	13	6.7	
Benzene$^-$		4.0	(+)2.80[c]
Cyclooctatetraene$^-$		3.0	(+)1.28[d]
trans-Butadiene$^-$	1	18.6	
	2	−1.2	
Naphthalene$^-$	α	9.3	(+)7.10[e]
	β	−0.3	(−)1.20[f]
	9	−4.3	
Anthracene$^-$	1	4.6	3.57[g]
	2	0	−0.25[g]
	9	12.4	8.76[g]
	11	−3.4	−4.59[g]
Anthracene$^+$	2	0.2	(+)0.37[g]
	9	11.8	8.48[g]
	11	−3.3	(−)4.50[g]

Table 4.24   Observed and calculated isotropic hyperfine coupling constants for ^{13}C (continued)

Radical	Atom	A calc., gauss	A exptl., gauss
Phenanthrene$^-$	1	8.2	
	2	−5.7	
	3	6.9	
	4	−2.2	
	9	7.5	
	11	−3.8	
	12	2.1	
Pyrene$^-$	1	9.9	
	2	−7.1	
	4	2.9	
Stilbene$^-$	1	6.2	
	2	−5.2	
	3	7.4	
	4	−4.9	
	5	5.8	
	6	−3.2	
	7	7.4	
Biphenylene$^-$	1	−3.0	
	2	3.0	
	10	5.2	
Azulene$^-$	1	−1.8	
	2	4.9	
	9	1.3	
	4	11.7	
	5	−10.2	
	6	16.9	
Fluoranthrene$^-$	1	7.5	
	2	−6.4	
	3	12.0	
	7	−1.2	
	8	1.3	
	11	−7.0	
	12	1.6	
	13	−0.4	
	14	2.4	
Benzonitrile$^-$	1	8.4	
	2	3.6	
	3	−5.2	
	4	14.0	
	—CN	−6.6	(−)6.12[h]
Phthalonitrile$^-$	1	8.5	
	3	−6.1	
	4	6.0	
	—CN	−6.4	
Isophthalonitrile$^-$	1	4.9	
	2	−5.8	
	4	12.3	
	5	−9.1	
	—CN	−4.3	

Table 4.24 Observed and calculated isotropic hyperfine coupling constants for ^{13}C (continued)

Radical	Atom	A calc., gauss	A exptl., gauss
Terephthalonitrile⁻	—CN	−6.7	(−)7.83[h]
	1	9.7	8.81[h]
	2	−0.7	(−)1.98[h]
1,2,4,5-Tetracyanobenzene⁻	1	7.2	
	3	−7.3	
	—CN	−5.3	
p-Nitrobenzonitrile⁻	1	7.5	
	2	−5.2	
	3	5.5	
	4	−2.3	
	—CN	−4.5	
Nitrobenzene⁻	1	−5.2	
	2	6.1	
	3	−5.2	
	4	7.1	
m-Dinitrobenzene⁻	1	0.3	
	2	−2.4	
	4	13.2	
	5	−9.4	
p-Dinitrobenzene⁻	1	6.1	
	2	0.1	
o-Benzosemiquinone⁻	1	−6.6	
	3	3.2	
	4	−1.1	
p-Benzosemiquinone⁻	1	−6.9	(−)0.59[i]
	2	1.0	(+)0.40[i]
2,5-Dioxo-1,4-Benzosemiquinone⁼	1	3.1	
	3	−7.9	
1,4-Naphthosemiquinone⁻	1	−8.3	
	2	1.3	
	5	−1.5	
	6	0.2	
	9	1.4	
9,10-Anthrasemiquinone⁻	1	−1.7	
	2	0.4	
	9	−9.6	
	11	1.8	
Pyrazine⁻		−1.8	(−)2.88[i]
N,N-Dihydropyrazine⁺		0.1	
Pyridazine⁻	3	−7.6	
	4	5.1	
s-Tetrazine⁻		−12.2	
1,5-Diazanaphthalene⁻	2	−2.5	
	3	0.9	
	4	6.5	
	9	−4.8	
Phthalazine⁻	1	11.9	
	5	9.1	

Table 4.24   Observed and calculated isotropic hyperfine coupling constants for ^{13}C (continued)

Radical	Atom	A calc., gauss	A exptl., gauss
	6	−0.2	
	9	−4.5	
Quinoxaline⁻	2	−1.2	
	5	3.3	
	6	−0.2	
	9	−4.1	
Dihydroquinoxaline⁺	2	0.2	
	5	−0.1	
	6	0.2	
	9	−0.2	
Phenazine⁻	1	2.6	
	2	−0.2	
	11	−3.8	
1,4,5,8-Tetraazaanthracene⁻	2	−0.2	
	9	8.4	
	11	−4.3	
p-Dicyanotetrazine⁻	RING	−10.6	
	—CN	3.5	
p-Nitrobenzaldehyde⁻	—CHO	−9.5	
p-Cyanobenzaldehyde⁻	—CHO	−2.7	
	—CN	−4.1	
4-Cyanopyridine⁻	—CN	−10.1	

[a] R. W. Fessenden, *J. Phys. Chem.*, **71**:74 (1967).
[b] R. W. Fessenden and R. H. Schuler, *J. Chem. Phys.*, **43**:2704 (1965).
[c] J. R. Bolton, *Mol. Phys.*, **6**:219 (1963).
[d] H. L. Strauss and G. K. Fraenkel, *J. Chem. Phys.*, **35**:1738 (1963).
[e] T. R. Tuttle, Jr., and S. I. Weissman, *J. Chem. Phys.*, **25**:189 (1956).
[f] T. R. Tuttle, Jr., *J. Chem. Phys.*, **32**:1579 (1960).
[g] See Ref. [22].
[h] P. H. Rieger, I. Bernal, W. H. Reinmuth, and G. K. Fraenkel, *J. Am. Chem. Soc.*, **85**:683 (1963).
[i] M. R. Das and B. Venkatareman, *Bull. Colloq. Amp. Eindhoven*, **1962**:21.
[j] E. W. Stone and A. H. Maki, *J. Chem. Phys.*, **39**:1635 (1963).

on the basis of the calculated spin densities for cases where the assignment of experimentally observed hyperfine coupling constants was not unequivocally established. In addition, the signs of most of the hyperfine coupling constants listed are not known experimentally, and here again assignments were made entirely on the basis of the calculations.

Considering the level of approximation involved, the overall results are seen to be quite satisfactory. An indication of the quality of the results follows from the linear relationship between the observed a_N and calculated $\rho_{s_N s_N}^{spin}$, as reflected in the standard deviations and

Table 4.25   Observed and calculated isotropic hyperfine coupling constants for ^{14}N

Radical	Atom	A calc., gauss	A exptl., gauss
Benzonitrile$^-$		2.4	(+)2.15[a]
Phthalonitrile$^-$		1.9	(+)1.80[b]
Isophthalonitrile$^-$		1.3	(+)1.02[a]
Terephthalonitrile$^-$		2.0	(+)1.81[a]
1,2,4,5-Tetracyanobenzene$^-$		1.4	(+)1.15[a]
p-Nitrobenzonitrile$^-$	—CN	1.1	(+)0.76[c]
	—NO$_2$	4.7	(+)7.15[c]
Nitrobenzene$^-$		7.1	(+)10.32[c]
m-Dinitrobenzene$^-$		0.5	(+)4.68[d]
p-Dinitrobenzene$^-$		−0.0	(−)1.74[d]
m-Fluoronitrobenzene$^-$		6.6	(+)12.60[e]
p-Fluoronitrobenzene$^-$		7.1	(+)9.95[f]
3,5-Difluoronitrobenzene$^-$		6.1	(+)8.09[f]
Pyrazine$^-$		8.3	(+)7.21[g]
N,N-Dihydropyrazine$^+$		7.8	(+)7.60[h]
Pyridazine$^-$		7.7	(+)5.90[g]
s-Tetrazine$^-$		5.8	(+)5.28[g]
1,5-Diazanaphthalene$^-$		5.9	(+)3.37[i]
Phthalazine$^-$		0.3	(+)0.88[g]
Quinoxaline$^-$		7.3	(+)5.64[j]
Dihydroquinoxaline$^+$		7.7	(+)6.65[k]
Phenazine$^-$		7.2	(+)5.14[j]
1,4,5,8-Tetraazaanthracene$^-$		3.3	(+)2.41[j]
p-Dicyanotetrazine$^-$	RING	5.9	(+)5.88[l]
	—CN	−0.9	(−)0.16[l]
p-Nitrobenazaldehyde$^-$		−0.5	(+)5.83[c]
p-Cyanobenzaldehyde$^-$		1.0	(+)1.40[m]
4-Cyanopyridine$^-$	RING	8.3	(+)5.67[a]
	—CN	2.7	(+)2.33[a]

[a] P. H. Rieger, I. Bernal, W. H. Reinmuth, and G. K. Fraenkel, *J. Am. Chem. Soc.*, **85**:683 (1963).

[b] A. Carrington and P. F. Todd, *Mol. Phys.*, **6**:161 (1963).

[c] A. H. Maki and D. H. Geske, *J. Am. Chem. Soc.*, **83**:1852, 3532 (1961).

[d] A. H. Maki and D. H. Geske, *J. Chem. Phys.*, **33**:825 (1960).

[e] P. B. Ayscough, F. P. Sargent, and R. Wilson, *J. Chem. Soc.*, **1963**:5418.

[f] M. Kaplan, J. R. Bolton, and G. K. Fraenkel, *J. Chem. Phys.*, **42**:955 (1965).

[g] E. W. Stone and A. H. Maki, *J. Chem. Phys.*, **39**:1635 (1963).

[h] J. R. Bolton, A. Carrington, and J. dos Santos-Veiga, *Mol. Phys.*, **5**:465 (1962).

[i] J. C. M. Henning, *J. Chem. Phys.*, **44**:2139 (1966).

[j] A. Carrington and J. dos Santos-Veiga, *Mol. Phys.*, **5**:21 (1962).

[k] B. L. Barton and G. K. Fraenkel, *J. Chem. Phys.*, **41**:1455 (1964).

[l] A. Carrington, P. Todd, and J. dos Santos-Veiga, *Mol. Phys.*, **6**:101 (1963).

[m] P. H. Rieger and G. K. Fraenkel, *J. Chem. Phys.*, **37**:2813 (1962).

Table 4.26   Observed and calculated isotropic hyperfine coupling constants for ^{17}O

Radical	Atom	A calc., gauss	A exptl., gauss
p-Benzosemiquinone$^-$		8.7	(+)9.53[†]
1,4-Naphthosemiquinone$^-$		9.3	(+)8.58[†]
9,10-Anthrasemiquinone$^-$		9.9	(+)7.53[†]
2,5-Dioxo-1,4-semiquinone$^=$		3.6	(+)4.57[†]
Nitrobenzene$^-$		4.3	(+)8.84[‡]

[†] M. Broze, Z. Luz, and B. L. Silver, *J. Chem. Phys.*, **46**:4891 (1967).
[‡] W. M. Garlick and D. H. Geske, *J. Am. Chem. Soc.*, **87**:4049 (1965).

correlation coefficients listed in Table 4.21.   From Table 4.23, we observe that 92 percent of the proton hyperfine coupling constants are calculated within 3 gauss, evidence that calculations of this type will be predictive in a semiquantitative sense.   For ^{13}C, ^{14}N, and ^{19}F, the number of data points is not as large as for protons but the overall results are satisfactory, especially in light of the fact that contributions from inner shells and vibronic effects are neglected.   The correlation is not as good for ^{17}O, where there is an insufficient number of data

Table 4.27   Observed and calculated isotropic hyperfine coupling constants for ^{19}F

Radical	Atom	A calc., gauss	A exptl., gauss
Fluoromethyl		71.3	(+)64.30[a]
Difluoromethyl		87.1	(+)84.20[a]
Trifluoromethyl		159.5	(+)142.40[a]
Monofluoroacetamide		34.4	54.60[b]
Difluoroacetamide	1'	31.5	75.00[c]
	1	39.0	75.00[c]
m-Fluoronitrobenzene$^-$		−4.0	(−)3.70[d]
p-Fluoronitrobenzene$^-$		6.3	(+)8.41[e]
3,5-Difluoronitrobenzene$^-$		−3.8	(−)2.73[f]

[a] R. W. Fessenden and R. H. Schuler, *J. Chem. Phys.*, **43**:2704 (1965).
[b] R. J. Cook, J. R. Rowlands, and D. H. Whiffen, *Mol. Phys.*, **7**:31 (1963).
[c] R. J. Lontz and W. Gordy, *J. Chem. Phys.*, **37**:1357 (1962).
[d] P. B. Ayscough, F. P. Sargent, and R. Wilson, *J. Chem. Soc.*, **1963**:5418.
[e] A. H. Maki and D. H. Geske, *J. Am. Chem. Soc.*, **83**:1852, 3532 (1961).
[f] M. Kaplan, J. R. Bolton, and G. K. Fraenkel, *J. Chem. Phys.*, **42**:955 (1965).

points for a critical test. Also included in Tables 4.23 to 4.27 are a number of calculated hyperfine coupling constants for which no experimental data have been reported.

Radicals and radical ions considered may be broadly divided into two classes. The first includes those in which the odd electron is primarily associated with a molecular orbital with nonvanishing amplitude at the nuclear positions (σ-type radicals such as vinyl, formyl, phenyl). The other, more numerous, class consists of planar systems in which the singly occupied molecular orbital is of π type, and hyperfine interaction only occurs by means of indirect effects (α and β electrons in the σ system experiencing different environments because of the different local α and β electron densities). Most previous theoretical calculations have treated these two types separately. Independent electron calculations of the extended Hückel type have given a partially satisfactory account of some of the σ systems, but these methods are inherently incapable of giving true values for π systems.

The second class of radicals is usually handled by considering the π electrons in detail and then using the McConnell relation [16] connecting the unpaired electron population of a carbon $2p\pi$ orbital with hyperfine interactions with carbon and hydrogen nuclei in the immediate vicinity. The method presented here, on the other hand, since it treats all valence electrons on an equal footing, is able to give a comprehensive account of both types of radicals within a single theoretical framework. The fact that moderately good agreement is achieved for both classes without additional parameterization is one of the most encouraging features.

The methyl radical, CH_3, directly illustrates the significant difference between INDO theory and CNDO theory. The CNDO molecular wavefunctions for the $^2A''$ ground state of a planar methyl radical (D_{3h}) indicates that the molecular orbital configuration is $(a_1'')^2(e')^4(a_2'')$. The a_1'' and e' molecular orbitals are linear combinations of the carbon $2s$, $2p_x$, $2p_y$ and hydrogen $1s$ atomic orbitals and together describe the three carbon-hydrogen σ bonds. The a_2'' orbital is singly occupied and is composed of only the carbon $2p_z$ atomic orbital. Since the node of the carbon $2p_z$ orbital is coincident with the molecular plane, the unpaired spin density at both the carbon nucleus and the proton is zero. However, the experimentally observed [17] isotropic hyperfine coupling constants are $(+)$ 38.5 gauss for carbon and $(-)$ 23.04 gauss for each of the protons, indicating that there exists considerable unpaired spin at these nuclei which is not properly accounted for by the CNDO wavefunction.

Table 4.28   Unpaired spin distribution in methyl radical†

Atomic orbital	ρ $\langle S^2 \rangle = 0.7553$	Observed isotropic hyperfine coupling constants‡
C_1 $2s$	0.0542	38.5
C_1 $2p_x$	0.0336	
C_1 $2p_y$	0.0336	
C_1 $2p_z$	1.0000	
H_2 $1s$	−0.0405	−23.04
H_3 $1s$	−0.0405	−23.04
H_4 $1s$	−0.0405	−23.04

† Based on wavefunctions calculated in the INDO approximation.
‡ See Ref. [17].

The unpaired spin distributions for the methyl radical computed from an unrestricted INDO molecular wavefunction and the corresponding observed isotropic hyperfine coupling constants are given in Table 4.28. The majority of unpaired spin density still remains localized in the carbon $2p_z$ atomic orbital, but a small amount has now been introduced into the atomic orbitals contributing to the σ system. Most important, there is now a finite unpaired spin density in the carbon $2s$ and hydrogen $1s$ orbitals, resulting in a finite spin density at the respective nuclei and allowing an isotropic hyperfine coupling between electron and nuclear spins. With an excess of α spin localized on the carbon atom, the σ orbitals associated with β spin tend to be polarized toward the hydrogens, resulting in a net negative spin density at the protons. Thus the calculated signs of the unpaired spin of the carbon nuclei and the protons agree with the signs of the observed coupling constants inferred from related experiments [18].

The example of methyl radical demonstrates that the INDO method is capable of giving wavefunctions that accommodate exchange polarization phenomena, which are commonly invoked to explain the mechanism of hyperfine coupling to α protons in π electron radicals. Another situation frequently encountered in organic systems is hyperfine coupling to β protons, for which a hyperconjugative delocalization of unpaired electron onto the β proton has been proposed. We consider now the case of the ethyl radical, in which hyperfine coupling to both α and β protons is observed in the same system.

Experimental measurements of hyperfine coupling constants for the ethyl radical [17] were taken under conditions such that the methyl group was rotating rapidly about the carbon-carbon σ bond.

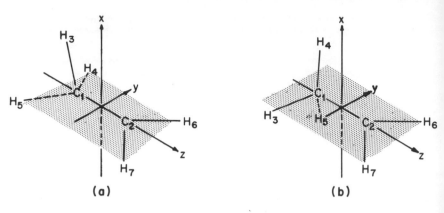

Fig. 4.10 Conformations considered in calculations on C_2H_5.

Thus INDO calculations were performed on the two configurations of the ethyl radical depicted in Fig. 4.10, and the final spin distribution was taken as the average of the spin densities computed from molecular wavefunctions for each configuration. The unpaired spin distributions in ethyl radical for both configurations based on INDO wavefunctions and the averaged spin distributions simulating the ethyl radical with a freely rotating methyl group are given in Table 4.29, together with the corresponding observed isotropic hyperfine coupling constants.

According to these results, the unpaired spin in the ethyl radical is localized mainly in the carbon $2p\pi$ orbital of the methylene group, and the negative spin density is observed in the $1s$ orbitals of the methylene protons and also in the $2s$ orbitals of the methylene protons and also in the $2s$ orbital of the methyl carbon, as expected from spin polarization. The unpaired spin density at the methyl proton is positive. This result could be attributed qualitatively either to a hyperconjugation mechanism in which the unpaired electron is delocalized in the π system or to a σ electron spin polarization effect in which no direct π interaction is required. The importance of these mechanisms can be partly distinguished by noting that in conformation B proton 3 lies in the nodal plane of the methylene $2p\pi$ orbital, so that the spin density in the corresponding hydrogen orbital is a measure of the contribution of the σ spin polarization effect. In fact this spin density is only $+0.0035$, an order of magnitude smaller than the spin density of the other protons. This figure indicates that the mechanism of hyperfine coupling to β protons is roughly 93 percent hyperconjugation and 7 percent spin polarization.

Table 4.29   Unpaired spin distribution in ethyl radical†

Atomic orbital		ρA $\langle S^2 \rangle = 0.7573$	ρB $\langle S^2 \rangle = 0.7573$	$\bar{\rho}$	Observed isotropic hyperfine coupling constant‡
C_1	$2s$	-0.0151	-0.0151	-0.0151	-13.57
C_2	$2s$	0.0487	0.0487	0.0487	$+39.07$
C_1	$2p_x$	-0.0461	-0.0460	-0.0461	
C_2	$2p_x$	0.9255	0.9255	0.9255	
C_1	$2p_y$	-0.0129	-0.0130	-0.0129	
C_2	$2p_y$	0.0302	0.0302	0.0302	
C_1	$2p_z$	-0.0333	-0.0333	-0.0333	
C_2	$2p_z$	0.0282	0.0282	0.0282	
H_3	$1s$	0.0989	0.0035	0.0511	26.87
H_4	$1s$	0.0272	0.0749	0.0511	26.87
H_5	$1s$	0.0272	0.0749	0.0511	26.87
H_6	$1s$	-0.0377	-0.0381	-0.0377	-22.38
H_7	$1s$	-0.0377	-0.0373	-0.0377	-22.38

† Based on wavefunctions calculated in the INDO approximation and corresponding observed isotropic hyperfine coupling constants.
‡ See Ref. [17].

For fluorinated methyl radicals, the results quoted are for calculated equilibrium bond angles leading to significant nonplanarity at the carbon atom as discussed in the previous section. For the remaining σ-type radicals, the theory reproduces a number of experimental features satisfactorily. The calculations on vinyl and formyl (using model B with all angles 120°) show the observed major difference between the hydrogen constants at the α position. The theory also distinguishes between the two hydrogen positions, predicting that the interaction is greatest trans to the site of the unpaired electron. The carbon calculations predict that the C_β constant in vinyl is negative, as it is in ethyl. The theoretical results for ethynyl show similar features. The C_β constant is predicted to be small and negative, but this is sensitive to bondlengths. A more realistic choice of 1.2 Å for the carbon-carbon triple bond gives positive constants for both C_α and C_β.

Application of the theory to phenyl radical gives better agreement with experiment than previous calculations. The hydrogen spin densities are all positive, with magnitudes in the order ortho > meta > para. The carbon predictions are interesting, as they indicate sign alternation around the ring (a result which cannot be obtained by any independent-electron calculations of the Hückel type). No experimental data on the carbon hyperfine constants for phenyl appear to be available.

For the π-type hydrocarbon radicals, the results of this theory mostly parallel previous calculations [19] which treat π electrons separately and handle σ-π interactions on a local basis. As previously mentioned, the McConnell relation in its simplest form

$$a_{\mathrm{H}} = Q \rho_{\mathrm{C}_\pi}{}^{\mathrm{spin}} \tag{4.14}$$

implies a direct proportionality between the unpaired electron population of the carbon $2p\pi$ orbital of a conjugated carbon atom $\rho_{\mathrm{C}_\pi}{}^{\mathrm{spin}}$ and the $1s$ orbital unpaired electron population $\rho_{\mathrm{H}_s}{}^{\mathrm{spin}}$ of hydrogen atoms bonded to the carbon atom in the principal valence structure, with Q being the constant of proportionality and usually taken to be about -23 gauss. Since both $\rho_{\mathrm{C}_\pi}{}^{\mathrm{spin}}$ and $\rho_{\mathrm{H}_s}{}^{\mathrm{spin}}$ are calculated explicitly in the course of an INDO molecular orbital calculation, the extent to which the McConnell relation holds up on this level of approximation may be directly examined. The quality of the linear relation obtained in plotting $\rho_{\mathrm{C}_\pi}{}^{\mathrm{spin}}$ versus the corresponding $\rho_{\mathrm{H}_s}{}^{\mathrm{spin}}$ for a number of positions in a variety of molecules reflects the extent to which the McConnell relation holds. A plot of this type, including all appropriate cases taken from the molecules listed in Table 4.23, is given in Fig. 4.11. The McConnell relation is observed to hold remarkably well, and the slope of the line leads to a theoretical value for Q of -22 gauss.

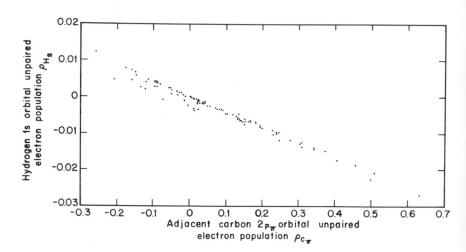

Fig. 4.11 Correlation of quantities entering McConnell relation.

Another notable feature of the calculations on π radicals is that the two hydrogens in the 1-position of allyl are separated in this theory, the prediction being the 1′ (cis to the third carbon atom C3) has the hyperfine constant of larger magnitude. However, the calculated separation between the two positions is considerably smaller than that observed experimentally. The results for benzyl predict that the magnitude of the proton hyperfine interaction at the para position is smaller than the corresponding magnitude at the ortho position. The experimental results show the opposite ordering. This failure of self-consistent field theories has also been noted in π electron treatments, and its origin is not yet understood. The theoretical results for the phenoxy radical show up the same difficulty.

The radicals cyclopentadienyl (C_5H_5) and tropyl (C_7H_7) were treated as having carbon structure as regular polygons. Both these systems are predicted to be in degenerate electronic states and are therefore distorted according to the Jahn-Teller theorem. This distortion is neglected, and the theoretical values quoted are averages over the two components of the Jahn-Teller state. The calculated proton hyperfine constants are approximately in the ratio 5:7 as observed experimentally.

Cyclohexadienyl shows a large hyperfine constant for the methylene protons. It was pointed out by Whiffen [20] that this was best interpreted in terms of a delocalized π-type molecular orbital in the pentadienyl fragment which interacted strongly with the CH_2 group. The results of the INDO calculations (using a regular hexagon for the carbon atoms and a tetrahedral H—C—H angle) overemphasize this effect and give too large a proton hyperfine constant. This is probably due to the unsatisfactory nature of the geometrical model which assumes a C—C bondlength of 1.40 Å for all C—C bonds. If the calculations are repeated with the same geometry for the pentadienyl C_5 fragment but with a length of 1.48 Å for the C—C bond to the CH_2 group, the predicted value of a_H (methylene) falls to 71.5.

The next section of the table deals with hydrocarbon anions and cations, for which there is an extensive body of experimental data. The calculations on butadiene anion give a rather smaller value for the proton constant at the 2-position than that observed. This may again be partly due to the unsatisfactory geometrical model which assumes three equal C—C bondlengths. Using model A geometry (a C—C single bondlength of 1.46 Å and a double bondlength of 1.34 Å), the calculated two-proton constant changes to -1.24 gauss. The carbon hyperfine constant in position 2 is predicted to be slightly negative, but this is also sensitive to bondlength and becomes positive if model A is used. The INDO calculations again differentiate between the two hydrogens in the 1-position, the 1′ (cis to C_3) having the hyperfine constant of largest magnitude.

For polycyclic anions and cations, the results of the present theory agree for the most part with previous π electron treatments. For naphthalene and anthracene, the general agreement is good for both carbon and hydrogen, the negative carbon constants observed in anthracene being correctly reproduced. However, calculated values at the 2-position are rather too small. For some of the higher polycyclic ions, assignments are still somewhat uncertain. Those given in the tables are made to give the best fit between the experimental data and the calculations of this paper. It may be noted that the assignment for phenanthrene anion differs from that proposed by Colpa and Bolton [21]. The results for the cations parallel those of the corresponding anions fairly closely, indicating that the pairing results discussed by Bolton and Fraenkel [22] hold well at this level of approximation.

The good results for the azines and cyanobenzenes ions in the tables are very encouraging, particularly since the calculations involve no additional parametrization to fit the data. The agreement covers hydrogen, carbon, and nitrogen constants in all the compounds considered. We are not able to report the results for some other nitrile anions studied experimentally (such as tetracyanoethylene) because of convergence difficulties with the calculations. The experimental data on nitrobenzene and dinitrobenzene anions are also fairly well reproduced. It is particularly interesting that the sharp drop in the nitrogen hyperfine constant from nitrobenzene to paradinitrobenzene is accounted for. The standard model for all these compounds is planar, and so this effect can be interpreted without appealing to nonplanarity at the nitrogen atoms as proposed by Symons. The calculations on metadinitrobenzene suggest that the assignment of the two- and five-proton hyperfine constants by Maki and Geske may be incorrect.

The results for quinones are less satisfactory. Calculated proton hyperfine constants for hydrogens in parabenzosemiquinone ion are less than experimental values as are those of the corresponding protons (2,3) in 1,4-naphthosemiquinone. Fairly large negative carbon constants are predicted for the carbon atoms in the carbonyl groups, but only a small value is found experimentally in parabenzosemiquinone.

The fluorine isotropic hyperfine coupling constants are generally well reproduced with the notable exception of the two fluoroacetamide radicals, which are calculated to be much lower than the observed values.   Although these radicals are thought to be planar in the crystal, the fluorine coupling constants observed for the monofluoro and difluoro species are quite comparable with those observed for fluoromethyl and difluoromethyl radicals, respectively, and the latter are almost certainly nonplanar.   Thus the planar model B geometry may be an inappropriate choice for these molecules.

On the basis of the agreement between calculated and observed hyperfine coupling constants listed in Tables 4.23 to 4.27, one may conclude that spin-unrestricted molecular orbital calculations carried out with the INDO approximations for atomic and molecular integrals are quite capable of accommodating isotropic hyperfine coupling phenomena in polyatomic molecules.   Calculations on this level of approximation should be useful in providing a basis for the assignment of positions and signs of hyperfine coupling constants when used in close conjunction with the available experimental data.   It also seems likely that wavefunctions of this type could be used to calculate and interpret anisotropic hyperfine coupling constants, g tensors, and other features of the electronic structure of free radicals.

4.4 NUCLEAR-SPIN—NUCLEAR-SPIN INTERACTIONS [23]

We turn now to the calculation of nuclear spin-nuclear-spin interactions via approximate molecular orbital theory.   The study of the electron coupled interactions between nuclear spins in a molecule, as observed in the NMR spectra of fluids, can be a powerful aid in understanding molecular structure.   The theory of these couplings, as originally formulated by Ramsey [24], is based on three types of interaction between electron and nuclear spins: (1) a magnetic dipole-dipole interaction between the magnetic dipoles of the spinning electron and the nuclear spin, (2) an orbital-dipole interaction between the magnetic fields due to the orbital motion of the electrons and the nuclear magnetic dipole, and (3) a Fermi contact interaction between the electron and nuclear spins.   Of these three basic interactions, the Fermi contact term seems to be predominant (especially if protons are involved), and most attempts at calculating coupling constants are based on this term alone.   In the present treatment, we also consider only this interaction.   Since the nuclear spin coupling constants involve the distortion of the electron distribution through these interactions, they are a second-order property and must be treated either variationally or by perturbation theory.

Although there have been successful variational calculations of nuclear spin coupling constants for small molecules [25], problems of mathematical complexity and choice of a trial function seem to preclude extension of such methods to larger systems at this time without introducing severe approximations. Consequently, most studies of nuclear spin coupling in larger molecules are based on second-order perturbation theory in which the coupling constant between two atoms A and B is expressed as (assuming a Fermi contact interaction only)

$$K_{AB} = -\left(\frac{8\pi}{3}\right)^2 \frac{8\beta^2}{3} \sum_n \frac{\langle \Psi_0 | \sum_k \delta(\mathbf{r}_{kA})\mathbf{s}_k | \Psi_n \rangle \cdot \langle \Psi_n | \sum_k \delta(\mathbf{r}_{kB})\mathbf{s}_k | \Psi_0 \rangle}{E_n - E_0}$$

$$(4.15)$$

where the summation over n extends over all the excited states of the molecule. β is the Bohr magneton, and $\delta(\mathbf{r}_{kA})$ is the Dirac delta function representing the "contact" between electron k and nucleus A. $\mathbf{s}_k$ is the spin angular momentum of electron k, and E_0 and E_n are the energies of the ground and nth excited states, respectively. K_{AB} is the reduced isotropic coupling constant between atoms A and B which is defined as the proportionality constant between the interaction energy of the two nuclear spins and the product of their magnetic moments,

$$E_{\text{int}} = K_{AB}\mu_A\mu_B \tag{4.16}$$

the magnetic moments being taken to be directed along the positive z axis. The relation of the reduced coupling constant K_{AB} to the usual value J_{AB} (measured in cycles per sec) is

$$J_{AB} = \frac{h}{2\pi} \gamma_A\gamma_B K_{AB} \tag{4.17}$$

where γ_A and γ_B are the nuclear magnetogyric ratios for the nuclei A and B, respectively.

Early calculations of spin-spin coupling constants [26] use an average excitation energy approximation in the perturbation expression (4.15). Although this approximation greatly simplifies the treatment and gives good results in many cases, there is a certain degree of arbitrariness in the choice of an appropriate energy value. Furthermore, in single-determinant molecular orbital theory, this approximation necessarily always leads to positive coupling constants, whereas many negative values are known experimentally. More recent calculations, using both the valence bond and molecular orbital methods, do not make this approximation and improved results are obtained [27]. Problems arise, however, due to the sensitivity of the computation to cancellation of large terms of opposite sign in the summation over n [28].

An alternative perturbation method which avoids the necessity of using expressions such as Eq. (4.15) with its associated difficulties has recently been proposed [29], and this method, known as *finite perturbation theory*, may be readily used with self-consistent molecular orbital wavefunctions. In the present paper we apply this technique to the calculation of nuclear spin coupling constants using simplified CNDO and INDO self-consistent molecular orbital methods.

The application of the finite perturbation method as to the calculation of nuclear spin coupling constants proceeds as follows. If we only consider the Fermi contact effect, the total hamiltonian is

$$\mathcal{H} = \mathcal{H}_0 + \frac{16\pi}{3} \beta \sum_k \sum_N \delta(\mathbf{r}_{kN}) \mathbf{s}_k \cdot \boldsymbol{\mu}_N \tag{4.18}$$

where $\mathcal{H}_0$ is appropriate for the unperturbed system and $\boldsymbol{\mu}_N$ are the nuclear magnetic moments. It is convenient to consider a molecule with two nuclear moments μ_A and μ_B both directed along the z axis, so that the hamiltonian becomes

$$\mathcal{H} = \mathcal{H}_0 + \mu_A \mathcal{H}'_A + \mu_B \mathcal{H}'_B \tag{4.19}$$

where

$$\mathcal{H}'_A = \frac{16\pi}{3} \beta \sum_k \delta(\mathbf{R}_{kA}) \mathbf{s}_{kz} \tag{4.20}$$

and similarly for $\mathcal{H}'_B$.

Now from Eqs. (4.16) and (4.15) and the Hellman-Feynman theorem [30], it can be shown that the reduced coupling constants can be written

$$K_{AB} = \frac{\partial}{\partial \mu_B} \left(\langle \Psi(\mu_B) | \mathcal{H}'_A | \Psi(\mu_B) \rangle \right)_{\mu_B=0} \tag{4.21}$$

where $\Psi(\mu_B)$ is the wavefunction when only the nuclear moment is present, so that the hamiltonian used is

$$\mathcal{H}(\mu_B) = \mathcal{H}_0 + \mu_B \mathcal{H}'_B \tag{4.22}$$

Equation (4.21) is the basis of our method of calculating coupling constants.

The wavefunction $\Psi(\mu_B)$ will be calculated as a spin-unrestricted self-consistent molecular orbital function, as is necessary, in order to accommodate the uneven distribution of α and β electrons induced by the perturbation $\mu_B \mathcal{H}'_B$.

If the perturbation is present, the spin-unrestricted SCF equations (2.93) are modified only by a change in the one-electron core part of the Fock matrices, and Eqs. (2.93) are modified to the form

$$F_{\mu\nu}{}^{\alpha} = H_{\mu\nu}{}^{\text{core}} + \frac{8\pi}{3} \beta\mu_{\text{B}} \int \phi_\mu \delta(r_{\text{B}}) \phi_\nu \, dr$$
$$+ \sum_{\lambda\sigma} [P_{\lambda\sigma}(\mu\nu|\lambda\sigma) - P_{\lambda\sigma}{}^{\alpha}(\mu\sigma|\lambda\nu)] \quad (4.23)$$

$$F_{\mu\nu}{}^{\beta} = H_{\mu\nu}{}^{\text{core}} - \frac{8\pi}{3} \beta\mu_{\text{B}} \int \phi_\mu \delta(r_{\text{B}}) \phi_\nu \, dr$$
$$+ \sum_{\lambda\sigma} [P_{\lambda\sigma}(\mu\nu|\lambda\sigma) - P_{\lambda\sigma}{}^{\beta}(\mu\sigma|\lambda\nu)] \quad (4.24)$$

where $H_{\mu\nu}{}^{\text{core}}$ and $(\mu\nu|\lambda\sigma)$ have the usual meanings. Using this type of wavefunction, the expression (4.21) for the coupling constant becomes

$$K_{\text{AB}} = \frac{8\pi}{3} \beta \sum_{\mu\nu} \int \phi_\mu(\mathbf{R}_\text{A}) \phi_\nu(\mathbf{R}_\text{A}) \, d\mathbf{R} \cdot \left[\frac{\partial}{\partial\mu_{\text{B}}} \rho_{\mu\nu}{}^{\text{spin}}(\mu_{\text{B}}) \right]_{\mu_{\text{B}}=0}$$
$$(4.25)$$

This formula can be used with unrestricted LCAOSCF wavefunctions for any basis set and at any level of approximation. The INDO method was used for the calculations reported herein.

Within the framework of the approximation of the INDO method, the integral in (4.25) becomes

$$\int \phi_\mu \delta(\mathbf{R}_\text{B}) \phi_\nu \, dr = s_{\text{B}}{}^2(0) \qquad \text{if } \phi_\mu = \phi_\nu, \ \phi_\mu \text{ being a valence}$$
$$\text{s orbital on atom B} \qquad (4.26)$$
$$= 0 \qquad \text{otherwise}$$

where $s_{\text{B}}{}^2(0)$ is the density at the nucleus of the valence s orbital of atom B. This means that the perturbation matrix elements in Eqs. 4.23 and 4.24 are zero unless $\mu = \nu = $ a valence s orbital of atom B. Thus, in this theory, the implementation of the perturbation involves simply the addition of a quantity

$$h_{\text{B}} = \frac{8\pi}{3} \beta\mu_{\text{B}}s_{\text{B}}{}^2(0) \qquad (4.27)$$

to the diagonal matrix element representing the s orbital of atom B of the core hamiltonian for α orbitals. At the same time $(-h_{\text{B}})$ is added to the corresponding matrix element of the β core hamiltonian.

The expression for the coupling constant now becomes

$$K_{\text{AB}} = \left(\frac{8\pi\beta}{3}\right)^2 s_\text{A}{}^2(0)s_\text{B}{}^2(0) \left[\frac{\partial}{\partial h_{\text{B}}} \rho_{s_\text{A}s_\text{A}}^{\text{spin}}(h_{\text{B}}) \right]_{h_{\text{B}}=0} \qquad (4.28)$$

i.e., it is just proportional to the derivative of the diagonal element of the spin density matrix corresponding to the valence s orbital of atom A.

The derivative in Eq. (4.28) was evaluated using the method of finite differences described in detail in Ref. [29]. Since $\rho_{s_A s_A}^{\text{spin}}(h_B)$ is an odd function of h, only one value of h was used in calculating Ψ. The expression (4.28) for the coupling constant is then approximated by

$$K_{AB} = \left(\frac{8\pi\beta}{3}\right)^2 s_A{}^2(0) \, \frac{\rho_{s_A s_A}^{\text{spin}}(h_B)}{h_B} \tag{4.29}$$

If an independent electron molecular orbital model is used (that is, a Hückel-type method in which the LCAO eigenfunctions are determined from a one-electron hamiltonian), the derivative can be evaluated explicitly. In fact, since the α and β densities behave independently, this derivative is equivalent to the *mutual polarizability* π_{s_A, s_B} as introduced by Coulson and Longuet-Higgins [31],

$$\pi_{\mu\nu} = 4 \sum_i^{\text{occ}} \sum_j^{\text{unocc}} (\varepsilon_i - \varepsilon_j)^{-1} c_{\mu i} c_{\mu j} \, c_{\nu i} c_{\nu j} \tag{4.30}$$

ε_i being the one-electron eigenvalues. Evaluation of (4.28) is then identical with that used in an earlier independent electron treatment of spin coupling [27, 28].

In this study all coupling constants were calculated directly from Eq. (4.29). If one makes the reasonable assumption that the valence s orbital densities $s_A{}^2(0)$ are invariant from molecule to molecule and depend only on the nature of atom A, then in the INDO approximation the derivatives in Eq. (4.28) or their approximate values $\rho_{s_A s_A}(h_B)/h_B$ give a complete electronic description of the contact contribution to nuclear spin coupling. All trends can be studied by looking at these derivatives. For the purpose of making a general comparison of our results with experiment, the s orbital densities were treated as parameters which were adjusted (in the least-squares sense) to give the best overall fit of the calculated couplings K_{AB} to the available experimental results. Calculations were done on a large number of molecules containing hydrogen, carbon, and fluorine. The s orbital densities obtained are shown in Table 4.30. Boron, nitrogen, and oxygen values were chosen so that the constants for B, C, N, O, and F form a geometric series. This procedure is preferred at present because there is considerably less experimental data on these other nuclei. The values of $s^2(0)$ used for hydrogen is close to the theoretical value (0.318), but the others are somewhat greater than the Hartree-Fock values and also different from the optimum values for treating

Table 4.30 s orbital densities at the nucleus (a_0^{-3}) for nuclear spin coupling calculations

A	$s_A{}^2(0)$
H	0.3724
B	2.2825
C	4.0318
N	6.9265
O	12.0658
F	21.3126

electron nuclear hyperfine interactions (cf. Table 4.21). The reason for these discrepancies is not altogether clear at present, although it may be associated with the neglect of $1s$ orbitals in this simplified treatment.

Calculated coupling constants involving H, ^{13}C, ^{14}N, ^{17}O, and F (J values in cycles per sec) for some simple molecules are given in Table 4.31. These are all based on the standard geometrical model

Table 4.31   Calculated and experimental values of coupling constants J, cycles/sec

	Calc.	Exptl.†
Hydrogen H—H	408.60	+280[a]
Water H—O—H	−8.07	(−)7.2[b]
Methane H—C—H	−6.13	−12.4[c]
Ethane Geminal H—C—H	−5.22	
Methyl Fluoride H—C—H	−1.86	−9.6[d]
Ethylene H—C—H	3.24	+2.5[e]
Formaldehyde H—C—H	31.86	+40.2[f]
Ethane H—C—C—H (gauche)	3.25	
Ethane H—C—C—H (trans)	18.63	
Ethane H—C—C—H (average)	8.37	+8[e]
Ethylene H—C—C—H (cis)	9.31	+11.7[e]
Ethylene H—C—C—H (trans)	25.15	+19.1[e]
Acetylene H—C—C—H	10.99	+9.5[e]
Allene H—C—C—C—H	−9.69	−7.0[g]
Benzene H—C—C—H	8.15	+7.54[h]
Benzene H—C—C—C—H	2.13	+1.37[h]
Benzene H—C—C—C—C—H	1.15	+0.69[h]
Methane C—H	122.92	+125[i]
Ethane C—H	122.12	+124.9[e]
Ethylene C—H	156.71	+156.4[e]
Acetylene C—H	232.65	+248.7[e]
Benzene C—H	140.29	+157.5[i]
Ethane C—C	41.45	+34.6[e]

Ethylene C—C	82.14	+67.6[e]
Acetylene C—C	163.75	+171.5[e]
Ethane C—C—H	−7.20	−4.5[e]
Ethylene C—C—H	−11.57	−2.4[e]
Acetylene C—C—H	2.52	+49.3[e]
Benzene C—C—H	−4.94	+1.0[j]
Benzene C—C—C—H	9.40	+7.4[j]
Benzene C—C—C—C—H	−2.27	−1.1[j]
Ammonia N—H	30.40	(+)43.6[k]
Water O—H	−12.84	(−)73.5[l]
Hydrogen Fluoride F—H	−150.22	(−)521[m]
Nitrogen Trifluoride N—F	−239.16	(−)155[n]
Methyl Fluoride C—F	−237.15	−158[o]
Methyl Fluoride H—C—F	4.68	+46.4[p]
Vinyl Fluoride H—C—F	16.61	+84.7[q]
Vinyl Fluoride H—C—C—F (cis)	26.7	+20.1[q]
Vinyl Fluoride H—C—C—F (trans)	66.20	+52.4[q]
1,1-Difluoroethylene F—C—F	−13.42	+36.4[r]
1,2-Difluoroethylene (cis) F—C—C—F	10.28	+18.7[s]
1,2-Difluoroethylene (trans) F—C—C—F	−32.42	−124.8[s]

† Only limited experimental evidence is available on the absolute signs of coupling constants. Those signs given without parentheses are mostly based on the assumption that directly bonded C—H constants are positive. In some cases, there is only evidence about the sign in molecules other than the one quoted. Signs in parentheses are not experimental at all, but are chosen to agree with the values calculated by this theory.

[a] T. F. Wimett, *Phys. Rev.*, **91**:476 (1953).

[b] J. R. Holmes, D. Rivelson, and W. C. Drinkard, *J. Chem. Phys.*, **37**:150 (1962).

[c] M. Karplus, D. H. Anderson, T. C. Farrar, and H. S. Gutowsky, *J. Chem. Phys.*, **27**:597 (1957).

[d] H. J. Bernstein and N. Sheppard, *J. Chem. Phys.*, **37**:3012 (1962).

[e] R. M. Lynden-Bell and N. Sheppard, *Proc. Roy. Soc. (London)*, **A269**:385 (1962).

[f] B. L. Shapiro, R. M. Kopchik, and S. J. Ebersole, *J. Chem. Phys.*, **39**:3154 (1963).

[g] E. B. Whipple, J. H. Goldstein, and W. E. Stewart, *J. Am. Chem. Soc.*, **81**:4761 (1959).

[h] J. M. Read, R. E. Mayo, and J. H. Goldstein, *J. Mol. Spectry.*, **22**:419 (1967).

[i] N. Muller and D. E. Pritchard, *J. Chem. Phys.*, **31**:768 (1959).

[j] F. J. Weigert and J. D. Roberts, *J. Am. Chem. Soc.*, **89**:2967 (1967).

[k] R. A. Bernheim and H. Batiz-Hernandez, *J. Chem. Phys.*, **40**:3446 (1964).

[l] J. Reuben, A. Tzalmone, and D. Samuel, *Proc. Chem. Soc.*, **1962**:353.

[m] C. MacLean and E. L. Mackor, *Proc. XI Colloq. Ampere*, **1962**:571.

[n] J. H. Noggle, J. D. Baldeschwieler, and C. B. Colburn, *J. Chem. Phys.*, **37**:182 (1962).

[o] N. Muller and D. T. Carr, *J. Phys. Chem.*, **67**:752 (1963).

[p] S. G. Frankiss, *J. Phys. Chem.*, **67**:752 (1963).

[q] C. N. Banwell and N. Sheppard, *Proc. Roy. Soc. (London)*, **A263**:136 (1961).

[r] G. W. Flynn and J. D. Baldeschwieler, *J. Chem. Phys.*, **38**:226 (1963).

[s] G. W. Flynn, M. Matsushima, and J. D. Baldeschwieler, *J. Chem. Phys.*, **38**:2295 (1963).

used in previous calculation on electric dipole moments. From this set of results it is clear that a number of well-established experimental trends are reproduced by the theory. Geminal H—H constants (separated by two bonds) are calculated to be negative in molecules with tetrahedral angles in agreement with observation. Positive values, however, are obtained for trigonal H—C—H groups, the calculated value in formaldehyde being much larger than ethylene as observed experimentally. For vicinal H—H constants (separated by three bonds), all calculated values are positive and greatest in the trans configuration. For longer-range H—H couplings, the results also appear promising. A large value is obtained for allene, and both meta and para couplings in benzene are calculated to be positive.

The theoretical values for directly bonded C—H constants increase along the series ethane, ethylene, and acetylene, with approximate proportionality to the s character of the bond in a simple hybridization picture. The directly bonded C—C constants behave in the same way. For the directly bonded series CH, NH, OH, and FH, there is a predicted trend toward negative values (note that the signs of J and K are opposite for O—H constants). A similar trend was noted previously in a simple independent electron treatment [28]. However, the absolute signs for NH_3, H_2O, and HF are not known experimentally. Directly bonded C—F and N—F constants are predicted to be negative and large in magnitude. This fits experimental evidence for C—F.

Longer-range coupling constants involving nuclei other than hydrogen are less well reproduced on the whole. Calculated two-bond C—C—H constants are less positive (or more negative) than experimental values, but the longer-range (three- and four-bonds) constants in benzene are given well. Similar deviations show up for H—F constants. Those for atoms separated by two bonds (H—C—F) are calculated to be positive but much smaller than experimental numbers. On the other hand, the positive three-bond H—C—C—F constants in vinyl fluoride are well reproduced. For F—F the sign of the two-bond F—C—F constant in 1,1-difluoroethylene is given incorrectly, but the different signs of cis and trans F—C—C—F are reproduced satisfactorily.

By modifying certain features of the underlying molecular orbital theory, it is possible to test some hypotheses that been have put forward about the mechanism of spin coupling. One such hypothesis is the suggestion that one-center atomic exchange integrals must be included in a molecular orbital description of spin coupling if a negative constant for the geminal H—H coupling in methane is to

be obtained.   The qualitative reason for this is that this type of
integral lowers the energy of configurations with parallel-spin electrons
in different orbitals on the same atom.   In valence bond terms, this
should lead to alternation of the coupling constant sign with the
number of bonds between the coupled atoms.   To test this hypothesis,
some of the coupling constants of Table 4.31 were recalculated using
the CNDO/2 method which is essentially the same as the INDO
method except that the one-center exchange integrals are not included.
Table 4.32 shows the result of these calculations.

As expected, all geminal proton-proton coupling constants
(protons separated by two bonds) are calculated to be more negative

**Table 4.32   Comparison of coupling constants calculated by the
INDO method with those calculated by the CNDO method**

	J (CNDO)	J (INDO)
Water H—O—H	1.31	−8.07
Ammonia H—N—H	1.60	−6.37
Methane H—C—H	1.17	−6.13
Ethane H—C—H	2.02	−5.22
Ethylene H—C—H	8.48	3.24
Ethane H—C—C—H (gauche)	2.43	3.25
Ethane H—C—C—H (trans)	15.43	18.63
Ethylene H—C—C—H (cis)	8.04	9.31
Ethylene H—C—C—H (trans)	19.50	25.15
Acetylene H—C—C—H	6.55	10.99
Benzene H—C—C—H	7.55	8.15
Benzene H—C—C—C—H	1.90	2.13
Benzene H—C—C—C—C—H	0.44	1.15
Methane C—H	93.19	122.92
Ethane C—H	93.30	122.12
Ethylene C—H	127.63	156.71
Acetylene C—H	205.49	232.65
Benzene C—H	116.00	140.29
Ethane C—C—H	−2.56	−7.20
Ethylene C—C—H	−3.85	−11.57
Acetylene C—C—H	5.51	2.52
Benzene C—C—H	−0.17	−4.94
Benzene C—C—C—H	5.51	9.40
Benzene C—C—C—C—H	−0.06	−2.27
Ammonia N—H	21.95	30.40
Water O—H	17.91	−12.84
Hydrogen fluoride F—H	19.67	−150.25
Methyl fluoride H—C—F	−0.89	4.68
Methyl fluoride C—F	−166.99	−237.16

(or less positive) by the INDO method compared with the CNDO method, some of the results even changing sign. A similar effect is noted for the C—C—H coupling constants. On the other hand, the results for directly bonded C—H and vicinal H—C—C—H and H—C—C—C coupling constants are more positive (or less negative) when calculated by the INDO method rather than CNDO. Thus, it appears from the results of Table 4.32 that not only is the inclusion of the one-center exchange integral consistent with the tendency of the signs of the coupling constant to alternate with the number of bonds separating the coupled atoms, but that this integral is an important contribution to the magnitude of the calculated coupling constants, at least for couplings involving hydrogen and carbon.

The results involving atoms other than hydrogen and carbon are not as straightforward. Although the directly bonded N—H coupling constant in ammonia becomes more positive in going from CNDO to INDO, the opposite is true for the O—H coupling constant in water and the HF constant in hydrogen fluoride. Further the C—F directly bonded constant in methyl fluoride becomes more negative in INDO and the two-bond H—C—F value becomes more positive. Clearly, the simple arguments that rationalize coupling constants involving carbon and hydrogen cannot be directly extended to other atoms.

A comparison of CNDO/2 and INDO calculations is also of value in studying the contribution of π electron spin polarization to long-range coupling. This mechanism, in which a spin density is induced in a local π orbital, transmitted through the π electron system and back to the σ electrons, was originally suggested by McConnell [32]. Since nonzero π spin density can only be induced by σ-π exchange integrals, such an effect is not taken into account in a CNDO theory. The smaller magnitudes of the long-range meta- and para-constants in benzene calculated by CNDO give an indication of the importance of this contribution.

From the study and calculations presented above, one may conclude that (1) the self-consistent finite perturbation method is a powerful and practical approach to the theory of nuclear spin coupling and the associated electron spin polarization. It requires only a single SCF calculation on an unrestricted determinantal wavefunction for all the coupling constants from a particular nucleus. In combination with the simplified integral treatment used in the INDO theory, it becomes possible to make calculations on couplings in large molecules with only modest computational effect. (2) The agreement between calculated and experimental coupling constants involving carbon and hydrogen is promising, most experimental trends being well reproduced. It should be possible to make a detailed study of the dependence of these constants on structural features, such as conformation and substitution. (3) Coupling constants involving fluorine nuclei are less well reproduced by this simple treatment although the observed negative values for directly bonded C—F are described satisfactorily. Longer-range couplings to fluorine are poorly calculated (particularly H—C—F), and further studies with more satisfactory wavefunctions are needed.

4.5 FURTHER APPLICATIONS OF APPROXIMATE MOLECULAR ORBITAL THEORY

The applications discussed in the preceding section were principally those which were organized in the course of the development and testing of the methods. In recent months, a number of applications of the CNDO method have been reported in the recent chemical literature, facilitated by the digital computer programs submitted to QCPE (Quantum Chemistry Program Exchange) by G. A. Segal [33]. In this section, we mention the work in this category in order to give an indication of articles of possible interest to the reader and to show the diverse directions that applications of approximate molecular orbital theory are taking. The literature survey was terminated on June 1, 1968.

Most of the research reported to date has been in the area of ground-state properties of organic molecules. Wiberg [34] has applied CNDO theory to a study of heats of formation of hydrocarbons and their cations; he achieves encouraging results after reparameterization. Another application by Wiberg [35] is concerned with cyclopropylcarbinyl and cyclobutyl cations and also bicyclobutane. Substituted benzenes have been treated by Davies [36], Bloor and Breen [37], and Kuznesof and Shriver [38], the latter study including some borazines as well. Calculations on heterocyclic systems have been reported by Hush and Yandel [40], and by Bloor and Breen [39]. These included azine, guanidines, furan, and pyrrole. Further work on pyrrole, indole, furan, and benzofuran has been published by Herrman [41], and Song [42] has treated some halogenated purines, pyrimidines, and flavins. The application of CNDO theory to some hydrogen-bonded systems has been reported by Devirk, Azman, and Hadzi [43], and Clark [44] has studied d orbital participation in the thiophene molecule. A study of optical rotatory power in methylcyclohexanones is due to Santry and Pao [45], and CNDO calculations of proton hyperfine constants have been published by Atherton [46]. Berthod, Gassner-Prettre, and Pullman [47] have reported CNDO calculations on uracil and flurouracil.   In the area of molecular vibrations, the calculation of infrared intensities by the CNDO method has been studied by Segal and Klein [48], and INDO study of vibronic effects on the isotropic hyperfine coupling constants in isotopically substituted methyl radicals has been reported by Beveridge and Miller [49].

A number of papers have been concerned wholly or in part with excited electronic states of molecules.   Calculations in the virtual orbital approximation have been reported by Kroto and Santry [50], followed up by a paper dealing with applications of an open-shell self-consistent field procedure in the CNDO approximation [51].   A consideration of the electronic excited states of benzene and ethylene has been studied by Clark and Ragle [52]; isomerization mechanism of diazacumulenes is due to Gordon and Fischer [53]; and calculations on cyclopropane, ethylene oxide, and ethylenimine have been reported by Clark [54].   A series of papers has been inaugurated by Del Bene and Jaffe [55] entitled "Use of the CNDO Method in Spectroscopy," and calculations on benzene, pyridine, and the diazines have been published with several more papers in the series in press.

This survey would not be complete without mentioning the approximate methods other than the CNDO, INDO, and NDDO methods presented in Chap. 3.   Extensive work in this area has been reported by Klopman [56] and Dewar and Klopman [57].   Approximate molecular orbital schemes including overlap have been set forth by Manne [58], and also Yonezawa, Kato, and collaborators [59].   A nonempirical molecular orbital method intended to reproduce self-consistent field calculations with appropriate parameterization at the Hückel level has been reported by Newton, de Boer, and Lipscomb [60].

REFERENCES

1. Wilson, E. B., Jr., J. C. Decius, and P. C. Cross: "Molecular Vibrations," McGraw-Hill Book Company, New York, 1955.
2. Mulliken, R. S.: *J. Chem. Phys.*, **23**:1833, 1841 (1955), **36**:3428 (1962).
3. Pople, J. A., and G. A. Segal: *J. Chem. Phys.*, **43**:S136 (1965).
4. Pople, J. A., and G. A. Segal: *J. Chem. Phys.*, **44**:3289 (1966).
5. Dressler, K., and D. A. Ramsey: *Phil. Trans. Roy. Soc. London,* **A251**:553 (1959).
6. Walsh, A. D.: *J. Chem. Soc.*, 2260, 2266, 2296, 2301 (1953).
7. Pople, J. A., and M. S. Gordon: *J. Chem. Phys.*, **49**:4643 (1968).
8. Beveridge, D. L., P. A. Dobosh, and J. A. Pople: *J. Chem. Phys.*, **48**:4802 (1968).
9. Pople, J. A., and M. S. Gordon: *J. Am. Chem. Soc.*, **89**:4253 (1967).
10. Dewar, M. J. S.: "Hyperconjugation," The Ronald Press Company, New York, 1962.

11. Ingold, C. K.: "Structure and Mechanism in Organic Chemistry," G. Bell & Sons, Ltd., London, 1953.
12. Pople, J. A., and A. A. Bothner-by: *J. Chem. Phys.*, **42**:1339 (1965).
13. Santry, D. P., and G. A. Segal: *J. Chem. Phys.*, **47**:158 (1967).
14. Pople, J. A., D. L. Beveridge, and P. A. Dobosh: *J. Am. Chem. Soc.*, **90**:4201 (1968).
15. Beveridge, D. L., and P. A. Dobosh: *J. Chem. Phys.*, in press.
16. McConnell, H. M.: *J. Chem. Phys.*, **28**:1188 (1956).
17. Fessenden, R. W., and R. H. Schuler: *J. Chem. Phys.*, **39**:2147 (1963); R. W. Fessenden: *J. Phys. Chem.*, **71**:74 (1967).
18. McConnell, H. M., C. Heller, T. Cole, and R. W. Fessenden: *J. Am. Chem. Soc.*, **82**:766 (1960).
19. Amos, A. T., and L. C. Snyder: *J. Chem. Phys.*, **42**:3670 (1965).
20. Whiffen, D. H.: *Mol. Phys.*, **6**:223 (1963).
21. Colpa, J. P., and J. R. Bolton: *Mol. Phys.*, **6**:273 (1963).
22. Bolton, J. R., and G. K. Fraenkel: *J. Chem. Phys.*, **40**:3307 (1964).
23. Pople, J. A., J. W. McIver, and N. S. Ostlund: *J. Chem. Phys.*, **49**:2965 (1968).
24. Ramsey, N. F.: *Phys. Rev.*, **91**:203 (1955).
25. O'Reilly, D. B.: *J. Chem. Phys.*, **36**:274 (1962), **38**:2583 (1963).
26. McConnell, H. M.: *J. Chem. Phys.*, **24**:460 (1956); M. Karplus and D. H. Anderson: *J. Chem. Phys.*, **30**:6 (1954).
27. Pople, J. A., and D. P. Santry: *Mol. Phys.*, **8**:1 (1964); Barfield, M.: *J. Chem. Phys.*, in press.
28. Pople, J. A., and D. P. Santry: *Mol. Phys.*, **9**:311 (1965).
29. Pople, J. A., J. W. McIver, and N. S. Ostlund: *Chem. Phys. Lett.*, **1**:465 (1967).
30. Feynman, R. P.: *Phys. Rev.*, **56**:340 (1939).
31. Coulson, C. A., and H. C. Longuet-Higgins: *Proc. Roy. Soc. (London)*, **A191**:39, **A192**:16 (1947).
32. McConnell, H. M.: *J. Mol. Spectry.*, **1**:11 (1952).
33. Segal, G. A.: Quantum Chemistry Program Exchange, No. 91, Department of Chemistry, University of Indiana, Bloomington, Ind.
34. Wiberg, K. B.: *J. Am. Chem. Soc.*, **90**:59 (1967).
35. Wiberg, K. B.: *Tetrahedron*, **24**:1083 (1968).
36. Davies, D. W.: *Mol. Phys.*, **13**:465 (1967).
37. Bloor, J. E., and D. L. Breen: *J. Phys. Chem.*, **72**:716 (1968).
38. Kuznesof, P. M., and D. F. Shriver: *J. Am. Chem. Soc.*, **90**:1683 (1968).
39. Bloor, J. E., and D. L. Breen: *J. Am. Chem. Soc.*, **89**:6835 (1967).
40. Hush, N. S., and J. R. Yandel: *Chem. Phys. Lett.*, **1**:493 (1967).
41. Herrman, R. B.: *Intern. J. Quant. Chem.*, **2**:165 (1968).
42. Song, P. S.: *J. Phys. Chem.*, **72**:536 (1968); *Intern. J. Quant. Chem.*, **2**:297 (1968).
43. Devirk, A., A. Azman, and D. Hadzi: *Theo. Chim. Acta*, **10**:187 (1967).
44. Clark, D. T.: *Tetrahedron*, **24**:2663 (1968).
45. Santry, D. P., and Y. Pao: *J. Am. Chem. Soc.*, **88**:4157 (1966).
46. Atherton, N. M.: *Mol. Phys.*, **12**:349 (1967).
47. Berthod, H., C. Gassner-Prettre, and A. Pullman: *Theo. Chim. Acta*, **8**:212 (1967).
48. Segal, G. A., and M. Klein: *J. Chem. Phys.*, **47**:4236 (1967).
49. Beveridge, D. L., and K. Miller: *Mol. Phys.*, **14**:401 (1968).
50. Kroto, H. W., and D. P. Santry: *J. Chem. Phys.*, **47**:792 (1967).

51. Kroto, H. W., and D. P. Santry: *J. Chem. Phys.*, **47**:2736 (1967).
52. Clark, P. A., and J. L. Ragle: *J. Chem. Phys.*, **46**:4235 (1967).
53. Gordon, M. S., and H. Fischer: *J. Am. Chem. Soc.*, **90**:2471 (1968).
54. Clark, D. T.: *Theo. Chim. Acta*, **10**:11 (1968).
55. Del Bene, J., and H. H. Jaffe: *J. Chem. Phys.*, **48**:1807 (1968).
56. Klopman, G.: *J. Am. Chem. Soc.*, **86**:4550 (1964), **87**:3300 (1965).
57. Dewar, M. J. S., and G. Klopman: *J. Am. Chem. Soc.*, **89**:3089 (1967).
58. Manne, R.: *Theo. Chim. Acta*, **6**:299, 312 (1966).
59. Yonezawa, T., K. Tamaguchi, and H. Kato: *Bull. Chem. Soc. Japan*, **40**:536 (1967); Kato, H., H. Konishi, and T. Yonezawa: *Bull. Chem. Soc. Japan*, **40**:1017, 2716; Yonezawa, T., H. Nakatsuji, and H. Kato: *J. Am. Chem. Soc.*, **90**:1239 (1968).
60. Newton, M. D., F. P. de Boer, and W. N. Lipscomb: *J. Am. Chem. Soc.*, **88**: 2367 (1966).

A Fortran-IV Computer Program for CNDO and INDO Calculations[†]

We present here a program written for the IBM System 360/65 digital computer for the calculation of CNDO and INDO molecular orbitals.[‡] The program is capable of computing CNDO wavefunctions for open- and closed-shell molecules containing the elements H to Cl and INDO open- and closed-shell calculations for molecules containing H to F.

The matrices in the program are large enough to allow molecules containing up to 35 atoms or 80 basis functions (whichever is smaller). One atomic orbital basis function is allowed for hydrogen ($1s$), four each to the elements Li through F ($2s$, $2p_x$, $2p_y$, $2p_z$), and nine each to the elements Na through Cl ($3s$, $2p_x$, $3p_y$, $3p_z$, $3d_{z^2}$, $3d_{xz}$, $3d_{yz}$, $3d_{x^2-y^2}$, $3d_{xy}$).

[†] Prepared in collaboration with Dr. Paul A. Dobosh.
[‡] Card copies of this program may be obtained from the Quantum Chemistry Program Exchange, Department of Chemistry, Indiana University, Bloomington, Ind. 47401. A FORTRAN-63 version allows for annihilation of the largest contaminating spin component in unrestricted calculations.

OPERATION OF THE PROGRAM

In MAIN, input data for a calculation is read in the following format: *First Card:* identification and comments; *Second Card:* method. Columns 1 to 4 should contain either "CNDO" or "INDO" and columns 6 to 11 should contain either "OPEN" (left justified) or "CLSD" depending on the type of calculation desired. *Third Card:* NATOMS (Number of Atoms), CHARGE and MULTIP (Multiplicity), Format (3I4); *Next* NATOMS *Cards:* AN (Atomic number), X, Y, Z (cartesian coordinates) of each atom, one atom to a card. Format (I4, 3 (3X, F12.7)). After reading the molecular data, the main program calls the subroutines (COEFFT and INTGRL) which compute the integrals needed for a molecular orbital calculation. It then calls the subroutines which perform the MO calculation (HUCKCL, SCFCLO, CPRINT for a closed-shell molecule; HUCKOP, SCFOPN, OPRINT for an open-shell molecule).

The following is a qualitative description of the operation of each subroutine:

COEFFT assigns the coefficients used in the calculation of overlap and coulomb integrals. In subroutine INTGRL the overlap matrix (stored in the first array of COMMON/ARRAYS/) and the coulomb integral (γ_{AB}) matrix (stored in COMMON/GAB/) are computed. The method of integral evaluation is discussed in detail in Appendix B. Integrals are calculated for pairs of atoms using a local diatomic coordinate system. Then the rotation matrix formed in subroutine HARMTR is used to transform the overlap integrals to the molecular coordinate system.

Subroutine HUCKCL first forms a ZDO extended Hückel-type approximation to the Fock matrix with diagonal elements formed from $-\frac{1}{2}(I + A)$ and off-diagonal elements formed from $(\beta_A{}^0 + \beta_B{}^0)S_{\mu\nu}/2$. This matrix is diagonalized and an initial density matrix is constructed. At this point corrections to the hamiltonian are added for CNDO and INDO calculations if one of these options is chosen. Since EIGN only works on the lower half of the matrix to be diagonalized, the core hamiltonian in the closed-shell segments is stored in the upper half of matrix A with the diagonal terms stored in a separate 80-element linear array.

Subroutine SCFCLO takes as input the initial density matrix and the CNDO or INDO core hamiltonian. The Fock matrix is formed by first adding the CNDO integrals and then the INDO corrections to these integrals depending upon which option is used. The Fock matrix is diagonalized and a new density matrix is formed which is used to construct a new Fock matrix. The procedure is repeated until the electronic energy converges to 10^{-6}.   At this point, the Fock matrix is printed, then diagonalized once more, and the resulting eigenvectors are printed.   The electronic energy is computed after each new Fock matrix is formed and before it is diagonalized.   A limit of 25 iterations is allowed (IT = 25).

Subroutine CPRINT computes dipole moments, atom densities, and nuclear repulsion energy.

HUCKOP is similar to HUCKCL except that α and β density matrices are formed from the initial Hückel eigenvectors.   The core hamiltonian is stored in its entirety in the third matrix of COMMON/ ARRAYS/.   The symmetrical α and β density matrices are stored by putting P^α in the lower-left triangle (including the diagonal elements of the second matrix in COMMON/ARRAYS/), while P^β is stored in the upper triangle with its diagonal terms stored in PDIAG.

SCFOPN has the same structure as SCFCLO except that it has to handle P^α, P^β, F^α, and F^β.   All are stored as described above for the P matrices.   The Fock matrices are formed simultaneously and then each half is separately diagonalized.

Subroutine OPRINT calculates the same properties as CPRINT. In addition, this segment forms a spin density matrix and from this computes isotropic hyperfine coupling constants (for H, C, N, O, F). The proportionality constants relating spin density to coupling constant are those listed in Table 4.31.   *These constants are for* INDO *calculations only.*

The subroutines SS, HARMTR, RELVEC, FACT, BINTGS, AINTGS, and MATOVT are called only by INTGRL. EIGN, SCFOUT, and EIGOUT are needed in the subroutines HUCKCL through OPRINT.

```
          BLOCK DATA
          COMMON/ORB/ORB(9)
          COMMON/PERTBL/EL(18)
          COMMON/OPTION/OPTION,OPNCLO,HUCKEL,CNDO,INDO,CLOSED,OPEN
          INTEGER OPTION,OPNCLO,HUCKEL,CNDO,INDO,CLOSED,OPEN
          INTEGER ORB,EL
          DATA CNDO/'CNDO'/
?  → DATA INDO/'INDO'/
          DATA OPEN/'OPEN'/
          DATA CLOSED/'CLSD'/
          DATA ORB/'  S','  PX','  PY','  PZ','DZ2',' DXZ',' DYZ','DX-Y',
         1 'DXY'/
          DATA EL/'  H','  HE','  LI','  BE','  B','  C','  N','  O',
         1 '  F','  NE','  NA','  MG','  AL','  SI','  P','  S','  CL',
         2 '  AR'/
          END


C     PROGRAM CNINDO
C
C
?  -  IMPLICIT REAL*8(A-H,O-Z)
          COMMON/ARRAYS/ABC(19200)
          COMMON/INFO/NATOMS,CHARGE,MULTIP,AN(35),C(35,3),N
          COMMON/PERTBL/EL(18)
          COMMON/ORB/ORB(9)
          COMMON/GAB/XYZ(2000)
          COMMON/INFO1/CZ(35),U(80),ULIM(35),LLIM(35),NELECS,OCCA,OCCB
          COMMON/OPTION/OPTION,OPNCLO,HUCKEL,CNDO,INDO,CLOSED,OPEN
          COMMON/AUXINT/A(17),B(17)
          INTEGER  OPTION,OPNCLO,HUCKEL,CNDO,INDO,CLOSED,OPEN
          INTEGER ORB,EL,AN,CHARGE,CZ,U,ULIM,OCCA,OCCB
C     INPUT IS READ IN THE FOLLOWING ORDER
C  (1)AN IDENTIFICATION CARD WHICH IS PRINTED AT THE BEGINNING OF THE RUN
C  (2)OPTION(WAVE FUNCTION OPTION) AND OPNCLO(OPEN OR CLOSED SHELL)
C         THE FORMAT IS A4,1X,A4   AND THE KEY WORDS ARE-
C             FOR THE WAVEFUNCTION(A4)    CNDO    INDO
C             FOR THE OPEN-CLOSED OPTION(A6)    OPEN    CLSD
C  (3)NATOMS,CHARGE,MULTIP    FORMAT(3I4)
C  (4)ATOMIC NUMBER, X COORDINATE, Y COORDINATE, Z COORDINATE - 1 CARD/ATC
C         FORMAT(I4,3(3X,F12.7))
?  -  READ(5,20) (AN(I),I=1,20)
          WRITE(6,30) (AN(I),I=1,20)
          READ(5,40) OPTION,OPNCLO
          WRITE(6,45) OPTION,OPNCLO
          READ(5,50) NATOMS,CHARGE,MULTIP
          WRITE(6,60) NATOMS,CHARGE,MULTIP
          DO 10 I = 1,NATOMS
          READ(5,70) AN(I),C(I,1),C(I,2),C(I,3)
          WRITE(6,70) AN(I),C(I,1),C(I,2),C(I,3)
C     CONVERSION OF COORDINATES FROM ANGSTROMS TO ATOMIC UNITS
          DO 9 J=1,3
        9 C(I,J) = C(I,J)/.529167D0
       10 CONTINUE
          IF (OPTION.EQ.CNDO) GO TO 6
        1 DO 5 I=1,NATOMS
          IF (AN(I).LE.9) GO TO 4
        2 WRITE(6,3)
        3 FORMAT(5X,46HTHIS PROGRAM DOES NOT DO INDO CALCULATIONS FOR,
         1  51H MOLECULES CONTAINING ELEMENTS HIGHER THAN FLUORINE)
          STOP
        4 CONTINUE
        5 CONTINUE
        6 CONTINUE
          CALL COEFFT
          CALL INTGRL
          IF (OPNCLO.EQ.OPEN) GO TO 90
```

```
   80 CALL HUCKCL
      CALL SCFCLO
      CALL CPRINT
      GO TO 100
   90 CALL HUCKOP
      CALL SCFOPN
      CALL CPRINT
  100 CONTINUE
   20 FORMAT(20A4)
   30 FORMAT(1H1,5X,20A4)
   40 FORMAT(A4,1X,A4)
   45 FORMAT(5X,A4,1X,A4)
   50 FORMAT(3I4)
   60 FORMAT(/5X,I4,18H ATOMS     CHARGE =,I4,18H     MULTIPLICITY =,I4/)
   70 FORMAT(I4,3(3X,F12.7))
      CALL EXIT
      STOP
      END


      SUBROUTINE COEFFT
      IMPLICIT REAL*8(A-H,O-Z)
      COMMON/ARRAYS/S(80,80),Y(9135),Z( 765),XX(2900)
      DO 1 I=1,9135
    1 Y(I)=0.0D0
      DO 2 I=1,765
    2 Z(I)=0.0D0
C     LOAD NON-ZERO Y COEFFICIENTS
      Y(7039)=    64.D0
      Y(7040)=    64.D0
      Y(7049)=   -64.D0
      Y(7032)=  -128.D0
      Y(7041)=   -64.D0
      Y(7033)=  -128.D0
      Y(7042)=   128.D0
      Y(7025)=    64.D0
      Y(7034)=   128.D0
      Y(7026)=    64.D0
      Y(7035)=   -64.D0
      Y(7027)=   -64.D0
      Y(6904)=   -96.D0
      Y(6913)=    32.D0
      Y(6896)=  -100.D0
      Y(6905)=   192.D0
      Y(6906)=   288.D0
      Y(6915)=   -96.D0
      Y(6889)=   192.D0
      Y(6907)=  -192.D0
      Y(6890)=    96.D0
      Y(6899)=  -288.D0
      Y(6891)=  -192.D0
      Y(6900)=   192.D0
      Y(6892)=   -32.D0
      Y(6901)=    96.D0
      Y(2854)=   -16.D0
      Y(2863)=    16.D0
      Y(2847)=    32.D0
      Y(2856)=   -16.D0
      Y(2865)=   -16.D0
      Y(2840)=   -16.D0
      Y(2849)=   -16.D0
      Y(2858)=    32.D0
      Y(2842)=    16.D0
      Y(2851)=   -16.D0
      Y(2710)=    48.D0
      Y(2719)=   -48.D0
      Y(2711)=    48.D0
```

Y(2720)=	-96.D0
Y(2729)=	48.D0
Y(2703)=	-48.D0
Y(2712)=	-48.D0
Y(2721)=	96.D0
Y(2704)=	-48.D0
Y(2713)=	48.D0
Y(2722)=	48.D0
Y(2731)=	-48.D0
Y(2705)=	96.D0
Y(2714)=	-48.D0
Y(2723)=	-48.D0
Y(2706)=	48.D0
Y(2715)=	-96.D0
Y(2724)=	48.D0
Y(2707)=	-48.D0
Y(2716)=	48.D0
Y(5329)=	64.D0
Y(5322)=	-128.D0
Y(5340)=	-64.D0
Y(5315)=	64.D0
Y(5333)=	128.D0
Y(5326)=	-64.D0
Y(5185)=	-96.D0
Y(5194)=	32.D0
Y(5186)=	-96.D0
Y(5195)=	64.D0
Y(5204)=	32.D0
Y(5178)=	96.D0
Y(5187)=	32.D0
Y(5196)=	64.D0
Y(5179)=	96.D0
Y(5188)=	-32.D0
Y(5197)=	32.D0
Y(5206)=	-96.D0
Y(5180)=	-64.D0
Y(5189)=	-32.D0
Y(5198)=	-96.D0
Y(5181)=	-32.D0
Y(5190)=	-64.D0
Y(5199)=	96.D0
Y(5182)=	-32.D0
Y(5191)=	96.D0
Y(4375)=	-144.D0
Y(4384)=	96.D0
Y(4393)=	-16.D0
Y(4368)=	144.D0
Y(4386)=	-48.D0
Y(4395)=	96.D0
Y(4370)=	-96.D0
Y(4379)=	48.D0
Y(4397)=	-144.D0
Y(4372)=	16.D0
Y(4381)=	-96.D0
Y(4390)=	144.D0
Y(1900)=	144.D0
Y(1909)=	-144.D0
Y(1893)=	-144.D0
Y(1920)=	144.D0
Y(1895)=	144.D0
Y(1922)=	-144.D0
Y(1906)=	-144.D0
Y(1915)=	144.D0
Y(955)=	-16.D0
Y(964)=	32.D0
Y(973)=	-16.D0
Y(948)=	16.D0
Y(966)=	-48.D0

Y(975)=	32.D0
Y(950)=	-32.D0
Y(959)=	48.D0
Y(977)=	-16.D0
Y(952)=	16.D0
Y(961)=	-32.D0
Y(970)=	16.D0
Y(8155)=	64.D0
Y(8156)=	-64.D0
Y(8165)=	-64.D0
Y(8148)=	-64.D0
Y(8157)=	64.D0
Y(8149)=	64.D0
Y(8158)=	64.D0
Y(8150)=	-64.D0
Y(8020)=	-96.D0
Y(8029)=	32.D0
Y(8021)=	128.D0
Y(8013)=	96.D0
Y(8031)=	-96.D0
Y(8014)=	-128.D0
Y(8015)=	-32.D0
Y(8024)=	96.D0
Y(7084)=	-64.D0
Y(7076)=	-128.D0
Y(7085)=	64.D0
Y(7086)=	128.D0
Y(7069)=	128.D0
Y(7070)=	64.D0
Y(7079)=	-128.D0
Y(7071)=	-64.D0
Y(3205)=	-16.D0
Y(3214)=	16.D0
Y(3206)=	16.D0
Y(3215)=	-16.D0
Y(3198)=	16.D0
Y(3216)=	-16.D0
Y(3199)=	-16.D0
Y(3217)=	16.D0
Y(3200)=	-16.D0
Y(3209)=	16.D0
Y(3201)=	16.D0
Y(3210)=	-16.D0
Y(7579)=	64.D0
Y(7580)=	-64.D0
Y(7572)=	-128.D0
Y(7573)=	128.D0
Y(7565)=	64.D0
Y(7566)=	-64.D0
Y(5680)=	64.D0
Y(5681)=	-64.D0
Y(5673)=	-64.D0
Y(5691)=	-64.D0
Y(5674)=	64.D0
Y(5692)=	64.D0
Y(5684)=	64.D0
Y(5685)=	-64.D0
Y(7435)=	-96.D0
Y(7444)=	32.D0
Y(7436)=	-96.D0
Y(7445)=	160.D0
Y(7428)=	96.D0
Y(7437)=	128.D0
Y(7446)=	-96.D0
Y(7429)=	96.D0
Y(7438)=	-128.D0
Y(7447)=	-96.D0
Y(7430)=	-160.D0

```
      Y(7439)=      96.D0
      Y(7431)=     -32.D0
      Y(7440)=      96.D0
      Y(5545)=     -96.D0
      Y(5554)=      32.D0
      Y(5546)=      32.D0
      Y(5555)=      32.D0
      Y(5538)=      96.D0
      Y(5556)=      32.D0
      Y(5539)=     -32.D0
      Y(5557)=     -96.D0
      Y(5540)=     -32.D0
      Y(5549)=     -32.D0
      Y(5541)=     -32.D0
      Y(5550)=      96.D0
      Y(3070)=      48.D0
      Y(3079)=     -48.D0
      Y(3071)=     -48.D0
      Y(3080)=      48.D0
      Y(3063)=     -48.D0
      Y(3081)=      48.D0
      Y(3064)=      48.D0
      Y(3082)=     -48.D0
      Y(3065)=      48.D0
      Y(3074)=     -48.D0
      Y(3066)=     -48.D0
      Y(3075)=      48.D0
      Y(8200)=     -64.D0
      Y(8201)=      64.D0
      Y(8193)=      64.D0
      Y(8194)=     -64.D0
      Y(7615)=     -64.D0
      Y(7616)=     -64.D0
      Y(7625)=      64.D0
      Y(7608)=      64.D0
      Y(7617)=      64.D0
      Y(7609)=      64.D0
      Y(7618)=     -64.D0
      Y(7610)=     -64.D0
      Y(3250)=      16.D0
      Y(3259)=     -16.D0
      Y(3243)=     -16.D0
      Y(3261)=      16.D0
      Y(3245)=      16.D0
      Y(3254)=     -16.D0
      Y(5725)=     -64.D0
      Y(5718)=      64.D0
      Y(5736)=      64.D0
      Y(5729)=     -64.D0
C     LOAD NON-ZERO Z COEFFICIENTS
      Z(341)=      -1.D0
      Z(343)=       3.D0
      Z(345)=      -3.D0
      Z(347)=       1.D0
      Z(664)=      -1.D0
      Z(665)=       5.D0
      Z(666)=     -10.D0
      Z(667)=      10.D0
      Z(668)=      -5.D0
      Z(669)=       1.D0
      Z(154)=      -1.D0
      Z(156)=       5.D0
      Z(158)=     -10.D0
      Z(160)=      10.D0
      Z(162)=      -5.D0
      Z(164)=       1.D0
      Z(222)=      -1.D0
      Z(223)=       1.D0
      Z(224)=       4.D0
      Z(225)=      -4.D0
      Z(226)=      -6.D0
      Z(227)=       6.D0
      Z(228)=       4.D0
      Z(229)=      -4.D0
      Z(230)=      -1.D0
      Z(231)=       1.D0
      Z(307)=      -1.D0
      Z(308)=       2.D0
      Z(309)=       2.D0
      Z(310)=      -6.D0
      Z(312)=       6.D0
      Z(313)=      -2.D0
      Z(314)=      -2.D0
      Z(315)=       1.D0
      Z(409)=      -1.D0
      Z(410)=       3.D0
      Z(411)=      -1.D0
      Z(412)=      -5.D0
      Z(413)=       5.D0
      Z(414)=       1.D0
      Z(415)=      -3.D0
      Z(416)=       1.D0
      Z(528)=      -1.D0
      Z(529)=       4.D0
      Z(530)=      -5.D0
      Z(532)=       5.D0
      Z(533)=      -4.D0
      Z(534)=       1.D0
      Z(562)=      -1.D0
      Z(563)=       2.D0
      Z(565)=      -2.D0
      Z(566)=       1.D0
      Z(732)=      -1.D0
      Z(733)=       1.D0
      Z(545)=       1.D0
      Z(546)=      -3.D0
      Z(547)=       2.D0
      Z(548)=       2.D0
      Z(549)=      -3.D0
      Z(550)=       1.D0
      Z(579)=       1.D0
      Z(580)=      -1.D0
      Z(581)=      -1.D0
      Z(582)=       1.D0
      Z(596)=      -1.D0
      Z(598)=       1.D0
      Z(443)=      -1.D0
      Z(444)=       1.D0
      Z(445)=       2.D0
      Z(446)=      -2.D0
      Z(447)=      -1.D0
      Z(448)=       1.D0
      Z(698)=      -1.D0
      Z(699)=       3.D0
      Z(700)=      -3.D0
      Z(701)=       1.D0
      Z(324)=       1.D0
      Z(325)=      -1.D0
      Z(326)=      -3.D0
      Z(327)=       3.D0
      Z(328)=       3.D0
      Z(329)=      -3.D0
      Z(330)=      -1.D0
      Z(331)=       1.D0
      Z(460)=       1.D0
      Z(462)=      -2.D0
      Z(464)=       1.D0
      RETURN
      END
```

```
      SUBROUTINE INTGRL
      IMPLICIT REAL*8(A-H,O-Z)
C     ATOMIC INTEGRALS FOR CNDO CALCULATIONS
      COMMON/ARRAYS/S(80,80),Y(9,5,203),Z(17,45),XX(2900)
      COMMON/INFO/NATOMS,CHARGE,MULTIP,AN(35),C(35,3),N
      COMMON/INFO1/CZ(35),U(80),ULIM(35),LLIM(35),NELECS,OCCA,OCCB
      COMMON/GAB/XXX(400),GAMMA(35,35),T(9,9),PAIRS(9,9),TEMP(9,9)
     1   ,C1(3),C2(3),YYY(126)
      COMMON/AUXINT/A(17),B(17)
      COMMON/OPTION/OPTION,OPNCLO,HUCKEL,CNDO,INDO,CLOSED,OPEN
      DIMENSION MU(18),NC(18),LC(9),MC(9),E(3)
      DIMENSION P(80,80)
      EQUIVALENCE (P(1),Y(1))
      REAL*8 MU,NUM,K1,K2
      INTEGER AN,ULIM,ULK,ULL,C7,U,CHARGE,ANL,ANK,OCCA,OCCB
      INTEGER  OPTION,OPNCLO,HUCKEL,CNDO,INDO,CLOSED,OPEN
C     DETERMINATION OF SIZE OF AO BASIS IN AND CORE CHARGE CZ
      N=0
      DO 60 I=1,NATOMS
      LLIM(I) = N+1
      K=1
      IF (AN(I).LT.11) GO TO 20
   10 N=N+9
      CZ(I)=AN(I)-10
      GO TO 50
   20 IF (AN(I).LT.3) GO TO 40
   30 N=N+4
      CZ(I) = AN(I)-2
      GO TO 50
   40 N=N+1
      CZ(I)= AN(I)
   50 CONTINUE
      ULIM(I) = N
   60 CONTINUE
C     FILL U ARRAY---U(J) IDENTIFIES THE ATOM TO WHICH ORBITAL J IS
C     ATTACHED E.G. ORBITAL 32 ATTACHED TO  ATOM 7, ETC.
      DO 70 K=1,NATOMS
      LLK = LLIM(K)
      ULK = ULIM(K)
      LIM = ULK+1-LLK
      DO 70 I=1,LIM
      J = LLK+I-1
   70 U(J) = K
C     ASSIGNMENT OF ORBITAL EXPONENTS TO ATOMS BY SLATERS RULES
      MU(2)=1.7D0
      MU(1)=1.2D0
      NC(1)=1
      NC(2)=1
      DO 80 I=3,10
      NC(I)=2
   80 MU(I)=.325D0*DFLOAT(I-1)
      DO 90 I=11,18
      NC(I)=3
   90 MU(I)=(.65D0*DFLOAT(I)-4.95D0)/3.D0
C     ASSIGNMENT OF ANGULAR MOMENTUM QUANTUM NOS. TO ATOMIC ORBITALS
      LC(1)=0
      LC(2)=1
      LC(3)=1
      LC(4)=1
      LC(5)=2
      LC(6)=2
      LC(7)=2
      LC(8)=2
      LC(9)=2
      MC(1)=0
      MC(2)=1
      MC(3)=-1
      MC(4)=0
```

```
        MC(5)=0
        MC(6)=1
        MC(7)=-1
        MC(8)=2
        MC(9)=-2
C     STEP THRU PAIRS OF ATOMS
        DO 320 K=1,NATOMS
        DO 320 L=K,NATOMS
        DO 100 I=1,3
        C1(I) = C(K,I)
  100 C2(I) = C(L,I)
C     CALCULATE UNIT VECTOR ALONG INTERATOM AXIS,E
        CALL RELVEC(R,E,C1,C2)
        LLK = LLIM(K)
        LLL = LLIM(L)
        ULK = ULIM(K)
        ULL = ULIM(L)
        NORBK=ULK-LLK+1
        NORBL=ULL-LLL+1
        ANK=AN(K)
        ANL=AN(L)
C     LOOP THRU PAIRS OF BASIS FUNCTIONS, ONE ON EACH ATOM
        DO 200 I=1,NORBK
        DO 200 J=1,NORBL
        IF(K.EQ.L) GO TO 160
  110 IF(MC(I).NE.MC(J)) GO TO 150
  120 IF(MC(I).LT.0) GO TO 140
  130 PAIRS(I,J)=DSQRT((MU(ANK)*R)**(2*NC(ANK)+1)*(MU(ANL)*R)**(2*NC(ANL
     1)+1)/(FACT(2*NC(ANK))*FACT(2*NC(ANL))))*(-1.D0)**(LC(J)+MC(J))
     2*SS(NC(ANK),LC(I),MC(I),NC(ANL),LC(J),MU(ANK)*R,MU(ANL)*R)
        GO TO 190
  140 PAIRS(I,J)=PAIRS(I-1,J-1)
        GO TO 190
  150 PAIRS(I,J)=0.0D0
        GO TO 190
  160 IF (I.EQ.J) GO TO 170
  180 PAIRS(I,J)=0.0D0
        GO TO 190
  170 PAIRS(I,J)=1.0D0
  190 CONTINUE
  200 CONTINUE
        LCULK=LC(NORBK)
        LCULL=LC(NORBL)
        MAXL=MAXO(LCULK,LCULL)
        IF(R.GT.0.000001D0) GO TO 220
  210 GO TO 250
C     ROTATE INTEGRALS FROM DIATOMIC BASIS TO MOLECULAR BASIS
  220 CALL HARMTR(T,MAXL,E)
        DO 230 I=1,NORBK
        DO 230 J=1,NORBL
        TEMP(I,J) = 0.D0
        DO 230 KK=1,NORBL
        TEMP(I,J) = TEMP(I,J)+T(J,KK)*PAIRS(I,KK)
  230 CONTINUE
        DO 240 I=1,NORBK
        DO 240 J=1,NORBL
        PAIRS(I,J) = 0.D0
        DO 240 KK=1,NORBK
        PAIRS(I,J) = PAIRS(I,J)+T(I,KK)*TEMP(KK,J)
  240 CONTINUE
C     FILL S MATRIX
  250 CONTINUE
        DO 260 I=1,NORBK
        LLKP=LLK+I-1
        DO 260 J=1,NORBL
        LLLP=LLL+J-1
  260 S(LLKP,LLLP)=PAIRS(I,J)
```

```
C       COMPUTATION OF 1-CENTER COULOMB INTEGRALS OVER SLATER S FUNCTIONS
        N1=NC(ANK)
        N2=NC(ANL)
        K1=MU(ANK)
        K2=MU(ANL)
        IF(K.NE.L) GO TO 290
  270   TERM1 = FACT(2*N1-1)/((2.D0*K2)**(2*N1))
        TERM2 = 0.D0
        LIM = 2*N1
        DO 280 J=1,LIM
        NUM =DFLOAT(J)*(2.D0*K1)**(2*N1-J)*FACT(4*N1-J-1)
        DEN = FACT(2*N1-J)*2.D0*DFLOAT(N1)*(2.D0*(K1+K2))**(4*N1-J)
        TERM2 = TERM2 + NUM/DEN
  280   CONTINUE
        GO TO 310
C       COMPUTATION OF 2-CENTER COULOMB INTEGRALS OVER SLATER S FUNCTIONS
  290   TERM1=(R/2.D0)**(2*N2)*SS(0,0,0,2*N2-1,0,0,D0,2.D0*K2*R)
        TERM2 = 0.D0
        LIM = 2*N1
        DO 300 J=1,LIM
  300   TERM2 = TERM2+(DFLOAT(J)*(2.D0*K1)**(2*N1-J)*(R/2.D0)**(2*
       1N1-J+2*N2))/ (FACT(2*N1-J)*2.D0*DFLOAT(N1))*SS(2*N1-J,0,0,2*N2-1,0
       2,2.D0*K1*R,2.D0*K2*R)
  310   GAMMA(K,L) = ((2.D0*K2)**(2*N2+1)/FACT(2*N2))*(TERM1-TERM2)
  320   CONTINUE
C       SYMMETRIZATION OF OVERLAP AND COULOMB INTEGRAL MATRICES
        DO 330 I=1,N
        DO 330 J=I,N
  330   S(J,I) = S(I,J)
        DO 340 I=1,NATOMS
        DO 340 J=I,NATOMS
  340   GAMMA(J,I) = GAMMA(I,J)
        WRITE(6,350)
  350   FORMAT(1H1,1X,23HOVERLAP INTEGRAL MATRIX)
        CALL MATOUT(N,1)
C       TRANSFER GAMMA TO 80X80 MATRIX P FOR PRINTING
        DO 360 I=1,NATOMS
        DO 360 J=1,NATOMS
  360   P(I,J)=GAMMA(I,J)
        WRITE(6,370)
  370   FORMAT(1X,23HCOULOMB INTEGRAL MATRIX)
        CALL MATOUT(NATOMS,2)
        RETURN
        END



        FUNCTION SS(NN1,LL1,MM,NN2,LL2,ALPHA,BETA)
        IMPLICIT REAL*8(A-H,O-Z)
C       PROCEDURE FOR CALCULATING REDUCED OVERLAP INTEGRALS
        COMMON/ARRAYS/S(80,80),Y(9,5,203),Z(17,45),XX(2900)
        COMMON/AUXINT/A(17),B(17)
        INTEGER ULIM
        N1=NN1
        L1=LL1
        M=MM
        N2=NN2
        L2=LL2
        P =(ALPHA + BETA)/2.D0
        PT=(ALPHA - BETA)/2.D0
        X = 0.D0
        M=IABS(M)
C       REVERSE QUANTUM NUMBERS IF NECESSARY
        IF((L2.LT.L1).OR.((L2.EQ.L1).AND.(N2.LT.N1))) GO TO 20
   10   GO TO 30
   20   K = N1
        N1= N2
        N2= K
```

```
      K= L1
      L1= L2
      L2= K
      PT=-PT
   30 CONTINUE
      K = MOD((N1+N2-L1-L2),2)
C     FIND A AND B INTEGRALS
      CALL AINTGS(P,N1+N2)
      CALL BINTGS(PT,N1+N2)
      IF((L1.GT.0).OR.(L2.GT.0)) GO TO 60
C     BEGIN SECTION USED FOR OVERLAP INTEGRALS INVOLVING S FUNCTIONS
C     FIND Z TABLE NUMBER L
   40 L = (90-17*N1+N1**2-2*N2)/2
      ULIM = N1+N2
      LLIM = 0
      DO 50 I=LLIM,ULIM
      NNI1=N1+N2-I+1
   50 X=X+Z(I+1,L)*A(I+1)*B(NNI1)/2.D0
      SS=X
      GO TO 80
C     BEGIN SECTION USED FOR OVERLAPS INVOLVING NON-S FUNCTIONS
C     FIND Y TABLE NUMBER L
   60 L=(5-M)*(24-10*M+M**2)*(83-30*M+3*M**2)/120+
     1  (30-9*L1+L1**2-2*N1)*(28-9*L1+L1**2-2*N1)/8+
     2  (30-9*L2+L2**2-2*N2)/2
      LLIM = 0
      DO 70 I=LLIM,8
      ULIM=4 - MOD(K+I,2)
      DO 70 J=LLIM,ULIM
      IIII=2*J+MOD(K+I,2)+1
   70 X=X+Y(I+1,J+1,L)*A(I+1)*B(IIII)
      SS = X*(FACT(M+1)/8.D0)**2*DSQRT(DFLOAT(2*L1+1)*FACT(L1-M)*
     1 DFLOAT(2*L2+1)*FACT(L2-M)/(4.D0*FACT(L1+M)*FACT(L2+M)))
   80 CONTINUE
      RETURN
      END




      SUBROUTINE HARMTR(T,MAXL,F)
      IMPLICIT REAL*8(A-H,O-Z)
      DIMENSION T(9,9),E(3)
      COST = E(3)
      IF((1.D0-COST**2).GT.0.00000000001) GO TO 20
   10 SINT = 0.D0
      GO TO 30
   20 SINT=DSQRT(1.D0-COST**2)
   30 CONTINUE
      IF(SINT.GT.0.000001D0)  GO TO 50
   40 COSP = 1.D0
      SINP = 0.D0
      GO TO 70
   50 COSP = E(1)/SINT
   60 SINP = E(2)/SINT
   70 CONTINUE
      DO 80 I=1,9
      DO 80 J=1,9
   80 T(I,J) = 0.D0
      T(1,1) =1.D0
      IF (MAXL.GT.1) GO TO 100
   90 IF (MAXL.GT.0) GO TO 110
      GO TO 120
  100 COS2T = COST**2-SINT**2
      SIN2T = 2.D0*SINT*COST
      COS2P = COSP**2-SINP**2
      SIN2P = 2.D0*SINP*COSP
```

```
C       TRANSFORMATION MATRIX ELEMENTS FOR D FUNCTIONS
        SQRT3=DSQRT(3.D0)
        T(5,5) = (3.D0*COST**2-1.D0)/2.D0
        T(5,6) = -SQRT3    *SIN2T/2.D0
        T(5,8) = SQRT3     *SINT**2/2.D0
        T(6,5) = SQRT3     *SIN2T*COSP/2.D0
        T(6,6) = COS2T*COSP
        T(6,7) = -COST*SINP
        T(6,8) =-T(6,5)/SQRT3
        T(6,9) = SINT*SINP
        T(7,5) = SQRT3     *SIN2T*SINP/2.D0
        T(7,6) = COS2T*SINP
        T(7,7) = COST*COSP
        T(7,8) = -T(7,5)/SQRT3
        T(7,9) = -SINT*COSP
        T(8,5) = SQRT3     *SINT**2*COS2P/2.D0
        T(8,6) = SIN2T*COS2P/2.D0
        T(8,7) = -SINT*SIN2P
         T(8,8) = (1.D0+COST**2)*COS2P/2.D0
        T(8,9) = -COST*SIN2P
        T(9,5) = SQRT3     *SINT**2*SIN2P/2.D0
        T(9,6) = SIN2T*SIN2P/2.D0
        T(9,7) = SINT*COS2P
        T(9,8) = (1.D0+COST**2)*SIN2P/2.D0
        T(9,9) = COST*COS2P
 110 CONTINUE
C       TRANSFORMATION MATRIX ELEMENTS FOR P FUNCTIONS
        T(2,2) = COST*COSP
        T(2,3) = -SINP
        T(2,4) = SINT*COSP
        T(3,2) = COST*SINP
        T(3,3) = COSP
        T(3,4) = SINT*SINP
        T(4,2) = -SINT
        T(4,4) = COST
 120 CONTINUE
        RETURN
        END



        SUBROUTINE RELVEC(R,E,C1,C2)
        IMPLICIT REAL*8(A-H,O-Z)
        DIMENSION E(3),C1(3),C2(3)
        X = 0.D0
        DO 10 I=1,3
        E(I) = C2(I)-C1(I)
        X = X+E(I)**2
 10 CONTINUE
        R=DSQRT(X)
        DO 40 I=1,3
        IF (R.GT..000001D0) GO TO 30
 20 GO TO 40
 30 E(I) =E(I)/R
 40 CONTINUE
        RETURN
        END



        FUNCTION FACT(N)
        IMPLICIT REAL*8(A-H,O-Z)
        PRODT = 1.D0
 20 DO 30 I=1,N
 30 PRODT=PRODT*DFLOAT(I)
 40 FACT=PRODT
        RETURN
        END
```

```
      SUBROUTINE BINTGS(X,K)
      IMPLICIT REAL*8(A-H,O-Z)
C     FILLS ARRAY OF B-INTEGRALS. NOTE THAT B(I) IS B(I-1) IN THE
C     USUAL NOTATION
C     FOR X.GT.3                        EXPONENTIAL FORMULA IS USED
C     FOR 2.LT.X.LE.3 AND K.LE.10       EXPONENTIAL FORMULA IS USED
C     FOR 2.LT.X.LE.3 AND K.GT.10       15 TERM SERIES IS USED
C     FOR 1.LT.X .E.2 AND K.LE.7        EXPONENTIAL FORMULA IS USED
C     FOR 1.LT.X.LE.2 AND K.GT.7        12 TERM SERIES IS USED
C     FOR .5.LT.X.LE.1 AND K.LE.5       EXPONENTIAL FORMULA IS USED
C     FOR .5.LT.X.LE.1 AND K.GT.5       7 TERM SERIES IS USED
C     FOR X.LE..5                       6 TERM SERIES IS USED
C     ***********************************************************
      COMMON/AUXINT/A(17),B(17)
      I0=0
      ABSX=DABS(X)
      IF(ABSX.GT.3.D0) GO TO 120
   10 IF(ABSX.GT.2.D0) GO TO 20
   40 IF(ABSX.GT.1.D0) GO TO 50
   70 IF(ABSX.GT..5D0) GO TO 80
  100 IF(ABSX.GT..000001D0) GO TO 110
      GO TO 170
  110 LAST=6
      GO TO 140
   80 IF(K.LE.5) GO TO 120
   90 LAST=7
      GO TO 140
   50 IF(K.LE.7) GO TO 120
   60 LAST=12
      GO TO 140
   20 IF(K.LE.10) GO TO 120
   30 LAST=15
      GO TO 140

  120 EXPX=DEXP(X)
      EXPMX=1.D0/EXPX
      B(1)=(EXPX-EXPMX)/X
      DO 130 I=1,K
  130 B(I+1)=(DFLOAT(I)*B(I)+(-1.D0)**I*EXPX-EXPMX)/X
      GO TO 190
  140 DO 160 I=I0,K
      Y=0.D0
      DO 150 M=I0,LAST
  150 Y=Y+(-X)**M*(1.D0-(-1.D0)**(M+I+1))/(FACT(M)*DFLOAT(M+I+1))
  160 B(I+1)=Y
      GO TO 190

  170 DO 180 I=I0,K
  180 B(I+1)=(1.D0-(-1.D0)**(I+1))/DFLOAT(I+1)
  190 CONTINUE
      RETURN
      END




      SUBROUTINE AINTGS(X,K)
      IMPLICIT REAL*8(A-H,O-Z)
      COMMON/AUXINT/A(17),B(17)
      A(1) =DEXP(-X)/X
      DO 10  I=1,K
   10 A(I+1) =(A(I)*DFLOAT(I)+DEXP(-X))/X
      RETURN
      END
```

```
      SUBROUTINE MATOUT(N,MATOP)
      IMPLICIT REAL*8(A-H,O-Z)
      COMMON/ARRAYS/A(80,80,3)
      DO 80 M=1,N,11
      K=M+10
      IF (K.LE.N) GO TO 30
   20 K=N
   30 CONTINUE
      WRITE(6,40) (J,J=M,K)
   40 FORMAT(///,7X,11(4X,I2,3X),//)
      DO 60 I=1,N
      WRITE(6,50) I,(A(I,J,MATOP),J=M,K)
   50 FORMAT(1X,I2,4X,50(F9.4))
   60 CONTINUE
      WRITE(6,70)
   70 FORMAT(//)
   80 CONTINUE
      RETURN
      END


      SUBROUTINE HUCKCL
      IMPLICIT REAL*8(A-H,O-Z)
C     EXTENDED HUCKEL THEORY FOR CLOSED SHELLS
C     OVERLAPS ARE IN MATRIX A, COULOMB INTEGRALS (GAMMA) ARE IN MATRIX G
      COMMON/ARRAYS/A(80,80),B(80,80),D(80,80)
      COMMON/INFO/NATOMS,CHARGE,MULTIP,AN(35),C(35,3),N
      COMMON/INFO1/CZ(35),U(80),ULIM(35),LLIM(35),NELECS,OCCA,OCCB
      COMMON/GAB/XXX(400),G(35,35),Q(80),YYY(80),ENERGY,XXY(214)
      COMMON/OPTION/OPTION,OPNCLO,HUCKEL,CNDO,INDO,CLOSED,OPEN
      DIMENSION ENEG(18,3),BETAN(18)
      DIMENSION G1(18),F2(18)
      INTEGER CHARGE,OCCA,OCCB,UL,AN,CZ,U,ULIM,ANI
      INTEGER  OPTION,OPNCLO,HUCKEL,CNDO,INDO,CLOSED,OPEN
      G1(3)=.092012       DO
      G1(4)=.1407         DO
      G1(5)=.199265       DO
      G1(6)=.267708       DO
      G1(7)=.346029       DO
      G1(8)=.43423        DO
      G1(9)=.532305       DO
      F2(3)=.049865       DO
      F2(4)=.089125       DO
      F2(5)=.13041        DO
      F2(6)=.17372        DO
      F2(7)=.219055       DO
      F2(8)=.266415       DO
      F2(9)=.31580        DO
      ENEG(1,1)=7.1761    DO
      ENEG(3,1)=3.1055    DO
      ENEG(3,2)=1.258     DO
      ENEG(4,1)=5.94557   DO
      ENEG(4,2)=2.563     DO
      ENEG(5,1)=9.59407   DO
      ENEG(5,2)=4.001     DO
      ENEG(6,1)=14.051    DO
      ENEG(6,2)=5.572     DO
      ENEG(7,1)=19.31637DO
      ENEG(7,2)=7.275     DO
      ENEG(8,1)=25.39017DO
      ENEG(8,2)=9.111     DO
      ENEG(9,1)=32.2724   DO
      ENEG(9,2)=11.08     DO
      ENEG(11,1)=2.804    DO
      ENEG(11,2)=1.302    DO
      ENEG(11,3)=0.150    DO
      ENEG(12,1)=5.1254   DO
```

```
      ENEG(12,2)=2.0516 D0
      ENEG(12,3)=0.16195D0
      ENEG(13,1)=7.7706 D0
      ENEG(13,2)=2.9951 D0
      ENEG(13,3)=0.22425D0
      ENEG(14,1)=10.0327D0
      ENEG(14,2)=4.1325 D0
      ENEG(14,3)=0.337  D0
      ENEG(15,1)=14.0327D0
      ENEG(15,2)=5.4638 D0
      ENEG(15,3)=0.500  D0
      ENEG(16,1)=17.6496D0
      ENEG(16,2)=6.989  D0
      ENEG(16,3)=0.71325D0
      ENEG(17,1)=21.5906D0
      ENEG(17,2)=8.7081 D0
      ENEG(17,3)=0.97695D0
      BETA0(1)= -9.       D0
      BETA0(3)= -9.       D0
      BETA0(4)= -13.      D0
      BETA0(5)= -17.      D0
      BETA0(6)= -21.      D0
      BETA0(7)= -25.      D0
      BETA0(8)= -31.      D0
      BETA0(9)= -39.      D0
      BETA0(11)=-7.7203 D0
      BETA0(12)=-9.4471 D0
      BETA0(13)=-11.3011D0
      BETA0(14)=-13.065 D0
      BETA0(15)=-15.070 D0
      BETA0(16)=-18.150 D0
      BETA0(17)=-22.330 D0
C     FIND NELECS AND FILL H CORE(DIAGONAL) WITH (I+A)/2
      NELECS=0
      DO 60 I=1,NATOMS
      NELECS=NELECS+CZ(I)
      LL =LLIM(I)
      UL =ULIM(I)
      ANI=AN(I)
      L=0
      DO 50 J=LL,UL
      L=L+1
      IF (L.EQ.1) GO TO 10
 20   IF (L.LT.5) GO TO 40
 30   A(J,J)=-ENEG(ANI,3)/27.21D0
      GO TO 50
 40   A(J,J)=-ENEG(ANI,2)/27.21D0
      GO TO 50
 10   A(J,J)  =-ENEG(ANI,1)/27.21D0
 50   CONTINUE
 60   CONTINUE
      NELECS=NELECS-CHARGE
      OCCA=NELECS/2
C     FORM HUCKEL HAMILTONIAN IN A (OFF DIAGONAL TWO CENTER TERMS)
      DO 90 I=2,N
      K=U(I)
      L=AN(K)
      UL=I-1
      DO 90 J=1,UL
      KK=U(J)
      LL=AN(KK)
      IF ((L.GT.9).OR.(LL.GT.9)) GO TO 70
 80   A(I,J)=A(I,J)*(BETA0(L)+BETA0(LL))/54.42D0
      A(J,I)=A(I,J)
      GO TO 90
 70   A(I,J)=0.75D0*A(I,J)*(BETA0(L)+BETA0(LL))/54.42D0
      A(J,I)=A(I,J)
```

```
   90 CONTINUE
      DO 100 I=1,N
  100 Q(I)=A(I,I)
      RHO=1.D-6
      CALL EIGN(N,RHO)
C     EIGENVECTORS (IN B) ARE CONVERTED INTO DENSITY MATRIX (IN B)
      DO 140 I=1,N
      DO 120 J=I,N
      XXX(J)=0.0D0
      DO 110 K=1,OCCA
  110 XXX(J)= XXX(J)+2.D0*B(I,K)*B(J,K)
  120 CONTINUE
      DO 130 J=I,N
  130 B(I,J)= XXX(J)
  140 CONTINUE
      DO 150 I=1,N
      DO 150 J=I,N
  150 B(J,I)=B(I,J)
C     ADD V(AB) TO HCORE--CNDO
      DO  170  I=1,N
      J=U(I)
      Q(I)=C(I)   +0.5D0*G(J,J)
      DO 160 K=1,NATOMS
  160 Q(I)=C(I)-DFLOAT(CZ(K))*G(J,K)
  170 CONTINUE
C     EXIT SEGMENT IF ONLY CNDO APPROXIMATIONS ARE DESIRED
      IF (OPTION.EQ.CNDO) GO TO 290
C     INDO MODIFICATION (CORRECTION TO U(I,I) )
  180 DO 280 I=1,NATOMS
      K=AN(I)
      J=LLIM(I)
      IF ((K.GT.1).AND.(K.LT.10)) GO TO 190
      GO TO 280
  190 IF (K.LE.3) GO TO 210
  200 Q(J)=C(J)   +(DFLOAT(CZ(I))-1.5D0)*G1(K)/6.D0
  210 IF(K.EQ.3) GO TO 220
  230 IF(K.EQ.4) GO TO 240
  250 TEMP=G1(K)/3.D0+(DFLOAT(CZ(I))-2.5D0)*2.D0*F2(K)/25.D0
      GO TO 260
  240 TEMP=G1(K)/4.D0
      GO TO 260
  220 TEMP=G1(K)/12.D0
  260 CONTINUE
      DO 270 L=1,3
  270 Q(J+L)=Q(J+L)+TEMP
  280 CONTINUE
  290 CONTINUE
      DO 310 I=1,N
      DO 300 J=I,N
  300 A(J,I)=A(I,J)
  310 A(I,I)=Q(I)
      WRITE(6,320)
  320 FORMAT(1X,18H CORE HAMILTONIAN /)
      CALL SCFOUT(0,1)
      RETURN
      END

      SUBROUTINE SCFCLO
      IMPLICIT REAL*8(A-H,O-Z)
C     CNDO/INDO CLOSED SHELL SCF SEGMENT
C     GAMMA MATRIX CONTAINED IN G, CORE HAMILTONIAN CONTAINED IN Q AND
C     UPPER TRIANGLE OF A, AND INITIAL DENSITY MATRIX CONTAINED IN B
C     OPTIONS   CNDO OR INDO
      COMMON/ARRAYS/A(80,80),B(80,80),D(80,80)
      COMMON/GAB/XXX(400),G(35,35),Q(80),YYY(80),ENERGY,XXY(214)
      COMMON/INFO/NATOMS,CHARGE,MULTIP,AN(35),C(35,3),N
      COMMON/INFO1/CZ(35),U(80),ULIM(35),LLIM(35),NELECS,OCCA,OCCB
```

```
      COMMON/OPTION/OPTION,OPNCLO,HUCKEL,CNDO,INDO,CLOSED,OPEN
      INTEGER  OPTION,OPNCLO,HUCKEL,CNDO,INDO,CLOSED,OPEN
      INTEGER CHARGE,OCCA,OCCB,UL,ULIM,U,AN,CZ,Z
      DIMENSION G1(18),F2(18)
      G1(3)=.092012D0
      G1(4)=.1407  D0
      G1(5)=.199265D0
      G1(6)=.267708D0
      G1(7)=.346029D0
      G1(8)=.43423 D0
      G1(9)=.532305D0
      F2(3)=.049865D0
      F2(4)=.089125D0
      F2(5)=.13041 D0
      F2(6)=.17372 D0
      F2(7)=.219055D0
      F2(8)=.266415D0
      F2(9)=.31580 D0
      Z=0
      IT=25
      RHO=1.D-6
   10 CONTINUE
      Z = Z+1
      ENERGY = 0.D0
C     TRANSFER CORE HAMILTONIAN TO LOWER TRIANGLE OF A
      DO 20 I=1,N
      A(I,I)=Q(I)
      DO 20 J=I,N
   20 A(J,I)=A(I,J)
      DO 30 I=1,N
      II=U(I)
      A(I,I)=A(I,I)-B(I,I)*G(II,II)*0.5D0
      DO 30 K=1,N
      JJ=U(K)
   30 A(I,I)=A(I,I)+B(K,K)*G(II,JJ)
      NM=N-1
      DO 40 I=1,NM
      II=U(I)
      LL=I+1
      DO 40 J=LL,N
      JJ=U(J)
   40 A(J,I)=A(J,I)-B(J,I)*G(II,JJ)*0.5D0
C     INDO MODIFICATION
      IF (OPTION.EQ.CNDO) GO TO 90
   50 DO 80 II=1,NATOMS
      K=AN(II)
      I=LLIM(II)
      IF (K.EQ.1) GO TO 80
   60 PAA=B(I,I)+B(I+1,I+1)+B(I+2,I+2)+B(I+3,I+3)
      A(I,I)=A(I,I)-(PAA-B(I,I)) *G1(K)/6.D0
      DO 70 J=1,3
      A(I+J,I+J)=A(I+J,I+J)-B(I,I)*G1(K)/6.D0-(PAA-B(I,I))*7.D0*
     1F2(K)/50.D0+B(I+J,I+J)*11.D0*F2(K)/50.D0
   70 A(I+J,I)=A(I+J,I)+B(I,I+J)*G1(K)/2.D0
      I1=I+1
      I2=I+2
      I3=I+3
      A(I2,I1)=A(I2,I1)+B(I2,I1)*11.D0*F2(K)/50.D0
      A(I3,I1)=A(I3,I1)+B(I3,I1)*11.D0*F2(K)/50.D0
      A(I3,I2)=A(I3,I2)+B(I3,I2)*11.D0*F2(K)/50.D0
   80 CONTINUE
   90 CONTINUE
      DO 100 I=1,N
  100 ENERGY=ENERGY+0.5D0*B(I,I)*(A(I,I)+Q(I))
      DO 105 I=1,NM
      LL=I+1
      DO 105 J=LL,N
```

```
     105 ENERGY=ENERGY+B(I,J)*(A(I,J)+A(J,I))
         WRITE(6,110) ENERGY
     110 FORMAT(//,10X,22H ELECTRONIC ENERGY      ,F16.10)
         IF(DABS(ENERGY-OLDENG).GE..000001D0) GO TO 150
     120 Z=26
     130 WRITE(6,140)
     140 FORMAT(5X,18H ENERGY SATISFIED /)
         GO TO 170
     150 CONTINUE
     160 OLDENG=ENERGY
     170 CONTINUE
         IF (Z.LE.IT) GO TO 210
C        SYMMETRIZE F FOR PRINTING (MATRIX A)
     180 DO 190 I=1,N
         DO 190 J=I,N
     190 A(I,J)=A(J,I)
         WRITE(6,200)
     200 FORMAT(1X,27H HARTREE-FOCK ENERGY MATRIX)
         CALL SCFOUT(0,1)
     210 CONTINUE
         CALL EIGN(N,RHO)
         IF (Z.LE.IT) GO TO 240
     220 WRITE(6,230)
     230 FORMAT(1X,28HEIGENVALUES AND EIGENVECTORS)
         CALL SCFOUT(1,2)
     240 CONTINUE
C        EIGENVECTORS (IN B) ARE CONVERTED INTO DENSITY MATRIX (IN B)
         DO 280 I=1,N
         DO 260 J=I,N
         XXX(J)=0.0D0
         DO 250 K=1,OCCA
     250 XXX(J)= XXX(J)+B(I,K)*B(J,K)*2.0D0
     260 CONTINUE
         DO 270 J=I,N
     270 B(I,J)= XXX(J)
     280 CONTINUE
         DO 290 I=1,N
         DO 290 J=I,N
     290 B(J,I)=B(I,J)
         IF (Z.LE.IT) GO TO 10
     300 CONTINUE
         RETURN
         END


         SUBROUTINE CPRINT
         IMPLICIT REAL*8(A-H,O-Z)
C        CNDO-INDO SCF CLOSED SHELL - PRINTOUT SEGMENT
         COMMON/ARRAYS/A(80,80),B(80,80),D(80,80)
         COMMON/GAB/XXX(400),G(35,35),Q(80),YYY(80),ENERGY,XXY(214)
         COMMON/INFO/NATOMS,CHARGE,MULTIP,AN(35),C(35,3),N
         COMMON/INFO1/CZ(35),U(80),ULIM(35),LLIM(35),NELECS,OCCA,OCCB
         COMMON/PERTBL/EL(18)
         COMMON/OPTION/OPTION,OPNCLO,HUCKEL,CNDO,INDO,CLOSED,OPEN
         INTEGER  OPTION,OPNCLO,HUCKEL,CNDO,INDO,CLOSED,OPEN
         INTEGER CHARGE,AN,U,ULIM,FL,OCCA,OCCB,UL,CZ,ANI
         DIMENSION DPM(3),DM(3),DMSP(3),DMPD(3)
         DIMENSION ATENG(18)
         IF (OPTION.EQ.CNDO) GO TO 20
         ATENG(1)=-0.6387302462   D0
         ATENG(3)=-.2321972405    D0
         ATENG(4)=-1.1219620354   D0
         ATENG(5)=-2.8725750048   D0
         ATENG(6)=-5.9349548261   D0
         ATENG(7)=-10.6731741251  D0
         ATENG(8)=-17.2920850650  D0
         ATENG(9)=-26.2574377875  D0
         GO TO 30
```

```
   20 CONTINUE
      ATENG(1)=-0.6387302462  D0
      ATENG(3)=-.2321972405   D0
      ATENG(4)=-1.1454120355  D0
      ATENG(5)=-2.9774239048  D0
      ATENG(6)=-6.1649936261  D0
      ATENG(7)=-11.0768746252 D0
      ATENG(8)=-18.0819658651 D0
      ATENG(9)=-27.5491302880 D0
      ATENG(11)=-.1977009568  D0
      ATENG(12)=-.8671913833  D0
      ATENG(13)=-2.0364557744 D0
      ATENG(14)=-3.8979034686 D0
      ATENG(15)=-6.7966009163 D0
      ATENG(16)=-10.7658174341D0
      ATENG(17)=-16.0467017940D0
   30 CONTINUE
      K=NATOMS-1
      WRITE(6,40)
   40 FORMAT(1X,15H DENSITY MATRIX)
      CALL SCFOUT(0,2)
      DO 50 I=1,K
      L=I+1
      DO 50 J=L,NATOMS
      RAD=DSQRT((C(I,1)-C(J,1))**2+(C(I,2)-C(J,2))**2
     1          +(C(I,3)-C(J,3))**2)
   50 ENERGY=ENERGY+(DFLOAT(CZ(I))*DFLOAT(CZ(J)))/RAD
      WRITE(6,60) ENERGY
   60 FORMAT(//,10X,16H TOTAL ENERGY = F16.10)
      DO 70 I=1,NATOMS
      ANI=AN(I)
   70 ENERGY=ENERGY-ATENG(ANI)
      WRITE(6,80) ENERGY
   80 FORMAT(//,10X,16HBINDING ENERGY= ,F16.10,5H A.U.)
      DO 110 I=1,NATOMS
      TCHG = 0.D0
      LL=LLIM(I)
      UL=ULIM(I)
      DO 90 J=LL,UL
   90 TCHG = TCHG+B(J,J)
      ANI=AN(I)
      WRITE(6,100) I,EL(ANI),TCHG
  100 FORMAT(I3,A4,8X,F7.4)
      XXX(I)=TCHG
  110 CONTINUE
      DO 120 I=1,3
      DM(I)=0.0D0
      DMSP(I)=0.0D0
  120 DMPD(I)=0.0D0
      DO 200 J=1,NATOMS
      IF (AN(J).LT.3) GO TO 180
  130 IF (AN(J).LT.11) GO TO 140
  160 SLTR1=(.65D0*DFLOAT(AN(J))-4.95D0)/3.D0
      FACTOR=2.5416D0*7.D0/(DSQRT(5.D0)*SLTR1)
      INDEX=LLIM(J)
      DO 170 K=1,3
  170 DMSP(K)=DMSP(K)-B(INDEX,INDEX+K)*10.27175D0/SLTR1
      DMPD(1)=DMPD(1)-FACTOR*(B(INDEX+2,INDEX+8)+B(INDEX+3,INDEX+5)
     1 +B(INDEX+1,INDEX+7)-1.D0/DSQRT(3.D0)*B(INDEX+1,INDEX+4))
      DMPD(2)=DMPD(2)-FACTOR*(B(INDEX+1,INDEX+8)+B(INDEX+3,INDEX+6)
     1 +B(INDEX+2,INDEX+7)-1.D0/DSQRT(3.D0)*B(INDEX+2,INDEX+4))
      DMPD(3)=DMPD(3)-FACTOR*(B(INDEX+1,INDEX+5)+B(INDEX+2,INDEX+6)
     1 +2.D0/DSQRT(3.D0)*B(INDEX+3,INDEX+4))
      GO TO 180
  140 INDEX=LLIM(J)
      DO 150 K=1,3
  150 DMSP(K)=DMSP(K)-B(INDEX,INDEX+K)*7.33697D0/
     1 (.325D0*DFLOAT(AN(J)-1))
```

```
  180 DO 190 I=1,3
  190 DM(I)=DM(I)+(DFLOAT(CZ(J))-XXX(J))*C(J,I)*2.5416D0
  200 CONTINUE
      DO 210 I=1,3
  210 DPM(I)=DM(I)+DMSP(I)+DMPD(I)
      WRITE(6,220)
  220 FORMAT(//,20X,16H  DIPOLE MOMENTS,/)
      WRITE(6,230)
  230 FORMAT(5X,11H COMPONENTS,3X,2H X,8X,2H Y,8X,2H Z)
      WRITE(6,240)DM(1),DM(2),DM(3)
  240 FORMAT(5X,10H DENSITIES,3(1X,F9.5))
      WRITE(6,250)DMSP(1),DMSP(2),DMSP(3)
  250 FORMAT(5X,4H S,P,6X,3(1X,F9.5))
      WRITE(6,260)DMPD(1),DMPD(2),DMPD(3)
  260 FORMAT(5X,4H P,D,6X,3(1X,F9.5))
      WRITE(6,270)DPM(1),DPM(2),DPM(3)
  270 FORMAT(5X,6H TOTAL,4X,3(1X,F9.5),/)
      DP=DSQRT(DPM(1)**2+DPM(2)**2+DPM(3)**2)
      WRITE(6,280) DP
  280 FORMAT(3X,15H DIPOLE MOMENT=,F9.5,7H DEBYES,//)
      RETURN
      END

      SUBROUTINE HUCKOP
      IMPLICIT REAL*8(A-H,O-Z)
C     EXTENDED HUCKEL THEORY FOR OPEN SHELLS
C     OVERLAP IS IN A, GAMMA MATRIX IS IN G
C     AN INITIAL F MATRIX IS FORMED FROM -(I+A)/2 AND S(U,V)*(1/2)*
C     (BETAOA+BETAOB). THIS F MATRIX IS USED TO GENERATE AN INITIAL
C     DENSITY MATRIX, AT THIS POINT, ADDITIONAL INTEGRALS AND COR-
C     RECTIONS ARE ADDED TO THE F MATRIX TO FORM EITHER THE CNDO OR INDO
C     CORE HAMILTONIAN. THESE ADDITIONS ARE THE INTEGRALS V(AB)FOR CNDO
C     AND CORRECTIONS TO U(I,I) FOR INDO.
      COMMON/ARRAYS/A(80,80),B(80,80),Q(80,80)
      COMMON/GAB/XXX(400),G(35,35),FDIAG(80),PDIAG(80),ENERGY,YYY(214)
      COMMON/INFO/NATOMS,CHARGE,MULTIP,AN(35),C(35,3),N
      COMMON/INFO1/CZ(35),U(80),ULIM(35),LLIM(35),NELECS,OCCA,OCCB
      COMMON/OPTION/OPTION,OPNCLO,HUCKEL,CNDO,INDO,CLOSED,OPEN
      DIMENSION ENEG(18,3),BETAA(18)
      DIMENSION G1(18),F2(18)
      INTEGER   OPTION,OPNCLO,HUCKEL,CNDO,INDO,CLOSED,OPEN
      INTEGER CHARGE,OCCA,OCCB,UL,AN,CZ,U,ULIM,ANI
      G1(3)=.092012     D0
      G1(4)=.1407       D0
      G1(5)=.199265     D0
      G1(6)=.267708     D0
      G1(7)=.346029     D0
      G1(8)=.43423      D0
      G1(9)=.532305     D0
      F2(3)=.049865     D0
      F2(4)=.089125     D0
      F2(5)=.13041      D0
      F2(6)=.17372      D0
      F2(7)=.219055     D0
      F2(8)=.266415     D0
      F2(9)=.31580      D0
      ENEG(1,1)=7.1761  D0
      ENEG(3,1)=3.1055  D0
      ENEG(3,2)=1.258   D0
      ENEG(4,1)=5.94557 D0
      ENEG(4,2)=2.563   D0
      ENEG(5,1)=9.59407 D0
      ENEG(5,2)=4.001   D0
      ENEG(6,1)=14.051  D0
      ENEG(6,2)=5.572   D0
      ENEG(7,1)=19.31637D0
      ENEG(7,2)=7.275   D0
```

```
      ENEG(8,1)=25.39017D0
      ENEG(8,2)=9.111    D0
      ENEG(9,1)=32.2724 D0
      ENEG(9,2)=11.08    D0
      ENEG(11,1)=2.804   D0
      ENEG(11,2)=1.302   D0
      ENEG(11,3)=0.150   D0
      ENEG(12,1)=5.1254 D0
      ENEG(12,2)=2.0516 D0
      ENEG(12,3)=0.16195D0
      ENEG(13,1)=7.7706 D0
      ENEG(13,2)=2.9951 D0
      ENEG(13,3)=0.22425D0
      ENEG(14,1)=10.0327D0
      ENEG(14,2)=4.1325 D0
      ENEG(14,3)=0.337   D0
      ENEG(15,1)=14.0327D0
      ENEG(15,2)=5.4638 D0
      ENEG(15,3)=0.500   D0
      ENEG(16,1)=17.6496D0
      ENEG(16,2)=6.989   D0
      ENEG(16,3)=0.71325D0
      ENEG(17,1)=21.5906D0
      ENEG(17,2)=8.7081 D0
      ENEG(17,3)=0.97695D0
      BETA0(1)= -9.      D0
      BETA0(3)= -9.      D0
      BETA0(4)= -13.     D0
      BETA0(5)= -17.     D0
      BETA0(6)= -21.     D0
      BETA0(7)= -25.     D0
      BETA0(8)= -31.     D0
      BETA0(9)= -39.     D0
      BETA0(11)=-7.7203 D0
      BETA0(12)=-9.4471 D0
      BETA0(13)=-11.3011D0
      BETA0(14)=-13.065 D0
      BETA0(15)=-15.070 D0
      BETA0(16)=-18.150 D0
      BETA0(17)=-22.330 D0
C     FIND NELECS AND FILL H CORE(DIAGONAL) WITH (I+A)/2
      NELECS=0
      DO 60 I=1,NATOMS
      NELECS=NELECS+CZ(I)
      LL =LLIM(I)
      UL =ULIM(I)
      ANI=AN(I)
      L=0
      DO 50 J=LL,UL
      L=L+1
      IF (L.EQ.1) GO TO 10
   20 IF (L.LT.5) GO TO 40
   30 A(J,J)=-ENEG(ANI,3)/27.21D0
      GO TO 50
   40 A(J,J)=-ENEG(ANI,2)/27.21D0
      GO TO 50
   10 A(J,J)   =-ENEG(ANI,1)/27.21D0
   50 CONTINUE
   60 CONTINUE
      NELECS=NELECS-CHARGE
      OCCA=(NELECS+MULTIP-1)/2
      OCCB=(NELECS-MULTIP+1)/2
C     FORM HUCKEL HAMILTONIAN IN A (OFF DIAGONAL TWO CENTER TERMS)
      DO 90 I=2,N
      K=U(I)
      L=AN(K)
```

```
      UL=I-1
      DO 90 J=1,UL
      KK=U(J)
      LL=AN(KK)
      IF ((L.GT.9).OR.(LL.GT.9)) GO TO 70
   80 A(I,J)=A(I,J)*(BETA0(L)+BETA0(LL))/54.42D0
      A(J,I)=A(I,J)
      GO TO 90
   70 A(I,J)=0.75D0*A(I,J)*(BETA0(L)+BETA0(LL))/54.42D0
      A(J,I)=A(I,J)
   90 CONTINUE
      DO 100 I=1,N
      DO 100 J=1,N
  100 Q(I,J)=A(I,J)
      RHO =1.D-6
      CALL EIGN(N,RHO)
      DO 110 I=1,N
      PDIAG(I)=0.0D0
      DO 110 J=1,N
      A(I,J)=B(I,J)
  110 B(I,J)=0.0D0
      DO 160 I=1,N
      DO 120 K=1,OCCA
  120 B(I,I)=B(I,I)+A(I,K)*A(I,K)
      DO 130 K=1,OCCB
  130 PDIAG(I)=PDIAG(I)+A(I,K)*A(I,K)
      LL=I+1
      DO 160 J=LL,N
      DO 140 K=1,OCCB
  140 B(I,J)=B(I,J)+A(I,K)*A(J,K)
      DO 150 K=1,OCCA
  150 B(J,I)=B(J,I)+A(I,K)*A(J,K)
  160 CONTINUE
C     ADD V(AB) TO HCORE--CNDO
      DO  180  I=1,N
      J=U(I)
      Q(I,I)=Q(I,I)+0.5D0*G(J,J)
      DO 170 K=1,NATOMS
  170 Q(I,I)=Q(I,I)-DFLOAT(CZ(K))*G(J,K)
  180 CONTINUE
C     EXIT SEGMENT IF ONLY CNDO APPROXIMATIONS ARE DESIRED
      IF (OPTION.EQ.CNDO) GO TO 300
C     INDO MODIFICATION (CORRECTION TO U(I,I) )
  190 DO 290 I=1,NATOMS
      K=AN(I)
      J=LLIM(I)
      IF ((K.GT.1).AND.(K.LT.10)) GO TO 200
      GO TO 290
  200 IF (K.LE.3) GO TO 220
  210 Q(J,J)=Q(J,J)+(DFLOAT(CZ(I))-1.5D0)*G1(K)/6.D0
  220 IF(K.EQ.3) GO TO 230
  240 IF(K.EQ.4) GO TO 250
  260 TEMP=  G1(K)/3.D0+(DFLOAT(CZ(I))-2.5D0)*2.D0*F2(K)/25.D0
      GO TO 270
  250 TEMP=G1(K)/4.D0
      GO TO 270
  230 TEMP=G1(K)/12.D0
  270 CONTINUE
      DO 280 L=1,3
  280 Q(J+L,J+L)=Q(J+L,J+L)+TEMP
  290 CONTINUE
  300 CONTINUE
      WRITE(6,310)
  310 FORMAT(1X,18H CORE HAMILTONIAN //)
      CALL SCFOUT(0,3)
      RETURN
      END
```

```
      SUBROUTINE SCFOPN
      IMPLICIT REAL*8(A-H,O-Z)
C     CNDO/INDO OPEN SHELL SCF SEGMENT
C     GAMMA MATRIX CONTAINED IN G, CORE HAMILTONIAN CONTAINED IN Q,
C      INITIAL DENSITY MATRICES IN B
C     OPTIONS    CNDO OR INDO
C     AND THE APPROPRIATE CORE HAMILTONIAN, THE TWO ELECTRON INTEGRALS
C     ARE ADDED TO THE F MATRIX (A) IN TWO PARTS - FIRST THE CNDO GAMMAS
C     ARE ADDED AND THEN THE INDO CORRECTIONS TO THE ONE-CENTER INTEGRALS
C     THE PROCEDURE IS THAT F(ALPHA) AND F(BETA) ARE FORMED, THEN
C     THE ELECTRONIC ENERGY IS COMPUTED.EIGN IS CALLED TO DIAGONALIZE
C     THE TWO F MATRICES AND THE ALPHA AND BETA BONDORDERS ARE FORMED.
C     THESE ARE USED TO FORM NEW F MATRICES AND THE CYCLE IS REPEATED
C     UNTIL THE ENERGY CONVERGES TO THE DESIRED VALUE (.000001 IN THIS
C     PROGRAM).
C     AN UPPER LIMIT OF 25 CYCLES IS INCLUDED (IT)
      COMMON/ARRAYS/A(80,80),B(80,80),Q(80,80)
      COMMON/GAB/XXX(400),G(35,35),FDIAG(80),PDIAG(80),ENERGY,YYY(214)
      COMMON/INFO/NATOMS,CHARGE,MULTIP,AN(35),C(35,3),N
      COMMON/INFO1/CZ(35),U(80),ULIM(35),LLIM(35),NELECS,OCCA,OCCB
      COMMON/OPTION/OPTION,OPNCLO,HUCKEL,CNDO,INDO,CLOSED,OPEN
      DIMENSION G1(18),F2(18)
      INTEGER   OPTION,OPNCLO,HUCKEL,CNDO,INDO,CLOSED,OPEN
      INTEGER CHARGE,OCCA,OCCB,UL,AN,CZ,U,ULIM,Z
      G1(3)=.092012D0
      G1(4)=.1407  D0
      G1(5)=.199265D0
      G1(6)=.267708D0
      G1(7)=.346029D0
      G1(8)=.43423 D0
      G1(9)=.532305D0
      F2(3)=.049865D0
      F2(4)=.089125D0
      F2(5)=.13041 D0
      F2(6)=.17372 D0
      F2(7)=.219055D0
      F2(8)=.266415D0
      F2(9)=.31580 D0
C     INITIALIZE COUNTER Z AND BEGIN SCF CYCLE AT 10
      Z = 0
      IT=25
      RHO=1.D-6
   10 CONTINUE
      Z = Z+1
      ENERGY = 0.D0
C     TRANSFER CORE HAMILTONIAN TO A
      DO 20 I=1,N
      FDIAG(I)=Q(I,I)
      DO 20 J=1,N
   20 A(I,J)=Q(I,J)
      DO 30 I=1,N
      II=U(I)
      A(I,I)=A(I,I)-B(I,I)*G(II,II)
      FDIAG(I)=FDIAG(I)-PDIAG(I)*G(II,II)
      DO 30 K=1,N
      JJ=U(K)
      A(I,I)=A(I,I)+     (PDIAG(K)+B(K,K))*G(II,JJ)
   30 FDIAG(I)=FDIAG(I)+(PDIAG(K)+B(K,K))*G(II,JJ)
      NM=N-1
      DO 50 I=1,NM
      II=U(I)
      LL=I+1
      DO 40 J=LL,N
      JJ=U(J)
      A(I,J)=A(I,J)-B(I,J)*G(II,JJ)
   40 A(J,I)=A(J,I)-B(J,I)*G(II,JJ)
   50 CONTINUE
C     INDO MODIFICATION
      IF (OPTION.EQ.CNDO) GO TO 100
```

```
   60 DO 90 II=1,NATOMS
      K=AN(II)
      I=LLIM(II)
      IF (K.EQ.1) GO TO 90
   70 PAA=B(I,I)+B(I+1,I+1)+B(I+2,I+2)+B(I+3,I+3)
      PAB=PDIAG(I)+PDIAG(I+1)+PDIAG(I+2)+PDIAG(I+3)
      A(I,I)=A(I,I)-(PAA-B(I,I))*G1(K)/3.D0
      FDIAG(I)=FDIAG(I)-(PAB-PDIAG(I))*G1(K)/3.D0
      DO 80 J=1,3
      A(I+J,I+J)= A(I+J,I+J)+(B(I+J,I+J)-(PAA-B(I,I)))*F2(K)/5.D0-B(I,I)
     1*G1(K)/3.D0+(6.D0*PDIAG(I+J)-2.D0*(PAB-PDIAG(I)))*F2(K)/25.D0
      FDIAG(I+J)=FDIAG(I+J)+(PDIAG(I+J)-(PAB-PDIAG(I)))*F2(K)/5.D0
     1 -PDIAG(I)*G1(K)/3.D0+(6.D0*B(I+J,I+J)-2.D0*(PAA-B(I,I)))
     2 *F2(K)/25.D0
      A(I,I+J)=A(I,I+J)+(B(I,I+J)+2.D0*B(I+J,I))*G1(K)/3.D0
      A(I+J,I)=A(I+J,I)+(B(I+J,I)+2.D0*B(I,I+J))*G1(K)/3.D0
      DO 80 L=1,3
      IF (J.EQ.L) GO TO 80
   75 A(I+L,I+J)=A(I+L,I+J)+(5.D0*B(I+L,I+J)+6.D0*B(I+J,I+L))
     1 *F2(K)/25.D0
   80 CONTINUE
   90 CONTINUE
  100 CONTINUE
      DO 110 I=1,N
  110 ENERGY=ENERGY+0.5D0*((A(I,I)+Q(I,I))*B(I,I)+(FDIAG(I)+Q(I,I))
     1 *PDIAG(I))
      DO 115 I=1,NM
      LL=I+1
      DO 115 J=LL,N
  115 ENERGY=ENERGY+((A(I,J)+Q(I,J))*B(I,J)+(A(J,I)+Q(J,I))*B(J,I))
      WRITE(6,120) ENERGY
  120 FORMAT(//,10X,22H ELECTRONIC ENERGY     ,F16.10)
      IF(DABS(ENERGY-OLDENG).GE.1.D-6)    GO TO 160
  130 Z=26
  140 WRITE(6,150)
  150 FORMAT(5X,18H ENERGY SATISFIED /)
      GO TO 180
  160 CONTINUE
  170 OLDENG=ENERGY
  180 CONTINUE
      IF (Z.LE.IT) GO TO 240
C     TRANSFER F(ALPHA) TO Q FOR PRINTING
  190 DO 200 I=1,N
      DO 200 J=I,N
      Q(I,J)=A(J,I)
  200 Q(J,I)=A(J,I)
      WRITE(6,210)
  210 FORMAT(1X,42H HARTREE-FOCK ENERGY MATRIX FOR ALPHA SPIN//)
      CALL SCFOUT(0,3)
C     TRANSFER F(BETA) TO Q FOR PRINTING
      DO 220 I=1,N
      Q(I,I)=FDIAG(I)
      LL=I+1
      DO 220 J=LL,N
      Q(I,J)=A(I,J)
  220 Q(J,I)=A(I,J)
      WRITE(6,230)
  230 FORMAT(1X,41H HARTREE-FOCK ENERGY MATRIX FOR BETA SPIN//)
      CALL SCFOUT(0,3)
  240 CONTINUE
      CALL EIGN(N,RHO)
      IF (Z.LE.IT) GO TO 270
  250 WRITE(6,260)
  260 FORMAT(1X,43HEIGENVALUES AND EIGENVECTORS FOR ALPHA SPIN//)
      CALL SCFOUT(1,2)
  270 CONTINUE
```

```
C       TRANSFER F(BETA) TO LOWER HALF OF A
        DO 280 I=1,N
        A(I,I)=FDIAG(I)
        FDIAG(I)=0.0D0
        K=I+1
        DO 280 J=K,N
        A(J,I)=A(I,J)
  280   A(I,J)=0.0D0
C       FORM ALPHA BONDORDERS IN TOP HALF OF A AND IN FDIAG    - TEMPORARY
        DO 300 I=1,N
        LL=I+1
        DO 290 K=1,OCCA
  290   FDIAG(I)=FDIAG(I)+B(I,K)*R(I,K)
        DO 300 J=LL,N
        DO 300 K=1,OCCA
  300   A(I,J)=A(I,J)+B(I,K)*B(J,K)
        CALL EIGN(N,RHO)
        IF (Z.LE.IT) GO TO 330
  310   WRITE(6,320)
  320   FORMAT(1X,43HEIGENVALUES AND EIGENVECTORS FOR BETA SPIN //)
        CALL SCFOUT(1,2)
  330   CONTINUE
C       FORM BETA BONDORDERS IN LOWER HALF OF A AND IN PDIAG
        DO 350 I=1,N
        LL=I+1
        PDIAG(I)=0.0D0
        DO 340 K=1,OCCB
  340   PDIAG(I)=PDIAG(I)+B(I,K)*R(I,K)
        DO 350 J=LL,N
        A(J,I)=0.0D0
        DO 350 K=1,OCCB
  350   A(J,I)=A(J,I)+B(I,K)*B(J,K)
C       TRANSFER BONDORDERS FROM A TO B
        DO 370 I=1,N
        DO 360 J=1,N
  360   B(I,J)=A(J,I)
  370   B(I,I)=FDIAG(I)
        IF (Z.LE.IT) GO TO 10
  380   CONTINUE
        RETURN
        END

        SUBROUTINE UPRINT
        IMPLICIT REAL*8(A-H,O-Z)
C       CNDO-INDO OPEN SHELL PRINTOUT SEGMENT
        COMMON/ARRAYS/A(80,80),B(80,80),Q(80,80)
        COMMON/GAB/XXX(400),G(35,35),FDIAG(80),PDIAG(80),ENERGY,YYY(214)
        COMMON/INFO/NATOMS,CHARGE,MULTIP,AN(35),C(35,3),N
        COMMON/INFO1/CZ(35),U(80),ULIM(35),LLIM(35),NELECS,CCCA,OCCB
        COMMON/OPTION/OPTION,OPNCLO,HUCKEL,CNDO,INDO,CLOSED,OPEN
        COMMON/PERTBL/EL(18)
        DIMENSION CISO(10)
        DIMENSION DPM(3),DM(3),DMSP(3),DMPD(3)
        DIMENSION ATENG(18)
        INTEGER OPTION,OPNCLO,HUCKEL,CNDO,INDO,CLOSED,OPEN
        INTEGER CHARGE,AN,U,ULIM,FL,OCCA,OCCB,UL,CZ,ANI
        IF (OPTION.EQ.CNDO) GO TO 20
        ATENG(1)=-0.6387302462    D0
        ATENG(3)=-.2321972405     D0
        ATENG(4)=-1.1219620354    D0
        ATENG(5)=-2.8725750048    D0
        ATENG(6)=-5.9349548261    D0
        ATENG(7)=-10.6731741251   D0
        ATENG(8)=-17.2920850650   D0
        ATENG(9)=-26.2574377875   D0
        GO TO 30
```

```
   20 CONTINUE
      ATENG(1)=-0.6387302462   D0
      ATENG(3)=-.2321972405    D0
      ATENG(4)=-1.1454120355   D0
      ATENG(5)=-2.9774239048   D0
      ATENG(6)=-6.1649936261   D0
      ATENG(7)=-11.0768746252  D0
      ATENG(8)=-18.0819658651  D0
      ATENG(9)=-27.5491302880  D0
      ATENG(11)=-.1977009568   D0
      ATENG(12)=-.8671913833   D0
      ATENG(13)=-2.0364557744  D0
      ATENG(14)=-3.8979034686  D0
      ATENG(15)=-6.7966009163  D0
      ATENG(16)=-10.7658174341D0
      ATENG(17)=-16.0467017940D0
   30 CONTINUE
      K=NATOMS-1
C     BONDORDER HALF MATRICES ARE NOW BEING STORED IN FULL MATRICES FOR
C     PRINTING---ALPHA IN B AND BETA IN A
      DO 40 I=1,N
      A(I,I)=PDIAG(I)
      LL=I+1
      DO 40 J=LL,N
      A(I,J)=B(I,J)
      A(J,I)=B(I,J)
   40 B(I,J)=B(J,I)
      WRITE(6,50)
   50 FORMAT(1X,23H ALPHA BONDORDER MATRIX//)
      CALL SCFOUT(0,2)
      WRITE(6,60)
   60 FORMAT(1X,22H BETA BONDORDER MATRIX//)
      CALL SCFOUT(0,1)
   70 CONTINUE
      DO 80 I=1,N
      DO 80 J=1,N
      B(I,J)=A(I,J)+B(I,J)
   80 A(I,J)=B(I,J)-2.D0*A(I,J)
      WRITE(6,90)
   90 FORMAT(1X,25H SCF TOTAL DENSITY MATRIX//)
      CALL SCFOUT(0,2)
      WRITE(6,100)
  100 FORMAT(1X,24H SCF SPIN DENSITY MATRIX//)
      CALL SCFOUT(0,1)
      DO 110 I=1,K
      L=I+1
      DO 110 J=L,NATOMS
      RAD=DSQRT((C(I,1)-C(J,1))**2+(C(I,2)-C(J,2))**2
     1        +(C(I,3)-C(J,3))**2)
  110 ENERGY=ENERGY+(DFLOAT(CZ(I))*DFLOAT(CZ(J)))/RAD
      WRITE(6,120) ENERGY
  120 FORMAT(//10X,16H TOTAL ENERGY = F16.10)
      DO 130 I=1,NATOMS
      ANI=AN(I)
  130 ENERGY=ENERGY-ATENG(ANI)
      WRITE(6,140) ENERGY
  140 FORMAT(//10X,16HBINDING ENERGY= ,F16.10,5H A.U.)
      CISO(1) = 539.8635D0
      CISO(6) = 820.0959D0
      CISO(7) = 379.3557D0
      CISO(8) = 888.6855D0
      CISO(9) = 44829.2 D0
      WRITE(6,150)
  150 FORMAT(15X,7HVALENCE,10X,9HS ORBITAL,10X,9HHYPERFINE)
      WRITE(6,160)
  160 FORMAT(10X,55H*ELECTRON DENSITY*  *SPIN DENSITY*  *COUPLING CONSTA
     1NT*)
      WRITE(6,170)
```

```
170 FORMAT(80X)
    DO 200 I=1,NATOMS
    TCHG = 0.D0
    LL=LLIM(I)
    UI=ULIM(I)
    ANI=AN(I)
    HFC=CISO(ANI)*A(LL,LL)
    IF (OPTION.EQ.INDO) GO TO 2
  1 HFC=0.0
  2 CONTINUE
    DO 180 J=LL,UL
180 TCHG = TCHG+B(J,J)
    WRITE(6,190) I,EL(ANI),TCHG,A(LL,LL),HFC
190 FORMAT(I3,A4,8X,F7.4,10X,F7.4,12X,F9.4)
    XXX(I)=TCHG
200 CONTINUE
    DO 210 I=1,3
    DM(I)=0.0D0
    DMSP(I)=0.0D0
210 DMPD(I)=0.0D0
    DO 290 J=1,NATOMS
    IF (AN(J).LT.3) GO TO 270
220 IF (AN(J).LT.11) GO TO 230
250 SLTR1=(.65D0*DFLOAT(AN(J))-4.95D0)/3.D0
    FACTOR=2.5416D0*7.D0/(DSQRT(5.D0)*SLTR1)
    INDEX=LLIM(J)
    DO 260 K=1,3
260 DMSP(K)=DMSP(K)-B(INDEX,INDEX+K)*10.27175D0/SLTR1
    DMPD(1)=DMPD(1)-FACTOR*(B(INDEX+2,INDEX+8)+B(INDEX+3,INDEX+5)
   1 +B(INDEX+1,INDEX+7)-1.D0/DSQRT(3.D0)*B(INDEX+1,INDEX+4))
    DMPD(2)=DMPD(2)-FACTOR*(B(INDEX+1,INDEX+8)+B(INDEX+3,INDEX+6)
   1 +B(INDEX+2,INDEX+7)-1.D0/DSQRT(3.D0)*B(INDEX+2,INDEX+4))
    DMPD(3)=DMPD(3)-FACTOR*(B(INDEX+1,INDEX+5)+B(INDEX+2,INDEX+6)
   1 +2.D0/DSQRT(3.D0)*B(INDEX+3,INDEX+4))
    GO TO 270
230 INDEX=LLIM(J)
    DO 240 K=1,3
240 DMSP(K)=DMSP(K)-B(INDEX,INDEX+K)*7.33697D0/
   1 (.325D0*DFLOAT(AN(J)-1))
270 DO 280 I=1,3
280 DM(I)=DM(I)+(DFLOAT(CZ(J))-XXX(J))*C(J,I)*2.5416D0
290 CONTINUE
    DO 300 I=1,3
300 DPM(I)=DM(I)+DMSP(I)+DMPD(I)
    WRITE(6,310)
310 FORMAT(//,20X,16H  DIPOLE MOMENTS,/)
    WRITE(6,320)
320 FORMAT(5X,11H COMPONENTS,3X,2H X,8X,2H Y,8X,2H Z)
    WRITE(6,330)DM(1),DM(2),DM(3)
330 FORMAT(5X,10H DENSITIES,3(1X,F9.5))
    WRITE(6,340)DMSP(1),DMSP(2),DMSP(3)
340 FORMAT(5X,4H S,P,6X,3(1X,F9.5))
    WRITE(6,350)DMPD(1),DMPD(2),DMPD(3)
350 FORMAT(5X,4H P,D,6X,3(1X,F9.5))
    WRITE(6,360)DPM(1),DPM(2),DPM(3)
360 FORMAT(5X,6H TOTAL,4X,3(1X,F9.5),/)
    DP=DSQRT(DPM(1)**2+DPM(2)**2+DPM(3)**2)
    WRITE(6,370) DP
370 FORMAT(3X,15H DIPOLE MOMENT=,F9.5,7H DEBYES,//)
    RETURN
    END
```

```
      SUBROUTINE EIGN(NN,RHO)
      IMPLICIT REAL*8(A-H,O-Z)
C     RHO= UPPER LIMIT FOR OFF-DIAGONAL ELEMENT
C     NN= SIZE OF MATRIX
C     A = F MATRIX (ONLY LOWER TRIANGLE IS USED + THIS IS DESTROYED)
C     EIG = RETURNED EIGENVALUES IN ALGEBRAIC ASCENDING ORDER
C     VEC = RETURNED EIGENVECTORS IN COLUMNS
      COMMON/ARRAYS/A(80,80),VEC(80,80),X(80,80)
      COMMON/GAB/GAMMA(80),BETA(80),BETASQ(80),EIG(80),W(80),XYZ(1600)
C     THE FOLLOWING DIMENSIONED VARIABLES ARE EQUIVALENCED
      DIMENSION P(80),Q(80)
      EQUIVALENCE (P(1),BETA(1)),(Q(1),BETA(1))
      DIMENSION IPOSV(80),IVPOS(80),IORD(80)
      EQUIVALENCE (IPOSV(1),GAMMA(1)),(IVPOS(1),BETA(1)),
     1(IORD(1),BETASQ(1))
      RHOSQ=RHO*RHO
      N=NN
      IF (N .EQ. 0) GO TO 640
   10 N1=N-1
      N2=N-2
      GAMMA(1)=A(1,1)
      IF(N2) 200,190,40
   40 DO 180 NR=1,N2
      B=A(NR+1,NR)
      S=0.D0
      DO 50 I=NR,N2
   50 S=S+A(I+2,NR)**2
C     PREPARE FOR POSSIBLE BYPASS OF TRANSFORMATION
      A(NR+1,NR)=0.D0
      IF (S) 170,170,60
   60 S=S+B*B
      SGN=+1.D0
      IF (B) 70,80,80
   70 SGN=-1.D0
   80 SQRTS=DSQRT(S)
      D=SGN/(SQRTS+SQRTS)
      TEMP=DSQRT(.5D0+B*D)
      W(NR)=TEMP
      A(NR+1,NR)=TEMP
      D=D/TEMP
      B=-SGN*SQRTS
C     D IS FACTOR OF PROPORTIONALITY. NOW COMPUTE AND SAVE W VECTOR.
C     EXTRA SINGLY SUBSCRIPTED W VECTOR USED FOR SPEED.
      DO 90 I=NR,N2
      TEMP=D*A(I+2,NR)
      W(I+1)=TEMP
   90 A(I+2,NR)=TEMP
C     PREMULTIPLY VECTOR W BY MATRIX A TO OBTAIN P VECTOR.
C     SIMULTANEOUSLY ACCUMULATE DOT PRODUCT WP,(THE SCALAR K)
      WTAW=0.D0
      DO 140 I=NR,N1
      SUM=0.D0
      DO 100 J=NR,I
  100 SUM=SUM+A(I+1,J+1)*W(J)
      I1=I+1
      IF(N1-I1) 130,110,110
  110 DO 120 J=I1,N1
  120 SUM=SUM+A(J+1,I+1)*W(J)
  130 P(I)=SUM
  140 WTAW=WTAW+SUM*W(I)
C     P VECTOR AND SCALAR K  NOW STORED. NEXT COMPUTE Q VECTOR
      DO 150 I=NR,N1
  150 Q(I)=P(I)-WTAW*W(I)
C     NOW FORM PAP MATRIX, REQUIRED PART
      DO 160 J=NR,N1
      QJ=Q(J)
      WJ=W(J)
      DO 160 I=J,N1
```

```
  160 A(I+1,J+1)=A(I+1,J+1)-2.D0*(W(I)*QJ+WJ*Q(I))
  170 BETA(NR)=B
      BETASQ(NR)=B*B
  180 GAMMA(NR+1)=A(NR+1,NR+1)
  190 B=A(N,N-1)
      BETA(N-1)=B
      BETASQ(N-1)=B*B
      GAMMA(N)=A(N,N)
  200 BETASQ(N)=0.D0
C     ADJOIN AN IDENTITY MATRIX TO BE POSTMULTIPLIED BY ROTATIONS.
      DO 220 I=1,N
      DO 210 J=1,N
  210 VEC(I,J)=0.D0
  220 VEC(I,I)=1.D0
      M=N
      SUM=0.D0
      NPAS=1
      GO TO 350
  230 SUM=SUM+SHIFT
      COSA=1.D0
      G=GAMMA(1)-SHIFT
      PP=G
      PPBS=PP*PP+BETASQ(1)
      PPBR=DSQRT(PPBS)
      DO 320 J=1,M
      COSAP=COSA
      IF (PPBS.GT.1.D-12) GO TO 250
  240 SINA=0.D0
      SINA2=0.D0
      COSA=1.D0
      GO TO 290
  250 SINA=BETA(J)/PPBR
      SINA2=BETASQ(J)/PPBS
      COSA=PP/PPBR
C     POSTMULTIPLY IDENTITY BY P-TRANSPOSE MATRIX
      NT=J+NPAS
      IF(NT .LT. N) GO TO 270
  260 NT=N
  270 DO 280 I=1,NT
      TEMP=COSA*VEC(I,J)+SINA*VEC(I,J+1)
      VEC(I,J+1)=-SINA*VEC(I,J)+COSA*VEC(I,J+1)
  280 VEC(I,J)=TEMP
  290 DIA=GAMMA(J+1)-SHIFT
      U=SINA2*(G+DIA)
      GAMMA(J)=G+U
      G=DIA-U
      PP=DIA*COSA-SINA*COSAP*BETA(J)
      IF(J .NE. M) GO TO 310
  300 BETA(J)=SINA*PP
      BETASQ(J)=SINA2*PP*PP
      GO TO 330
  310 PPBS=PP*PP+BETASQ(J+1)
      PPBR=DSQRT(PPBS)
      BETA(J)=SINA*PPBR
  320 BETASQ(J)=SINA2*PPBS
  330 GAMMA(M+1)=G
C     TEST FOR CONVERGENCE OF LAST DIAGONAL ELEMENT
      NPAS=NPAS+1
      IF(BETASQ(M) .GT. RHOSQ) GO TO 370
  340 EIG(M+1)=GAMMA(M+1)+SUM
  350 BETA(M)=0.D0
      BETASQ(M)=0.D0
      M=M-1
      IF(M .EQ. 0) GO TO 400
  360 IF(BETASQ(M) .LE. RHOSQ) GO TO 340
C     TAKE ROOT OF CORNER 2 BY 2 NEAREST TO LOWER DIAGONAL IN VALUE
C     AS ESTIMATE OF EIGENVALUE TO USE FOR SHIFT
```

```
 370 A2=GAMMA(M+1)
     R2=0.5D0*A2
     R1=0.5D0*GAMMA(M)
     R12=R1+R2
     DIF=R1-R2
     TEMP=DSQRT(DIF*DIF+BETASQ(M))
     R1=R12+TEMP
     R2=R12-TEMP
     DIF=DABS(A2-R1)-DABS(A2-R2)
     IF(DIF .LT. 0.D0) GO TO 390
 380 SHIFT=R2
     GO TO 230
 390 SHIFT=R1
     GO TO 230
 400 EIG(1)=GAMMA(1)+SUM
C    INITIALIZE AUXILIARY TABLES REQUIRED FOR REARRANGING THE VECTORS
     DO 410 J=1,N
     IPOSV(J)=J
     IVPOS(J)=J
 410 IORD(J)=J
C    USE A TRANSPOSITION SORT TO ORDER THE EIGENVALUES
     M=N
     GO TO 450
 420 DO 440 J=1,M
     IF (EIG(J) .LE. EIG(J+1)) GO TO 440
 430 TEMP=EIG(J)
     EIG(J)=EIG(J+1)
     EIG(J+1)=TEMP
     ITEMP=IORD(J)
     IORD(J)=IORD(J+1)
     IORD(J+1)=ITEMP
 440 CONTINUE
 450 M=M-1
     IF(M .NE. 0) GO TO 420
 460 IF(N1 .EQ. 0) GO TO 510
 470 DO 500 L=1,N1
     NV=IORD(L)
     NP=IPOSV(NV)
     IF(NP .EQ. L) GO TO 500
 480 LV=IVPOS(L)
     IVPOS(NP)=LV
     IPOSV(LV)=NP
     DO 490 I=1,N
     TEMP=VEC(I,L)
     VEC(I,L)=VEC(I,NP)
 490 VEC(I,NP)=TEMP
 500 CONTINUE
 510 CONTINUE
C    BACK TRANSFORM THE VECTORS OF THE TRIPLE DIAGONAL MATRIX
     DO 570 NRR=1,N
     K=N1
 520 K=K-1
     IF(K .LE. 0) GO TO 560
 530 SUM=0.D0
     DO 540 I=K,N1
 540 SUM=SUM+VEC(I+1,NRR)*A(I+1,K)
     SUM=SUM+SUM
     DO 550 I=K,N1
 550 VEC(I+1,NRR)=VEC(I+1,NRR)-SUM*A(I+1,K)
     GO TO 520
 560 CONTINUE
 570 CONTINUE
 640 RETURN
     END
```

```
      SUBROUTINE SCFOUT(OP,MOP)
      IMPLICIT REAL*8(A-H,O-Z)
C     THIS ROUTINE PRINTS THE ARRAY IN COMMON/ARRAYS/ WHICH IS DESIGNATE
C     MOP. IF OP = 1 THE EIGENVALUES CONTAINED IN COMMON/1/ ARE ALSO
C     PRINTED. IF OP= 0 THE EIGENVALUES ARE NOT PRINTED
      COMMON/ARRAYS/A(80,80,3)
      COMMON/GAB/XXX(2000)
      COMMON/INFO/NATOMS,CHARGE,MULTIP,AN(35),C(35,3),N
      COMMON/INFO1/CZ(35),U(80),ULIM(35),LLIM(35),NELECS,OCCA,OCCB
      COMMON/ORB/ORB(9)
      COMMON/PERTBL/EL(18)
      INTEGER OP,AN,ANII,CZ,U,ORB,ULIM,EL,CHARGE,OCCA,OCCB
      DO 120 M=1,N,11
      K=M+10
      IF (K.LE.N) GO TO 30
   20 K=N
   30 CONTINUE
      WRITE(6,100)
      IF (OP.EQ.1) GO TO 40
      GO TO 50
   40 CALL EIGOUT(M,K)
   50 CONTINUE
      WRITE(6,60) (I,I=M,K)
   60 FORMAT(13X,50I9)
      DO 110 I=1,N
      II=U(I)
      ANII=AN(II)
      L=I-LLIM(II)+1
   70 WRITE(6,80) I,II,EL(ANII),ORB(L),(A(I,J,MOP),J=M,K)
   80 FORMAT(1X,I2,I3,A4,1X,A4,50(F9.4))
      IF (I.EQ.ULIM(II)) GO TO 90
      GO TO 110
   90 WRITE(6,100)
  100 FORMAT(1X)
  110 CONTINUE
  120 CONTINUE
      WRITE(6,100)
      WRITE(6,100)
      RETURN
      END




      SUBROUTINE EIGOUT(M,K)
      IMPLICIT REAL*8(A-H,O-Z)
C     THIS ROUTINE IS CALLED IN SCFOUT TO PRINT THE EIGENVALUES M TO K
      COMMON/GAB/XXX(240),EPSILN(80),YYY(1680)
      WRITE(6,10) (EPSILN(I),I=M,K)
   10 FORMAT(//,15H EIGENVALUES---,20(F9.4),//)
      RETURN
      END
```

appendix B

Evaluation of One- and Two-center Integrals

This appendix is essentially a documentation of the integrals segment of the program presented in Appendix A, and covers the evaluation of overlap and coulomb integrals over Slater functions required for CNDO and INDO calculations.

B.1 BASIS FUNCTIONS

The integrals discussed herein are based on the Slater-type analytical form for the atomic functions referred to as the spherical polar coordinate system (r,θ,ϕ) centered on atom A.

$$\chi_a(r,\theta,\phi) = N_a r^{n_a-1} \exp(-\zeta_a r) Y_{l_a m}(\theta,\phi) \tag{B.1}$$

where n_a, l_a, and m are the principal, azimuthal, and magnetic quantum numbers, respectively, and ζ_a is the orbital exponent. The radial normalization constant is

$$N_a = \frac{(2\zeta_a)^{n_a+\frac{1}{2}}}{\sqrt{(2n_a)!}}$$ (B.2)

and the $Y_l{}^m(\theta,\phi)$ are the *real* normalized spherical harmonics,

$$Y_l{}^m(\theta,\phi) = \Theta_{lm}(\cos\theta)\Phi_m(\phi)$$ (B.3)

where

$$\Theta_{lm}(\cos\theta) = \left[\frac{(2l+1)(l-m)!}{2(l+m)!}\right]^{\frac{1}{2}} P_l{}^m(\cos\theta)$$ (B.4)

$$\Phi_m(\phi) = \begin{cases} \pi^{-\frac{1}{2}}\cos m\phi & m \neq 0 \\ (2\pi)^{-\frac{1}{2}} & m = 0 \end{cases}$$ (B.5)

The quantities $P_l{}^m(\cos\theta)$ are the normalized associated Legendre polynomials, taken in the form

$$P_l{}^m(\cos\theta) = \frac{(m+1)!}{8}\sin^m\theta \sum_{u=0}^{l-m} C_{lmu}\cos^u\theta$$ (B.6)

B.2 COORDINATE SYSTEMS

One-center integrals are referred to the spherical polar coordinate system (r,θ,ϕ). The volume element is

$$d\tau = r^2\sin\theta\,d\theta\,d\phi\,dr$$ (B.7)

and the limits of integration are $r: 0$ to ∞, $\theta: 0$ to π, and $\phi: 0$ to 2π. The two-center integrals are referred to the prolate spheroidal coordinate system (μ,ν,ψ). The relations between the prolate spheroidal system and two spherical polar systems centered at atoms A and B separated by a distance R are

$$\mu = \frac{r_A + r_B}{R} \qquad \nu = \frac{r_A - r_B}{R} \qquad \phi = \phi$$ (B.8)

as is illustrated in Fig. B.1 Other useful relations in converting from spherical polar coordinates to prolate spheroidal coordinates are

$$r_A = \frac{R(\mu+\nu)}{2} \qquad r_B = \frac{R(\mu-\nu)}{2}$$ (B.9)

$$\cos\theta_A = \frac{1+\mu\nu}{\mu+\nu} \qquad \cos\theta_B = \frac{1-\mu\nu}{\mu-\nu}$$ (B.10)

$$\sin\theta_A = \frac{[(\mu^2-1)(1-\nu^2)]^{\frac{1}{2}}}{\mu+\nu}$$

$$\sin\theta_B = \frac{[(\mu^2-1)(1-\nu^2)]^{\frac{1}{2}}}{\mu-\nu}$$ (B.11)

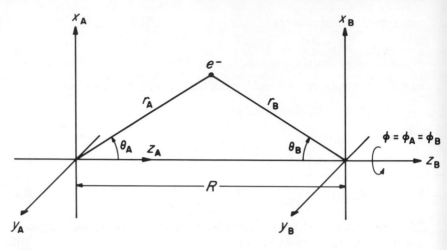

Fig. B.1

The volume element for integration in prolate spheroidal coordinates is

$$dr = \frac{R^3}{8} (\mu^2 - \nu^2)\, d\mu\, d\nu\, d\phi \tag{B.12}$$

and the limits of integration are μ: 1 to ∞, ν: -1 to 1, and ϕ: 0 to 2π.

It is of interest at this point to express the product of two spherical harmonic functions centered on a and b in terms of a function of prolate spheroidal coordinates $T(\mu,\nu)$

$$T(\mu,\nu) = \Theta_{l_a}{}^m(\cos\theta_A)\Theta_{l_b}{}^m(\cos\theta_B) \tag{B.13}$$

Substituting Eq. (B.6) into (B.4) and using (B.10) and (B.11),

$$
\begin{aligned}
\Theta_{l_a}{}^m&(\cos\theta_A) \\
&= \left[\frac{(2l_a + 1)(l_a - m)!}{2(l_a + m)!}\right]^{1/2} \frac{(m + 1)!}{8} \frac{[(\mu^2 - 1)(1 - \nu^2)]^{m/2}}{(\mu + \nu)^m} \\
&\qquad\qquad\qquad \times \sum_{u=0}^{l_a - m} C_{l_a m u} \frac{(1 + \mu\nu)^u}{(\mu + \nu)^u}
\end{aligned} \tag{B.14}
$$

and an analogous expression may be developed for $\Theta_{l_b}{}^m(\cos\theta_B)$. The product $T(\mu,\nu)$ may be written in the form

$$
\begin{aligned}
T(\mu,\nu) = D(l_a,l_b,m) \sum_{u}^{l_a - m} \sum_{v}^{l_b - m} C_{l_a m u} C_{l_b m v}(\mu^2 - 1)^m \\
\times (1 - \nu^2)^m(1 + \mu\nu)^u(1 - \mu\nu)^v(\mu + \nu)^{-m-u}(\mu - \nu)^{-m-v}
\end{aligned} \tag{B.15}
$$

where

$$D(l_a,l_b,m) = \left[\frac{(m+1)!}{8}\right]^2 \left[\frac{2l_a+1}{2}\frac{(l_a-m)!}{(l_a+m)!}\right]^{\frac{1}{2}}$$
$$\times \left[\frac{(2l_b+1)}{2}\frac{(l_b-m)!}{(l_b+m)!}\right]^{\frac{1}{2}} \quad (B.16)$$

B.3 THE REDUCED OVERLAP INTEGRAL

All the two-center integrals to be considered herein may be algebraically reduced to expressions involving one or more basic two-center integrals, known as reduced overlap integrals, denoted s. The general form of the reduced overlap integral is

$$s(n_a,l_a,m,n_b,l_b,\alpha,\beta) = \int_1^\infty \int_{-1}^1 (\mu+\nu)^{n_a}(\mu-\nu)^{n_b}$$
$$\times \exp\left[-\tfrac{1}{2}(\alpha+\beta)\mu - \tfrac{1}{2}(\alpha-\beta)\nu\right]T(\mu,\nu)\, d\mu\, d\nu \quad (B.17)$$

where

$$\alpha = \zeta_a R \qquad \beta = \zeta_b R \quad (B.18)$$

Substituting Eq. (B.15) into Eq. (B.17),

$$s(n_a,l_a,m,n_b,l_b,\alpha,\beta) = D(l_a,l_b,m) \sum_u^{l_a-m} \sum_v^{l_b-m} C_{l_amu}C_{l_bmv}$$
$$\times \int_1^\infty \int_{-1}^1 \exp\left[-\tfrac{1}{2}(\alpha+\beta)\mu - \tfrac{1}{2}(\alpha-\beta)\nu\right](\mu^2-1)^m$$
$$\times (1-\nu^2)^m(1+\mu\nu)^u(1-\mu\nu)^v(\mu+\nu)^{n_a-m-u}(\mu-\nu)^{n_b-m-v}\, d\mu\, d\nu$$
$$(B.19)$$

For a given l_a, l_b, and m,

$$\sum_u^{l_a-m} \sum_v^{l_b-m} C_{l_amu}C_{l_bmv}(\mu^2-1)^m(1-\nu^2)^m(1+\mu\nu)^u(1-\mu\nu)^v$$
$$\times (\mu+\nu)^{n_a-m-u}(\mu-\nu)^{n_b-m-v} = \sum_{i,j=0} Y_{ij\lambda}\mu^i\nu^j \quad (B.20)$$

where λ is a function of n_a, n_b, l_a, l_b, and m and serves as an algorithm to reference the appropriate Y matrix. The development of the elements of the Y matrix was accomplished by systematic manipulation of the matrices representative of the various polynomials involved.

The reduced overlap integral at this point can be expressed as

$$s(n_a,l_a,m,n_b,l_b) = D(l_a,l_b,m) \sum_{ij} Y_{ij\lambda} \int_1^\infty \mu^i$$
$$\times \exp\left[-\tfrac{1}{2}(\alpha+\beta)\mu\right] d\mu \int_{-1}^1 \nu^j \exp\left[-\tfrac{1}{2}(\alpha-\beta)\nu\right] d\nu \quad (B.21)$$

Introducing the auxiliary A and B functions [1],

$$A_k(\rho) = \int_1^\infty x^k \exp(-\rho x)\, dx = \exp(-\rho) \sum_{\mu=1}^{k+1} \frac{k!}{\rho^\mu(k - \mu + 1)!}$$

$$(B.22)$$

and

$$B_k(\rho) = \int_{-1}^1 x^k \exp(-\rho x)\, dx = -\exp(-\rho) \sum_{\mu=1}^{k+1} \frac{k!}{\rho^\mu(k - \mu + 1)!}$$

$$- \exp(\rho) \sum_{\mu=1}^{k+1} \frac{(-1)^{k-\mu}k!}{\rho^\mu(k - \mu + 1)!} \quad (B.23)$$

with $B_k(0) = 2/(k + 1)$ for k even and $B_k(0) = 0$ for k odd, the reduced overlap integral becomes

$$s(n_a,l_a,m,n_b,l_b,\alpha,\beta) = D(l_a,l_b,m) \sum_{ij} Y_{ij\lambda} A_i[\tfrac{1}{2}(\alpha + \beta)]B_j$$

$$\times [\tfrac{1}{2}(\alpha - \beta)] \quad (B.24)$$

and is programmed in this form as a subroutine in the segment INTGRL.

For the case in which the reduced overlap integral is to be used to evaluate integrals involving only s functions ($l_a = l_b = m = 0$),

$$T(\mu,\nu) = \tfrac{1}{2} \tag{B.25}$$

and Eq. (B.17) reduces to

$$s(n_a,0,0,n_b,0,\alpha,\beta) = \tfrac{1}{2} \int_1^\infty \int_{-1}^1 (\mu + \nu)^{n_a}(\mu - \nu)^{n_b}$$

$$\times \exp[-\tfrac{1}{2}(\alpha + \beta)\mu - \tfrac{1}{2}(\alpha - \beta)\nu]\, d\mu\, d\nu \quad (B.26)$$

Using the binomial expansion and collecting terms

$$(\mu + \nu)^{n_a}(\mu - \nu)^{n_b} = \sum_{k=0}^{n_a+n_b} Z_{k\lambda}\mu^k \nu^{(n_a+n_b-k)} \tag{B.27}$$

where

$$Z_{k\lambda} = \sum_i \sum_j \delta_{k,(i+j)}(-1)^{n_b-j} \frac{n_a!n_b!}{i!(n_a - i)!j!(n_b - j)!} \tag{B.28}$$

The reduced overlap integral with l and m equal to zero may thus be written

$$s(n_a,0,0,n_b,0,\alpha,\beta) = \tfrac{1}{2} \sum_k^{n_a+n_b} Z_{k\lambda} \int_1^\infty \mu^k \exp[-\tfrac{1}{2}(\alpha + \beta)\mu]\, d\mu$$

$$\times \int_{-1}^1 \nu^{n_a-n_b-k} \exp[-\tfrac{1}{2}(\alpha - \beta)\nu]\, d\nu \quad (B.29)$$

which in terms of the auxiliary A and B functions is

$$s(n_a,0,0,n_b,0,\alpha,\beta) = \tfrac{1}{2} \sum_k^{n_a+n_b} Z_{k\lambda} A_k \left[\tfrac{1}{2}(\alpha + \beta)\right] B_{n_a+n_b-k}$$
$$\times \left[\tfrac{1}{2}(\alpha - \beta)\right] \quad \text{(B.30)}$$

The coefficients are stored in the Z matrix (segment 1 of the integrals program) and references via the index k and a second index l, the latter being an algorithm involving n_a and n_b.

A convenient equality to be used extensively in the subsequent discussion is

$$\int r_A{}^{n_a-1} \exp\left(-\zeta_a r_A\right) r_B{}^{n_b-1} \exp\left(-\zeta_b r_B\right) Y_{l_a m}(\theta_A, \phi)$$
$$\times Y_{l_b m}(\theta_B, \phi)\, d\tau = \left(\frac{R}{2}\right)^{n_a+n_b+1} s(n_a,l_a,m,n_b,l_b,\alpha,\beta) \quad \text{(B.31)}$$

B.4 OVERLAP INTEGRALS

We now consider the general case of the evaluation of the overlap integral

$$S_{ab} = \int \Omega_{ab}(1)\, dt \quad \text{(B.32)}$$

where the charge distribution function Ω_{ab} is a product of any two Slater functions χ_a and χ_b specified by the quantum numbers (n_a,l_a,m) and (n_b,l_b,m), respectively,

$$\Omega_{ab}(1) = \chi_a(1)\chi_b(1) \quad \text{(B.33)}$$

with χ_a on atom A and χ_b on atom B.

For the case in which $\chi_a(1)$ and $\chi_b(1)$ are both on the same center, A = B and

$$S_{ab} = \begin{cases} 0 & \chi_a \neq \chi_b \\ 1 & \chi_a = \chi_b \end{cases} \quad \text{(B.34)}$$

For the two-center case, the charge distribution may be written using Eq. (B.1) as

$$\Omega_{ab}(1) = N_a N_b r_A{}^{n_a-1} r_B{}^{n_b-1} \exp\left(-\zeta_a r_A - \zeta_b r_B\right)$$
$$\times \Theta_{l_a m}(\cos\theta_A)\Theta_{l_b m}(\cos\theta_B)\Phi_m{}^2(\phi) \quad \text{(B.35)}$$

Transforming the charge-distribution function to prolate spheroidal coordinates, the overlap integral becomes

$$S_{ab} = N_a N_b \left(\frac{R}{2}\right)^{n_a+n_b-2} \int_1^\infty \int_{-1}^1 \int_0^{2\pi} \frac{(\mu + \nu)^{n_a}(\mu - \nu)^{n_b}}{\mu^2 - \nu^2}$$
$$\times \exp\left[-\tfrac{1}{2}(\alpha + \beta)\mu - \tfrac{1}{2}(\alpha - \beta)\nu\right]T(\mu,\nu)\Phi_m^2(\phi)\left(\frac{R}{2}\right)^3$$
$$\times (\mu^2 - \nu^2)\, d\mu\, d\nu\, d\phi \quad \text{(B.36)}$$

where

$$N_a N_b = \frac{(2\zeta_a)^{n_a+\frac{1}{2}}(2\zeta_b)^{n_b+\frac{1}{2}}}{[(2n_a)!(2n_b)!]^{\frac{1}{2}}} \tag{B.37}$$

The integration over ϕ may be carried out directly,

$$\int_0^{2\pi} \Phi_m^2(\phi)\, d\phi = 1 \tag{B.38}$$

The overlap integral then reduces to

$$S_{ab} = N_a N_b \left(\frac{R}{2}\right)^{n_a+n_b+1} \int_1^\infty \int_{-1}^1 (\mu + \nu)^{n_a}(\mu - \nu)^{n_b}$$
$$\times \exp\left[-\tfrac{1}{2}(\alpha + \beta)\mu - \tfrac{1}{2}(\alpha - \beta)\nu\right]T(\mu,\nu)\, d\mu\, d\nu \quad \text{(B.39)}$$

in which the integral involved is just the reduced overlap integral developed in Sec. B.3.   Thus

$$S_{ab}(n_a,l_a,m,n_b,l_b,\alpha,\beta) = \frac{(2\zeta_a)^{n_a+\frac{1}{2}}(2\zeta_b)^{n_b+\frac{1}{2}}}{[(2n_a)!(2n_b)!]^{\frac{1}{2}}}$$
$$\times \left(\frac{R}{2}\right)^{n_a+n_b+1} s(n_a,l_a,m,n_b,l_b,\alpha,\beta) \quad \text{(B.40)}$$

and the overlap integral is programmed in this general form, using the subroutine for the reduced overlap integral.

B.5 TWO–CENTER COULOMB INTEGRALS INVOLVING s FUNCTIONS

Two-center electron-electron interaction integrals of the coulomb type over Slater s functions are used in CNDO and INDO approximate self-consistent field schemes.   These are integrals of the form

$$\gamma(n_a,n_b,\zeta_a,\zeta_b,R) = \iint \Omega_{aa}(1)r_{12}^{-1}\Omega_{bb}(2)\, d\tau_1\, d\tau_2 \tag{B.41}$$

where the charge distribution $\Omega_{aa}(1)$ and $\Omega_{bb}(2)$ are products of Slater s functions.   The interelectronic repulsion operator r_{12}^{-1} is developed according to the Laplace-Newman expansion [2] as

$$r_{12}^{-1} = \sum_{l=0}^\infty \sum_{m=-l}^l \frac{4\pi}{2l + 1} \frac{r_<^l}{r_>^{l+1}} Y_{l_1m}(\theta_1,\phi) Y_{l_2m}(\theta_2,\phi) \tag{B.42}$$

where $r_>$ and $r_<$ denote the larger and smaller of (r_1, r_2), respectively. Since the spherical harmonics are an orthogonal set, it is only necessary to carry the summation over l as far as the maximum l appearing in the electron density functions, which in the case of just s functions is zero. Thus Eq. (B.42) reduces to just one term,

$$r_{12}^{-1} = r_>^{-1} \tag{B.43}$$

Substituting Eq. (B.43) into Eq. (B.41) and rearranging slightly, the coulomb integral may be written in the form

$$\gamma(n_a, n_b, \zeta_a, \zeta_b, R) = \int \Omega_{aa}(1) I(n_b, \zeta_b, 1) \, d\tau_1 \tag{B.44}$$

where

$$I(n_b, \zeta_b, 1) = \int r_>^{-1} \Omega_{bb}(2) \, d\tau_2 \tag{B.45}$$

which represents the potential energy of electron 2 at the position of electron 1. The evaluation of the coulomb integral is accomplished in two steps: (1) evaluation of the potential by the integration of Eq. (B.45) over spherical polar coordinates centered on b and (2) multiplication of the expression for the potential by $\Omega_{aa}(2)$ and integration over the coordinates of electron 2 in prolate spheroidal coordinates according to Eq. (B.44).

1. *Evaluation of the potential.* The density function $\Omega_{bb}(1)$ is given by Eq. (B.35) with $a = b$, and substituting this into Eq. (B.45) results in

$$I(n_b, \zeta_b, 1) = \frac{(2\zeta_b)^{2n_b+1}}{(2n_b)! \, 4\pi} \int r_>^{-1} r_{B2}^{2n_b-2} \exp\left(-2\zeta_b r_{B2}\right) d\tau_2$$

$$= \frac{(2\zeta_b)^{2n_b+1}}{(2n_b)! \, 4\pi} \int_0^\infty \int_0^\pi \int_0^{2\pi} r_>^{-1} r_{B2}^{2n_b-2}$$
$$\times \exp\left(-2\zeta_b r_{B2}\right) r_{B2}^2 \sin \theta_B \, dr_{B2} \, d\theta_B \, d\phi \tag{B.46}$$

The integral from 0 to ∞ is divided into two regions, 0 to r_{B1}, wherein $r_> = r_{B1}$, and r_{B1} to ∞, wherein $r_> = r_{B2}$. Thus Eq. (B.46) becomes

$$I(n_b, \zeta_b, 1) = [(2\zeta_b)^{2n_b+1}/(2n_b)!] \left\{ r_{B1}^{-1} \int_0^{r_{B1}} r_{B2}^{2n_b} \exp\left(-2\zeta_b r_{B2}\right) dr_{B2} \right.$$
$$\left. + \int_{r_{B1}}^\infty r_{B2}^{2n_b-1} \exp\left(-2\zeta_b r_{B2}\right) dr_{B2} \right\} \tag{B.47}$$

With the transformation of variable $r_{B2} = r_{B1} u$,

$$I(n_b, \zeta_b, 1) = \frac{(2\zeta_b)^{2n_b+1}}{(2n_b)!} r_{B1}^{2n_b} \left[\int_0^1 u^{2n_b} \exp\left(-2\alpha u\right) du \right.$$
$$\left. + \int_1^\infty u^{2n_b-1} \exp\left(-2\alpha u\right) du \right] \tag{B.48}$$

where $\alpha = \zeta_b r_{B1}$. The integral from 0 to 1 is readily evaluated in terms of the auxiliary A integrals given in Eq. (B.22),

$$\int_0^1 u^{2n_b} \exp(-2\alpha u)\, du = \frac{(2n_b)!}{(2\alpha)^{2n_b+1}} - A_{2n_b}(2\alpha) \tag{B.49}$$

Substituting (B.49) into (B.48), the expression for the potential reduces to

$$I(n_b,\zeta_b,1) = r_{B1}^{-1}\left\{1 - \frac{(2\alpha)^{2n_b+1}}{(2n_b)!}\left[A_{2n_b}(2\alpha) - A_{2n_b-1}(2\alpha)\right]\right\} \tag{B.50}$$

It may be shown that

$$A_{2n_b}(2\alpha) - A_{2n_b-1}(2\alpha) = \frac{(2n_b)!}{(2\alpha)}\exp(-2\alpha)$$

$$\times \sum_{l=1}^{2n_b} \frac{l}{(2\alpha)^l (2n_b - l)!\, 2n_b} \tag{B.51}$$

and using Eq. (B.51) and rearranging, the final expression for the potential reduces to

$$I(n_b,\zeta_b,1) = r_{B1}^{-1} - \frac{\exp(-2\zeta_b r_{B1})}{(2n_b)} \sum_{l=1}^{2n_b} \frac{l(2\zeta_b)^{2n_b-l} r_{B1}^{2n_b-l-1}}{(2n_b - l)!} \tag{B.52}$$

2. *Evaluation of the coulomb integral.* Substituting Eq. (B.52) into Eq. (B.44) and introducing the analytical expression for $\Omega_{aa}(1)$ results, after integration over angular coordinates, in

$$\gamma(n_a,n_b,\zeta_a,\zeta_b,R) = \frac{(2\zeta_a)^{2n_a+1}}{(2n_a)!\,4\pi}\left[\int r_{B1}^{-1} r_{A1}^{2n_a-2} \exp(-2\zeta_a r_{A1})\, d\tau_1\right.$$

$$-\sum_{l=1}^{2n_b} \frac{l(2\zeta_b)^{2n_b-l}}{(2n_b - l)!(2n_b)} \int r_{B1}^{2n_b-l-1} \exp(-2\zeta_b r_{B1}) r_{A1}^{2n_a-2}$$

$$\left.\times \exp(-2\zeta_a r_{A1})\, d\tau_1\right] \tag{B.53}$$

The integrals in Eq. (B.53) are readily evaluated from Eq. (B.31) in terms of the reduced overlap integral,†

† Note this treatment depends on $Y_{lm}{}^2(\theta_A,\phi)$ being equivalent to

$$Y_{l_a m}(\theta_A,\phi)\, Y_{l_b m}(\theta_B,\phi)$$

and thus holds only for s functions. For two-electron integrals involving p or higher functions, it is more convenient to use C functions [3], integrating over the spherical harmonics separately.

$$(4\pi)^{-1}\int r_{B1}{}^{-1}r_{A1}{}^{2n_a-2} \exp\left(-2\zeta_a r_{A1}\right) d\tau_1$$

$$= \left(\frac{R}{2}\right)^{2n_a} s(2n_a - 1, 0, 0, 0, 0, 2\zeta_a R, 0) \quad \text{(B.54)}$$

$$(4\pi)^{-1}\int r_{B2}{}^{2n_b-l-1} \exp\left(-2\zeta_b r_{B2}\right) r_{A2}{}^{2n_a-2} \exp\left(-2\zeta_a r_{A2}\right) d\tau_2$$

$$= \left(\frac{R}{2}\right)^{2n_b-l+2n_a} s(2n_a - 1, 0, 0, 2n_b - l, 0, 2\zeta_a R, 2\zeta_b R) \quad \text{(B.55)}$$

Substituting (B.54) and (B.55) back into (B.53), the final general expression for the two-center coulomb integral over Slater s functions is

$$\gamma(n_a,n_b,\zeta_a,\zeta_b,R) = \frac{(2\zeta_a)^{2n_a+1}}{(2n_a)!}\left[\left(\frac{R}{2}\right)^{2n_a} s(2n_a - 1, 0, 0, 0, 0, 2\zeta_a R, 0)\right.$$

$$- \sum_{l=1}^{2n_b} \frac{l(2\zeta_b)^{2n_b-l}}{(2n_b - l)!2n_b}\left(\frac{R}{2}\right)^{2n_b-l+2n_a}$$

$$\left. \times s(2n_a - 1, 0, 0, 2n_b - l, 0, 2\zeta_a R, 2\zeta_b R)\right] \quad \text{(B.56)}$$

and the integral is programmed in this form in segment 5.

B.6 ONE–CENTER COULOMB INTEGRALS INVOLVING s FUNCTIONS

A general expression for one-center coulomb integrals over Slater s functions may be developed along lines similar to those described in the preceding section. The integral has the form

$$\gamma(n_a,n_b,\zeta_a,\zeta_b,0) = \int \Omega_{aa}(1)\int r_>{}^{-1}\Omega_{bb}(2)\, d\tau_1\, d\tau_2 \quad \text{(B.57)}$$

wherein the potential part is identical to the preceding Eq. (B.52), with the general expression for the integrated form given in Eq. (B.57). Multiplying Eq. (B.52) by $\Omega_{aa}(1)$ and integrating over the coordinates of electron 2 results in

$$\gamma(n_a,n_b,\zeta_a,\zeta_b,0) = \frac{(2\zeta_a)^{2n_a+1}}{(2n_a)!4\pi}\left[\int r_{A1}{}^{2n_a-3} \exp\left(-2\zeta_a r_{A1}\right) d\tau_1\right.$$

$$\left. - \sum_{l=1}^{2n_b} \frac{l(2\zeta_b)^{2n_b-l}}{(2n_b - l)!2n_b}\int r_{A1}{}^{2n_b-l-3+2n_a} \exp\left[-2(\zeta_a + \zeta_b)r_{A1}\right] d\tau_2\right]$$

$$\text{(B.58)}$$

Integrating over θ and ϕ in spherical polar coordinates,

$$\gamma(n_a,n_a,\zeta_a,\zeta_a,0) = \frac{(2\zeta_a)^{2n_a+1}}{(2n_a)!}\left[\int_0^\infty r_{A1}{}^{2n_a-1}\right.$$

$$\times \exp\left(-2\zeta_a r_{A1}\right) dr_{A1}$$

$$- \sum_{l=1}^{2n_b} \frac{l(2\zeta_b)^{2n_b-l}}{(2n_b - l)!2n_b}\int_0^\infty r_{A1}{}^{2n_a+2n_b-l-1}$$

$$\left. \times \exp\left[-2(\zeta_1 + \zeta_2)r_{A1}\right] dr_{A1}\right] \quad \text{(B.59)}$$

Both of these integrations are of a type tabulated in standard integrals {i.e., the $C(k,g)$ given by Mulliken et al. [2]}

$$\int_0^\infty r_{A1}{}^{2n_a-1} \exp\left(-2\zeta_a r_{A1}\right) dr_{A1} = \frac{(2n_a - 1)!}{(2\zeta_a)^{2n_a}} \tag{B.60}$$

$$\int_0^\infty r_{A2}{}^{2(n_a+n_b)-l-1} \exp\left[-2(\zeta_a + \zeta_b)r_{A2}\right] dr_{A2}$$
$$= \frac{[2(n_a + n_b) - l - 1]!}{[2(\zeta_a + \zeta_b)]^{2(n_a+n_b)-l}} \tag{B.61}$$

Substituting (B.60) and (B.61) into (B.59) and rearranging, the general form of the one-center coulomb integral over Slater s functions is

$$\gamma(n_a,n_b,\zeta_a,\zeta_b,0) = \frac{(2\zeta_a)^{2n_a+1}}{(2n_a)!} \left[\frac{(2n_a - 1)!}{(2\zeta_a)^{2n_a}} \right.$$
$$\left. - \sum_{l=1}^{2n_b} \frac{l(2\zeta_b)^{2n_b-l}[2(n_a + n_b) - l - 1]!}{(2n_b - l)!2n_b[2(\zeta_a + \zeta_b)]^{2(n_a+n_a-l)}} \right] \tag{B.62}$$

and is programmed in this form.

B.7 IMPLEMENTATION OF INTEGRAL EVALUATIONS IN CNDO AND INDO MOLECULAR ORBITAL CALCULATIONS

The integrals discussed in Secs. B.1 to B.6 are used in parametric form in the course of molecular orbital calculations. Overlap integrals are required for all pairs of basis functions χ_μ, χ_ν of the atomic orbital basis set, and comprise the elements of a two-dimensional array $\mathbf{S}$, referred to the system in which coordinates of the atomic nuclei are specified (the molecular frame). In the evaluation of the elements of the overlap matrix, pairs of atoms A, B in the molecule are considered, and the complete set of S_{ab} involving orbitals χ_a on A and χ_b on B are evaluated with respect to the local atomic coordinate systems with the z axes of the respective atomic system parallel to the internuclear line. The overlap integrals in the local atomic frame are then transformed back to the molecular frame by an orthogonal transformation involving the matrix $\mathbf{T}$

$$S_{\mu\nu} = \sum_{ab} T_{\mu a} S_{ab} T_{b\nu} \tag{B.63}$$

The elements of the matrix $\mathbf{T}$ involved in such transformations for s, p, and d functions are generated by the subroutine HARMTR in the program.

The integral segment of the program is organized in the following manner for CNDO and INDO calculations: (1) Input data, comprised of the coordinates and atomic numbers of each of the atoms of the molecule, are obtained from MAIN via common; (2) the basis functions on each atom are specified by filling arrays indicating the atom number on which the basis function is centered, principal, azimuthal, and magnetic quantum numbers and orbital exponents; (3) the program then loops over pairs of atoms and computes all the overlap integrals between the sets of atomic functions centered on the two atoms under consideration, in the local atomic frame. Finally the overlap integrals in the atomic frame are transformed back to the molecular frame, using HARMTR; (4) the program then loops over pairs of atoms again, calculating the coulomb integrals over valence s function for each pair; (5) the overlap and coulomb matrices are printed out and made available to the subsequent segments of the system. These steps in the program are referenced in the source deck with comment cards.

REFERENCES

1. Mulliken, R. S., C. A. Rieke, D. Orloff, and M. Orloff: *J. Chem. Phys.*, **17**:1248 (1949).
2. Eyring, H., J. Walter, and G. E. Kimball: "Quantum Chemistry," John Wiley & Sons, Inc., New York, 1944.
3. Ruedenberg, C., C. C. J. Roothaan, and W. Jaunzemis: *J. Chem. Phys.*, **24**:201 (1956).

Name Index

Subject Index

Antisymmetry principle, 16–18
Atomic units, 7

Basis:
  extended, 42
  functions, 12
  minimal, 42
  valence, 42
Binding energy, 86
Bondangles:
  calculated, 85–109
  standard, 110–112
Bondlengths:
  calculated, 85–109
  standard, 110, 111
Born-Oppenheimer approximation, 6

CNDO/1, 69–75
CNDO/2, 75–89
Computer program, CNDO/INDO,
  163–216

Dipole moments, 87, 96, 114–117, 127
Dirac notation, 9

Electron affinity, 77
Electron spin, 14
Electronegativity, 77
Electronic charge distribution, 85–127
Electronic configurations, 19–22
  closed shell, 19, 32
  open shell, 20, 55
Electronic energy, 7
  closed shell, 32–37
  open shell, 53, 54
Electronic states, 19–22
Equivalent orbitals, 41
Expectation value, 9

Hartree-Fock theory:
  restricted, 37–41
  unrestricted, 51–56
Hartree product, 12
Hyperfine coupling constants, 128–149

INDO, 80–83
Integrals:
  core, 36
  coulomb, 36, 203, 204
  energy, 9, 33
  exchange, 36
  overlap, 32, 199–203
  penetration, 67
Ionization potential, 36, 71

LCAO approximation, 23

Molecular geometry, 85–110
Multiplicity, 16

NDDO, 83
Nodes, 25
Normalization, 8, 32

Operators, 7–11
  commuting, 10, 11
  core, 33
  coulomb, 38
  exchange, 38
  hamiltonian, 5, 6
  Hartree-Fock, 39
  linear, 4
  permutation, 16
  spin, 14, 15
Orbital energies, 41
Orbitals, 12–14
  atomic, 22–25
  gaussian, 30

213